CHILD LANGUAGE AND DEVELOPMENTAL DYSPHASIA

STUDIES IN SPEECH PATHOLOGY AND CLINICAL LINGUISTICS

Aims and Scope

The establishment of this series reflects the growth of both interest and research into disorders of speech and language. It is intended that the series will provide a platform for the development of academic debate and enquiry into the related fields of speech pathology and clinical linguistics.
To this end, the series will publish book length studies or collections of papers on aspects of disordered communication, and the relation between language theory and language pathology.

Volume 2

Harald Clahsen

Child Language and Developmental Dysphasia

CHILD LANGUAGE AND DEVELOPMENTAL DYSPHASIA

Linguistic Studies of the Acquisition of German

HARALD CLAHSEN
University of Düsseldorf

Translated by

KARIN RICHMAN

JOHN BENJAMINS PUBLISHING COMPANY
AMSTERDAM/PHILADELPHIA

1991

Autorisierte Übersetzung nach der deutschen Originalausgabe: Harald Clahsen, *Normale und gestörte Kindersprache*.

The translation of this book into English was supported by Inter Nationes, Bonn. Germany.

Library of Congress Cataloging-in-Publication Data

Clahsen, Harald.
[Normale und gestörte Kindersprache. English]
Child language and developmental dysphasia : linguistic studies of the acquisition of German / Harald Clahsen : translated by Karin Richman.
p. cm. -- (Studies in speech pathology and clinical linguistics ; v. 2)
Translation of: Normale und gestörte Kindersprache.
Includes bibliographical references and index.
1. Language acquisition. 2. Grammar, Comparative and general. 3. German language -- Acquisition. 4. Language disorders in children. I. Title. II. Series.
[DNLM: 1. Aphasia, Childhood. 2. Language Development -- in infancy & childhood. WL 340.5 C584n]
P118.C5413 1991
401'.93 -- dc20
DNLM/DLC 91-22437
ISBN 90 272 4332 8 (Eur.) / 1-55619-388-2 (US) (alk. paper) CIP

Preface

This book is a slightly revised version of my postdoctoral thesis (Habilitationsschrift) as submitted to the faculty of philosophy at the University of Düsseldorf in January 1987. The study was written and researched mainly in 1985 and 1986. I am grateful that the John Benjamins Publishing Company makes this book available to the English-speaking reader. The book does not squeeze all that goes under the rubrics of 'child language' and 'developmental dysphasia'; its focus is rather on the acquisition of German with particular reference to the research situation in West Germany. I hope that the book is of some interest for the English-speaking reader. Some passages from the original which had to do with my work on second language development have been omitted in the translated version, since in the meantime this work has been published at other places.

The present study owes its existence to the assistance and support of several people. First of all, I want to thank Dieter Wunderlich who was my supervisor and ensured that the circumstances for my research at the institute in Düsseldorf were always optimal. Many thanks also to Tilman Höhle who spent considerable time discussing the present work with me. The data on dysphasia to be analysed in the following were gathered and transcribed for the most part by the members of our research group. Earlier members of the project included Birgit Mohnhaus, Beate Uzarewicz, Andreas Collings, Detlef Hansen, Karin Martens and Andreas Schubert; the present members of the project are Monika Rothweiler, Stefan Schmitz, Jutta Pollmann and Andreas Woest. Further data came from institutes working in collaboration with our project: the Institute for Speech Therapy in Aachen and the Max-Planck-Institute for Psychiatry in Munich. In addition, Frieder Dannenbauer, Iris Füssenich and Hildegard Heidtmann made data from dysphasic children available to me.

My thanks to all the aforementioned.

The research was supported by a grant from the Max-Planck-Institute for Psycholinguistics in Nijmegen and by the German Science Foundation which sponsors our projects on language acquisition and on dysphasia financially. A computer was donated by the Rank Xerox Company, Düsseldorf, for the analysis of language data. The preparation of the English translation was supported by a grant from 'Inter Nationes'. I also gratefully acknowledge having received an award from the 'Society of Friends and Supporters of the University of Düsseldorf' for the present study.

Düsseldorf, January 1991 *Harald Clahsen*

Table of Contents

Introduction

The subject of this work is the acquisition of language structure. The development of syntax and morphology under two conditions is to be examined: (i) in normal children in the acquisition of their native language, and (ii) in children with grammatical deficiencies in language development. The thread of the research is that a rich mental capacity is available to the child in order that s/he can reconstruct the structure of the language with which s/he is confronted. The various studies presented here should provide insights into the basic principles of the language acquisition device and its development.

Linguistic investigations into child grammar acquisition can now draw upon the research of about 20 to 30 years. Early attempts to explain child language acquisition within a framework of simple behaviouristic theories of learning (Skinner 1957, Staats/Staats 1963) are no longer in favour nowadays. It is assumed instead that humans possess a specific 'mechanism' which enables them to acquire the grammar of any given language with relative ease. The language learning mechanism can thereby be taken as a part of the human biological make-up; there is neuropsychological evidence for this in, for example, Stachowiak (1987). The consensus of modern language acquisition research goes little further than these conclusions, however. Basically, the controversies arise regarding the question of the learning mechanism's internal structure and its development.

The question of the *autonomy* of grammar acquisition remains disputed. Some approaches – those which are more psychologically orientated – accept that grammar is learnt with the aid of general problem-solving and learning strategies, along with which non-linguistic abilities are acquired. On the other hand, linguistic approaches start on the basis that the mechanism for the acquisition of grammar is an autonomous cognitive component. Closely connected with this is the problem of *modularity* and the question as to which components the ability to acquire language consists of. Theoretical concepts which base themselves upon the autonomy hypothesis see the learning mechanism for the acquisition of grammar as a cognitive module, which itself contains a series of highly specialised components. These interact in a predetermined way and thus enable the normal acquisition of syntax and morphology. The opposing stance tries to explain grammar acquisition purely by means of pragmatic and semantic preconditions, thereby disposing of those learning mechanisms which specialise in the acquisition of formal language parameters.

A second complex of controversial questions concerns the *development of the language learning device*. In most approaches, including those endorsing the autonomy hypothesis, the basis is that the learning mechanisms for grammar acquisition develop step-by-step. Acquisition sequences are formulated, and in some studies even, an explicit maturation plan is produced (see Borer/Wexler 1987, Felix 1984). Other approaches, especially Pinker (1984), however, suggest the so-called *continuity hypothesis*, which tries to accomplish its aim without a specific maturation plan. Here it is assumed that all the mechanisms for learning are (latently) present from the start and that they do not undergo any qualitative changes during development. The progress seen during the period of language acquisition is primarily due to the expansion of lexical knowledge. It is shown that the learning mechanisms can only be triggered when the child has identified certain lexical elements, or rather their characteristics, in the input. This assumption has become known as the *lexical learning hypothesis*. Indeed, in comparison to the continuity hypothesis, it is the more interesting theoretical approach. Whether it can be maintained as such can only be decided by means of suitable empirical evidence from language acquisition investigations.

In this vein the question arises which deficiencies of grammar acquisition are possible in the process of development. An appropriate theory of grammar acquisition ought to be able to make specific predictions on this matter. Theoretical approaches which perceive the language acquisition mechanism as an autonomous and internally structured system of modules would predict the possibility of selective deficiencies in individual components, for example. Other approaches, in which grammar acquisition is explained by general problem-solving strategies, would then have to try to attribute the disorders in grammar development to (much more general) deficiencies in the child's information processing system.

The research situation in the area of language disorders is unsatisfactory. On the basis of the available empirical results it cannot be decided which of the two aforementioned ideas is the more appropriate. Thus far, linguistic acquisition research has injustifiably neglected the question of disorders in language learning, and left the area open for other disciplines (psychology, education, medicine). In my opinion it must be possible to describe the development of grammar under pathological conditions in the context of appropriate theories of grammar acquisition. Moreover, the predictions on possible disorders stemming from these theories can be tested empirically; the investigations into language development disorders are, in this respect, also a yard-stick against which competing theoretical constructs can be measured.

The aforementioned questions and problems outline the subject which this work will look at. It is methodically conceived of as a *comparative acquisition study* in which I concentrate on the investigations on children without language problems and on children with what is termed developmental dysphasia. This kind of comparative acquisition study can provide insights into the structure and development of the language acquisition device, which cannot be obtained by isolated analyses of only one type of learning. In this respect the study should be understood as a contribution to the efforts to extend the perspectives of language acquisition research (see Wode 1981), which strives towards an integrated theory of language acquisition in which human language learning under differing conditions can be explained. The special theoretical framework for my investigations is the *learnability approach*, in which acquisition models are proposed which are heavily influenced by theoretical linguistics. All proposed analyses in this direction use the autonomy hypothesis and the assumption of modularity as a starting-point. Pinker's approach (1984) to which I refer here, assumes furthermore the continuity hypothesis and the theory of lexical learning. I will be arguing in favour of these ideas.

I will show in the first part of the study that child grammar acquisition can be explained in the framework of learnability theory. Starting with an overall view of the theoretical discussion in language acquisition research, I investigate several central areas of syntactical and morphological development in German child language, in particular the acquisition of word order, syntactic categories and inflection.

Part II deals with deficiencies in normal grammar acquisition. Syntax and inflectional morphology in dysphasic children are investigated, and cross-sectional and longitudinal data on ten dysphasic children analysed. Learnability theory serves as the theoretical framework within which the deficiencies occurring can be precisely described and interpreted.

PART I

FIRST LANGUAGE ACQUISITION

1. Theoretical approaches in language acquisition research

Child language acquisition results from the combination of inborn abilities and the child's experiences in its physical and social environment. Every serious approach must credit the child with genetic preconditions for language acquisition. For this, one need only bear in mind that a child is capable of learning a language in domestic surroundings, unlike dogs, budgerigars and other domestic animals, for example. Nevertheless, environmental experiences also play a role, because as a rule children living in France do after all learn French, whilst children growing up in a German-speaking environment learn German. These conclusions are certainly undeniable; they are, however, also trivial.

Modern language acquisition research no longer asks *whether* genetic preconditions and environmental experiences are relevant, but *what* knowledge and *which* capabilities the child must be credited with, and *what* information from the input is necessary in order to learn language. Language acquisition studies are interested in discovering the child's underlying representations and learning mechanisms, as well as their development. The theoretical discussion in language acquisition research is defined by three lines of thought:

- learnability theory, an attempt on the development of learning models following ideas of theoretical linguistics (Wexler/Culicover 1980, Pinker 1984);
- the theory of Operating Principles (Slobin 1985), known as the cognitive approach in language acquisition research;
- the functionalist approach which is more orientated towards psychology and is formulated as a research programme in studies by Bates/MacWhinney (1979, 1982).

The decisive theoretical controversy concerns child *grammar* acquisition. In linguistic approaches it is accepted that children's grammatical competence is represented in a separate module, which functions independently of any other components and which consists of modules itself. The development of grammatical competence can proceed virtually independent of development in other cognitive areas. The development of grammar is steered by mechanisms which specialise in the acquisition of grammatical knowledge. These hypotheses are represented most clearly in learnability theory. They are also to be found in the theory of Operating Principles, although Slobin does not explicitly restrict himself to a specific theory of grammar.

On the other hand, there is a clearly opposing viewpoint represented in the functionalist approach. It is assumed in the radical version of (psychological) functionalism (see also Bates/MacWhinney/Smith 1983) that grammatical categories are generally unsuitable in representing children's linguistic knowledge, and that cognitive categories and strategies must be established for this purpose. In addition, those problem-solving strategies which would be engaged in grammar acquisition are those with which the child acquires other cognitive abilities. These ideas are to be described as the *functionalist hypothesis* of child language learning.

The subject of the following discussion will be the three aforementioned theories and the controversies in the explanation of child grammar acquisition. In this, I shall be arguing for the existence of an autonomous system of grammatical knowledge in children and – in connection with this – also for the existence of learning mechanisms with the specific task of learning grammar. That elements of grammatical theory make a fundamental contribution to the precision of learning models is also to be demonstrated.

1.1 The functionalist approach

We owe to the functionalist approach and the language acquisition studies linked with this approach the following insights: (a) that in the acquisition of formal language properties, pragmatic conditions of those communicative settings in which the children find themselves play an essential role, and (b) that children, in acquiring language structure, use the form-function relations which they find in the input. Moreover, the functional method of analysing child language data is propagated here, according to which various formal devices and their combination within the marking of pragmatic and semantic functions are investigated. The functionalist studies can be taken as a reaction against an all too rigid separation of form and function in language acquisition research in the sixties and seventies, in which individual formal devices, such as grammatical morphemes of English, were investigated in isolation and often without consideration for their function within child language. The functionalist approach provides the possibility of asking anew the question of the acquisition of formal aspects of language.

In the field of language acquisition research, Bates and MacWhinney (1979, 1982) formulate functionalism as a research programme and apply it to a large amount of data. Here, I want to look briefly at two examples.

Bates (1976) makes it clear that *word order* has a pragmatic function in early developmental phases; it serves especially to differentiate clearly between focus- and topic-elements. Bates shows that children in the one-word phase verbalise the most important element in each separate situation. The topic is provided here by the speech context and the child expresses the new information simply. Consequently, cognitive developments take place and enable the child to advance beyond the immediate context of action. To this end, new verbal means of expression, including word order, also become available. Bates demonstrates that word order in early two- and multi-word utterances serves to differentiate between old and new information, whereby the new information as a rule precedes the topic element. This result corresponds with the ideas of the functionalist approach, in particular with hypothesis (a).

Bates and MacWhinney (1979) illustrate their hypothesis (b) with the use of *subjects* in early child language. Their premise is that, in the linguistic input with which a child learning English is confronted, the syntactic subject expresses both the semantic role Agent and the pragmatic function Topic at the same time. There are therefore strong correlations in the input between the syntactic form and semantic, or rather pragmatic, functions of which the children take advantage. The authors show that children clearly mark Agent- and/or Topic-elements early on, by means of a fixed word order pattern. On the other hand, other kinds of subjects, for example Theme-arguments or subject-coding properties (agreement) are not marked. It is concluded from this that grammatical categories, for example subject, are not appropriate in the representation of children's linguistic knowledge.

The aforementioned results may be viewed as confirmation of the hypotheses (a) and (b). However, the conclusions which are drawn from them in the radical version of functionalism are controversial. Bates and MacWhinney (1982) assume that the relation between form and function is one-sidedly causal, so that in principle all formal characteristics of a language can be predicted as the necessary results of functional conditions. Regarding child language development, the strong version of the functionalist approach maintains (a*) that grammar acquisition can only be explained by semantic/pragmatic prerequisites, and that special mechanisms for the acquisition of formal language properties are superfluous; (b*) that child language can be represented completely in pragmatic or semantic categories just as in cognitive operations for language processing, and that grammatical categories are not necessary.

These ideas have already been rejected in language acquisition research as untenable. Here I will only sketch briefly some arguments against Bates and MacWhinney's position; a more in-depth discussion is to be found in Pinker (1984:138ff.), Meisel (1986) and Clahsen (1982).

Firstly, the strong functionalist approach does not explain how children learn the grammar of *adult* language in which syntactical categories and rules occur which cannot be described in semantic or pragmatic terms. The mechanisms offered in Bates and MacWhinney's model do not enable the acquisition of formal characteristics of language which have no semantic or pragmatic correlate. At most one could imagine that, at some particular point in development, the language learning mechanism changes fundamentally and that functional learning becomes grammatical learning. This idea would, however, contradict the strong functionalist position.

Secondly, the empirical evidence offered by Bates and MacWhinney is dubious. For example, at most preferential statistical tendencies are given for subject marking in early child language; they are not absolute generalisations which would justify not using grammatical categories. Pinker (1984:131ff.) carried out corresponding quantitative analyses on the use of the subject in early phases of English child language. It can be seen that animate Agent-arguments are used preferentially as subjects; however, absolute subject/object asymmetries are imperceptible in the analyses. Instead, elements which are used typically as objects also occur sometimes as the subject. The quantitative preference for Agent subjects does not have as much to do with the structure of the child's grammar as it has to do with the predominant use of verbs of action in children's early speech. In any case, Bates and MacWhinney's results do not force us to do away with grammatical categories in the representation of children's linguistic knowledge.

Thirdly, even in the earliest phase of syntax acquisition, the child has rules which draw upon grammatical categories and which cannot be described solely in semantic or pragmatic terms. These include positional principles for subjects, independent of their thematic role, and verbal elements (see Clahsen 1982).

Finally, the influence of pragmatic factors upon grammar acquisition is overestimated in functionalism, whilst on the other hand the child's ability for grammatical structure formation is underestimated. Meisel (1986) makes this argument clear with numerous examples from his investigation on bilingual language learning (German/French). As mentioned above, Bates (1976) claims that at early developmental stages word order fulfills pragmatic purposes. For example, verb-object-subject sequences in Italian child language are interpreted as being pragmatically motivated, whereby Focus- and Topic-elements are clearly differentiated through word order. Meisel shows that these sequences also appear in the data on bilingual children, though only in the French. There were no VOS patterns to be found in these children's German, although one would naturally expect them here, too, if they were really to be due to pragmatic considerations. Meisel interprets his results as an indication that children at an early developmental stage are already capable of separating the different grammatical structures of both languages. This enables them to recognise that right-dislocated subjects belong to the syntax of French, but not to that of German.

Functionalism, at least in its strong version, has to be rejected. The learning model of this approach does not have the scope to explain child grammar acquisition. Instead, mechanisms which specialise in the acquisition of formal linguistic features and individual categories, with which children's grammatical knowledge can be represented, are needed. I agree that the functional method of data analysis propagated by Bates and MacWhinney has benefited language acquisition research. Alternative theoretical concepts today can neither be allowed to fall back into the sterile paradigm of early language acquisition research nor should they investigate the acquisition of formal devices removed from their function in child language.

1.2 The theory of Operating Principles

The second theoretical approach currently discussed in language acquisition research arose from the comparative language acquisition studies within Dan Slobin's project at the University of California, Berkeley. The project has now been completed and publication of the results (Slobin 1985) gave the theoretical approach being developed here a whole new impetus.

The aim of the study was to formulate universal strategies and principles, termed by Slobin Operating Principles (OPs), with which the child approaches the task of learning a language. Information about universal OPs is obtained through comparative investigations into the acquisition of linguistic devices of expression in structurally differing languages. OPs are obtained inductively from the available data and from observations of errors and successive development. The first somewhat unsystematic collection of OPs was presented as early as Slobin (1973). Subsequently, the collection was expanded to a more coherent approach (Slobin 1985).

1.2.1 *A sketch of Slobin's model*

In accordance with the autonomy hypothesis, Slobin presupposes that the child possesses a mental mechanism, the *Language Making Capacity* (LMC), which specialises in acquiring language competence. LMC is related to Chomsky's notion of the Language Acquisition Device (LAD). Both mechanisms attempt to indicate what knowledge and which abilities the child brings to the task of learning a language. The fundamental difference from Chomsky's notion is that Slobin's LMC does not specifically refer to a grammatical theory. The LMC consists of a semantic space, in which basic semantic concepts are founded, and of a formal space which contains linguistic forms and devices of expression. Both spaces have an internal order based upon hierarchies of markedness. Moreover, the LMC encompasses OPs which create links between the semantic and formal spaces. OPs are the actual mechanisms for the formation of language; they include statements as to how the child perceives, analyses, and reconstructs language.

Slobin stresses that gradual attainment of language competence in early development can be explained by OPs. Chomsky's concept of the LAD, at least in its early versions (Chomsky 1965) took on an idealisation, the so-called "instantaneous" assumption. Thereafter the study of language learning was reducable to an analysis of the initial state and the final state, reached by having acquired adult language. Nothing about actual development was stated. Thus, Chomsky's original approach provided no theory of real language learning (see Clahsen 1982:13ff.). Slobin's concept ignores this idealisation and claims, with the aid of OPs, to be able to explain the continual growth in the child's linguistic competence.

Three groups of OPs are defined as follows:

(a) *Filters of perception and storage* control the information from the linguistic input to which the child pays attention, and the form in which that information is stored.
(b) *Strategies for the construction of grammar* control how the stored information is used in the construction of linguistic rule-systems; amongst other things, they draw upon linguistic units, form-function relations and positional principles.
(c) *General problem-solving strategies* are not specific for language learning; they are used among other things to review continuously the results of learning.

The elements of Slobin's model can be represented as in the following diagram:

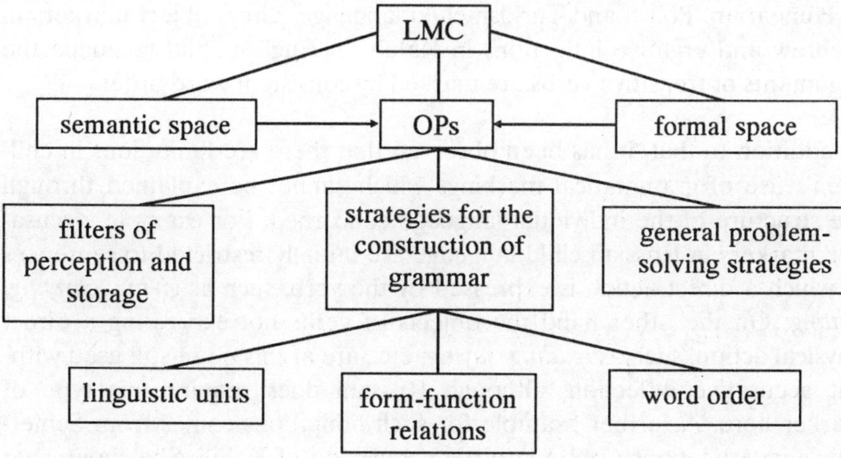

New in Slobin's theory are the assumptions of the so-called *Basic Child Grammar* (BCG). Slobin conceives of a predetermined number *of OPs in* child language development which is initially applied to the input from the individual language to be learned. Thereby, a grammar – the BCG – arises, which, from the point of view of the LMC learning mechanism, can be considered the ideal underlying form of human language. The BCG encompasses a number of fundamental semantic concepts which are clearly mapped onto linguistic forms. In this respect, the BCG is related to Bickerton's concept of a "Language Bioprogram" (Bickerton 1981, 1984). On the basis of these investigations into pidgin and creole languages, claims can also be made as to the ideal form of grammar.

These comments provide a rough view of the fundamental elements of Slobin's theory. In the following, the grammar acquisition mechanisms are to be examined in more detail; as an example, I will investigate transitivity markers in child language.

1.2.2 *On the analysis of transitivity markers*

Investigations into the acquisition of various individual languages, as summarised in Slobin (1985), show that grammatical markings which occur typically in transitive sentences are already available to children at an early age. Thus, even at early developmental stages, accusative forms are found in Hungarian, Polish and Turkish child language, direct object markers in Hebrew and ergative inflections in Kaluli. In English child language the arguments of transitive verbs are marked by consistent word order.

In addition to that, it has been observed that there are limitations in children's use of grammatical markings which cannot be explained through the structure of the individual language concerned. For example, accusative markers in Russian child language are initially restricted to sentences in which a direct action is expressed by the verb, such as *giving, carrying, putting*. On the other hand the objects of verbs not expressing a direct physical action, such as *reading, saying*, etc., are at this point still used without accusative inflection, although Russian does require this type of marker here. A further example for such limitations comes from Schieffelin's investigations (1981) into the acquisition of Kaluli. She shows that the ergative in child language is used from the start only in transitive sentences. It is not transferred to the arguments of intransitive verbs, not even in the case of an Agent-argument.

Slobin (1981) concludes from these observations that it is not only just the thematic role of the argument which is decisive for the surface structure marking chosen by the child. Far more relevant are the characteristics of the entire sentence, particularly the *semantic transitivity* of the predicate-argument structure.

Within Slobin's theoretical approach, transitivity belongs to the fundamental concepts of the semantic space in the LMC. Here transitivity is understood according to Hopper and Thompson's (1980) account. They define semantic transitivity by means of a cluster of characteristics; hence, highly transitive sentences comprise, amongst other things, an action verb, two or more arguments, an animate Agent, etc. Slobin believes that the child – independent of the individual language to be learned – looks for a means of expression for high transitivity. He considers transitivity to be an elementary concept which can be fitted into a grammatical scheme and regards it as an integral part of the universal BCG.

Slobin supports this thesis by sketching a prototypical action pattern, the so-called Manipulative Activity Scene, which corresponds to semantic transitivity. In this prototypical schema, an animate protagonist carries out a visible activity with an object. According to Slobin, such a schema occurs often in the child's experience. It also includes relevant basic concepts, which are, in the above case, the Agent and the physical object, which to a large extent has been handled by the child itself. Slobin considers action patterns of this type to be the crucial components of grammar acquisition.

Based on these considerations, Slobin formulates OPs with which mappings can be made between semantic transitivity and a number of formal linguistic devices. Particularly relevant here is the OP for function words with which amongst other things inflectional elements can be acquired. Transitivity as a basic concept and the OP both belong in the BCG and are therefore universals of child language.

One of the particular advantages of Slobin's approach, which should be apparent from the above example, is that these principles are based on broad and varied analyses of child language. Data from the acqusition of structurally different languages has not been compiled and systemised to such an extent in any other language acquisition approach. The OPs can therefore be regarded as valid and particularly well-grounded statements on child language.

A further advantage is that the principles refer to functional, largely semantic parameters *and* to formal characteristics of language. Both are autonomous areas of the LMC. In particular, Slobin does not make the same (in my opinion misguided) attempt as is made in functionalist approaches, whereby formal parameters are dismissed as arbitrary problem-solving areas not necessary for a child learning language.

The *objections* to Slobin's approach can also be made clear using the example of transitivity markers. Bowerman (1985) especially criticises the hypotheses on BCG. She offers a number of arguments against the claims of universal dispositions for certain semantic concepts and preferred mappings between form and function. Bowerman also contends that a child even at an early developmental stage pays heed to the specific structure of the individual language concerned.

Hence investigations on, for example, the use of transitivity markers show that children, even at early developmental stages, are receptive to the difference between a Nominative-Accusative and an Ergative-Absolutus system. As mentioned above, the ergative is not tranferred onto the subjects of intransitive verbs in the acquisition of Kaluli or in Samoan child language (cf. Ochs 1982), for example. Rather, the Agent-argument is marked (in the ergative). On the other hand, in Russian child language as in the learning of other Nominative-Accusative languages, the *object* is marked (in the accusative). This contrast illustrates that children single out *several different* elements of the so-called Manipulative Activity Scene, and that this is only because they heed the structure of the language being learnt.

Additional problems concerning the concepts assumed in the BCG and their formal marking are made clear through the results attained by Budwig (1985) on the acquisition of English and by Clahsen (1986a) on German child language. They show that children do not only develop means of expression for highly transitive sentences, but that the intransitive construction can also be provided with formal markers.

At the earliest learning stage of German child language the children's utterances include *-t* as a verbal suffix, in addition to stem and infinitive forms. At first the inflections are not yet employed as agreement markers.

Rather, we find that the inflection *-t* occurs in sentences of *low* semantic transitivity. The occurrences with *-t* were investigated in terms of the parameters of the transitivity scale in Hopper & Thompson (1980). This then showed that *-t* occurs typically in sentences with one-place predicates and an inanimate Theme-argument in which no physical activity is expressed:

(1) a. fällt um
(The child asks his mother to give him a hand so that he does not fall over.)
b. fehlt was
(The child indicates a bridge of which a part is missing.)
c. dreht immer
(The child points at a roundabout which is revolving.)

These examples are taken from my data on German child language. I present them here to serve as an illustration of the phenomenon. Verb inflection will be investigated more thoroughly in Ch. 3.3.

The results of this study also show that children develop formal markers for the intransitive construction. In this respect Slobin's theory makes predictions which are false for German child language.

Budwig's results (1985) display a similar tendency. She establishes that the uses of the pronouns *I* and *my* in early English child language comply with parameters on the transitivity scale in Hopper & Thompson (1980): *my* occurs in highly transitive sentences (with two-place predicates, action verbs, Agent-arguments, etc.), whilst *I* is used in sentences which are less transitive. The following instances from Budwig (1985) clarify this asymmetry:

(2) a. *my* blew the candles out
b. *my* do it
c. *I* like peas

Budwig's results show, as do the observations on German child language, that children develop a marking system for transitivity/intransitivity, even when the adult language does not offer any such corresponding grammatical system. It can therefore be concluded that there are preferred semantic concepts in language (from a set of alternatives which are easy, compared to those which are difficult to access), and that semantic transitivity is one of these basic concepts. Here Slobin's claims are supported by the empirical results.

However, the claim that only the transitive sentences would be grammatically marked is not confirmed. It seems to be far more decisive that children construct a formal system with which the functional difference between the various values of the basic concept can be marked. It is possible that different forms are employed for low and high transitivity, as in English child language. It is also possible that only one transitivity value is marked formally, as in German child language. However, in both cases the functional differentiation of argument structures with regard to transitivity is assured.

On the whole, the results on the use of transitivity markers show that the relations between semantic concepts and formal devices for expression, even in early child language, are more complex than presumed in Slobin's theory. The idea of direct and universal mappings between form and function, as conceived in Slobin's BCG, in particular, must be retracted.

1.2.3 *On the theoretical status of Operating Principles*

In Slobin's approach, elements of grammatical theory and the considerations of learnability linked with these are not explicitly heeded. This leads to ambiguities in the theoretical status of OPs, the BCG and other elements of this theory.

Hence Bowerman (1985) comments, for example, that the BCG does not make any substantial statements about the acquisition of purely formal parameters. It is unclear how universal syntactic conditions, as they are formulated in grammatical theory, are to be represented in children's linguistic systems.

Additionally Bowerman criticizes the fact that it is hardly possible to falsify OPs. Using several examples she illustrates that evidence against a particular OP can be swept away by establishing a new OP. Thus, the arguments are tautological since OPs are available for all logically possible cases. Connected with this is the objection that identical phenomena, e.g. error-types, can be explained by means of completely different OPs.

I suggest that these problems occur because in Slobin's concept learnability constraints and insights from grammatical theory have not been sufficiently considered. If OPs are meant to be learning mechanisms then the conditions under which these mechanisms are triggered must also be given. It is conceivable, for example, that the child at a particular point in its development can identify material in the input which it has not considered before. Additionally it must be shown that the learning mechanisms can acquire the linguistic systems which emerge during development as easily as they acquire the system of adult language. Otherwise caesuras would occur in development and the learning mechanisms themselves would undergo changes. In any case, with learnability considerations of this type, it is possible to limit the class of possible OPs greatly.

In this respect Slobin does not clarify his ideas. Similarly,he does not consider the theoretical status of the BCG. Does the BCG fall within the scope of Universal Grammar? In other words, do the same principles apply to the BCG as to any other grammar in natural language? If the answer is yes, then the structure of the BCG could be correspondingly specified. Slobin does not, however, wish to commit himself to the theory of Universal Grammar. He mainly limits himself to composing OPs directly from the data. This approach is of course appropriate as a descriptive procedure, but as long as the aforementioned questions remain untackled, OPs and the BCG are merely generalisations about the data, but not central elements of a theory of language acquisition.

1.3 Learnability theory

Recently, in the area of learnability theory progress has been made from which language acquisition research could benefit. In this framework, precise, partly mechanistic models are developed, which can in principle acquire a language on the basis of a limited amount of linguistic input. Research in this area has been carried out in several disciplines: (a) learnability theorems in mathematical linguistics (Gross 1972), (b) computer simulation of language acquisition in A(rtificial)-I(ntelligence) research (Kelley 1967), (c) learning models in theoretical linguistics for transformational grammars (Wexler/Culicover 1980) and for Lexical-Functional Grammar (Pinker 1982).

Up to now learnability theories have received far less acknowledgement in language acquisition research than the two approaches previously described. That is in my belief not justified, since answers to basic questions regarding language acquisition are provided in learnability research. Pinker (1984) has proposed a far-reaching theory of language acquisition within the learnability approach which is not merely a mathematical learning model but which also employs extensive data on child language in order to validate the theoretically possible variants with empirical evidence.

Learnability theories consist of three components:

(A) They define *the set of possible grammars* which the language learner can acquire, one of which is that of the target language.
(B) They define the *linguistic input*, needed by the learner in order to acquire the set of possible grammars in (A).
(C) They involve *acquisition mechanisms* which describe the operations to be performed by the language learner in order to acquire one of the possible grammars in (A) on the basis of (B).

In addition, theoretically motivated *learnability constraints* are established, which must be fulfilled by the analyses suggested. In the following, the various elements of this approach will be described in more detail.

1.3.1 *Learnability constraints*

In grammatical theory, considerations about learnability serve as external criteria in the evaluation of competing descriptively adequate grammatical analyses. Priority is given to that grammatical description which fulfills the constraints of learnability (cf. Chomsky 1981).

Empirical studies on language acquisition research usually only deal with learnability considerations as a side-issue. The grammars formulated for child language comprise, for example, a mixture of categories from adult language, of ad hoc categories, semantic features and individual lexical units (cf. e.g. Bowerman 1973, Brown 1973). In addition to traditional grammatical rules, cognitive operations, processing strategies etc. are given. It may well be that all of these mechanisms are descriptively adequate. However, the decisive question is which of the categories and operations suggested actually represent the children's linguistic knowledge correctly. If word order in early child language can be described by a grammatical rule in which categories such as subject, object and so on occur, and at the same time by an Operating Principle, which exclusively refers to semantic features, then external criteria have to be formulated, as in grammatical theory, in order to decide which of the suggested, descriptively adequate analyses is to be given priority. Learnability constraints come into play at this point.

Theories of language acquisition must fulfill a number of empirical conditions. One of these is the fact that the learning mechanism must be able to learn any human language. Learning mechanisms which are only operational for specific languages do not fit this criterion, which Pinker (1979: 218) has named the condition of *equipotentiality*. Moreover, the acquisition of the basic elements of grammar takes place in a *temporally fixed period* of development, up until the age of about four. Children possess *limited general cognitive abilities* in this period. On top of this, the child only has access to a *restricted amount of linguistic input.*

Current approaches in language acquisition research seek first and foremost to do justice to these conditions. Hence, Slobin carries out comparative acquisition studies in order to be able to formulate Operating Principles with universal validity and thereby to fulfill the condition of equipotentiality. Also to be considered in functionalist approaches and in Slobin's theory are discoveries made in developmental psychology on children's perception and memory, for example, as well as investigations on linguistic input, available to the child.

The decisive criterion from the point of view of learnability theory, termed the *condition of learnability* by Pinker (1984), is neglected in other theoretical approaches. It is based on observations that child language learning is possible without any exertion, that it always leads to the acquisition of a human language and that it proceeds in the form of ordered stages of development. In order to fulfill the constraint of learnability, a suitable language acquisition theory must contain mechanisms with which not only those linguistic systems constructed by children at each individual stage of development are learnt, but also that of adult language grammar. Two solutions to this learnability problem are conceivable:

(a) The learning mechanisms change in the course of language development as a result of cognitive or neural maturational processes.
(b) The language learning mechanism itself undergoes no qualitative changes in the course of development. Rather the stages of development are more the result of gradual extensions of the child's lexicon and his/her processing capacities.

Most language acquisition models are based (explicitly or implicitly) on the maturation hypothesis, (a). Assumption (b) comprises the *continuity hypothesis* of Pinker's learnability theory. In the event of (a) and (b) being equally descriptively adequate for any set of child language data, analysis (b) is preferred for heuristic reasons, because it is more parsimonious. A theory of acquisition which falls under the continuity assumption must describe the initial and final states, as well as the learning mechanism itself. Approaches that follow assumption (a) must explain additionally those changes in the learning mechanism which are assumed to have occurred as a result of maturation.

Using the continuity hypothesis as a basis, the language acquisition mechanism is conceived of as being stationary and direct. It does not change during the course of development, nor does it produce any transitional structures or any developmental defects which could then disappear while learning progresses.

In the face of empirical results in language acquisition research these assumptions initially seem untenable. Numerous investigations have shown that the child constructs a number of transitional grammars in the course of acquisition before attaining the adult grammar for any given language, and that characteristic errors occur in children's utterances during development. If the learning mechanism is meant to be stationary and direct, one could ask, why does the child not learn the grammar of adult language immediately and how do errors occur in his/her verbal utterances?

Pinker does not contradict the aforementioned observations, but he does show that transitional grammars and developmental defects are possible options within parameterised principles of Universal Grammar (UG). The children's utterances do indeed contain errors in the sense of a particular target-language norm, and the children learn rules during development which as such do not apply to the adult language being learned. However, the crucial evidence is that the children's linguistic patterns fall from the start within the limits imposed by UG. One can therefore relinquish the idea that there exist special mechanisms in children for the learning of transitional grammars.

In addition to this Pinker argues for the *lexical learning hypothesis*. He shows that developmental progress is triggered by extensions of the child's lexicon. At the start of language learning, not all lexical units and the features linked with them are available to the child. Rather, the lexicon develops step-by-step. What is decisive is that certain learning mechanisms can only become effective when the child is able to categorize the corresponding lexical units. Conjunctions introducing subordinate clauses are for example not accessible to children in early developmental phases, and the relevant syntactic learning mechanisms are not yet operative. This leads to a lack of structural possibilities for sentence embedding in early child grammars. Only after conjunctions have been identified and categorized in the child's lexicon can the related parameters of Universal Grammar be fixed. In this way the lexicalist position facilitates an analysis of child transitional grammars which meshes with the continuity hypothesis.

The question as to the continuity of learning mechanisms belongs to the core of the discussion in learnability research. Some researchers delute the strong version of the hypothesis as represented here by Pinker. I will look briefly at Felix's approach (1984) as an example of this.

Felix agrees with the basic assumptions of learnability theory. He adds to the theory a maturational schedule according to which the principles of Universal Grammar are triggered. He describes the grammar of early two- and three-word utterances only in terms of semantic categories and relations. In his opinion, early child grammar does not fall under Universal Grammar. Felix tries to show that this grammar is completely restructured further on in the course of learning. The cause of this is the availability of the X-bar scheme, triggered by the maturational schedule. The X-bar scheme's function is to limit the variety of possible grammars. This scheme is then triggered sometime around the early two- and three-word phase. Through this – according to Felix – it is possible for the child to restructure its transitional grammar in such a way that it concurs with the principles of Universal Grammar.

This scenario clearly diverges from the continuity hypothesis and the related assumptions about learnability. A decision between the two alternatives can only be made on the basis of empirical evidence. For heuristic reasons, though, the continuity hypothesis is to be chosen in preference. As long as descriptively adequate analyses of child language data are possible under continuity, there is no need for an additional maturational schedule, such as that proposed by Felix.

The continuity hypothesis, together with the other aforementioned learnability conditions, provides external criteria with which possible learning mechanisms and grammatical analyses of child language can be evaluated. Learnability constraints alone cannot lead to a theory of grammar acquisition, but instead only to a number of theoretically motivated variants. Generalisations about child language data do not comprise a theory either, but rather just a number of competing (descriptively adequate) analyses. Only by means of a combination of learnability constraints together with descriptive analyses of child language can a theory of grammar acquisition be derived. The following diagram illustrates these observations (cf. Pinker 1984:10):

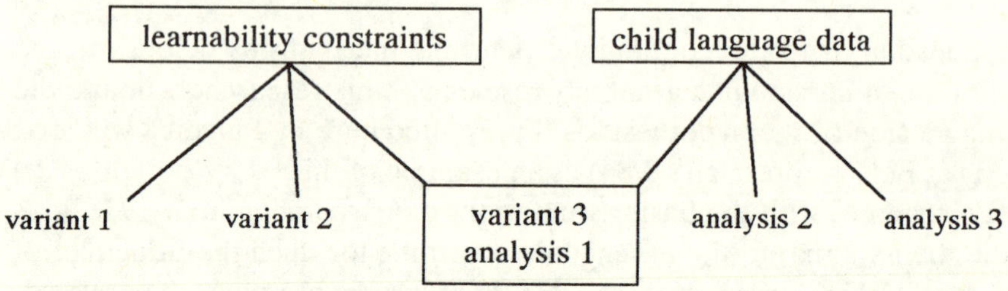

Variant 3 – analysis 1 fulfills the learnability constraints and provides a descriptively adequate analysis of the data. It should therefore be preferred to the other variants and analyses.

The particular advantage of Pinker's theory (1984) lies in the fact that it fulfills both requirements. Other learnability theories sometimes create rather abstract learning models which have little to say about actual language acquisition. Pinker does not limit himself only to considerations about learnability, but also deals with extensive data on child language and with the corresponding results in language acquisition research, in order to evaluate the theoretically possible variants on the basis of the empirical evidence available.

1.3.2 *Grammatical theory and learnability*

In learnability theory it is assumed that children's linguistic knowledge can be represented in terms of grammars. One of the tasks of learnability research is to specify the set of possible grammars which a language learner can acquire (cf. component A). A learnability theory is based here on insights from grammatical theory and assumes that the possibilities for the construction of grammars are limited from the start by principles of Universal Grammar (UG).

As already mentioned, the representation of the language learner's linguistic knowledge is controversial. Functionalism states, for example, that grammars are unsuited to this purpose. Here language competence is considered to be a set of processing strategies, i.e. distinct mechanisms for language production, language comprehension, for metalinguistic judgements, etc.

Learnability theory argues against these claims. Clearly, adults can produce, understand and judge the same number of well-formed sentences. Instead of assuming that there are three separate knowledge systems for these capabilities, in which redundancies would then have to occur automatically, it is surely more plausible to assume an independent grammatical module, upon which the aforementioned capabilities are based and in which it is specified what can count as a possible grammatical sentence in the language at hand.

As long as no empirical evidence is produced to counter it, this hypothesis can – simply for reasons of plausibility – apply to children, too. If one wished to maintain that children do not learn grammatical rules, but special production and comprehension strategies instead, then one would have to show the existence of qualitative asymmetries within the various processing modalities; linguistic structures or elements would, for example, have to be available in production but not in language comprehension. Furthermore, children's processing systems develop only gradually. Even if asymmetries between production and comprehension are observed, they can simply be explained by the fact that, despite the availability of grammatical competence, children do not have access to the corresponding processing strategies. Such asymmetries have not yet been demonstrated convincingly (cf. Deutsch 1985). So we shall therefore stick to the theory that children's linguistic knowledge can also be represented in the form of grammars.

The second controversy has to do with the structure of child grammars and the categories which they comprise. In language acquisition research it is commonly argued that the grammatical rules and categories of adult language are not suitable for the analysis of children's linguistic utterances. Rather, independent grammars for child language ought to be formulated with "child-fair" categories (cf. for example Braine 1963, 1976, Huss 1980). This premise has led to the child language grammars available in the literature comprising a strange mixture of semantic, syntactic and occasionally pragmatic categories, together with transformational rules, production strategies, etc. (cf. for example Miller 1976, Brown 1973, Braine 1976). It is obvious that these grammars cannot fulfill the learnability constraints specified in paragraph 1.3.1.

As a result of the continuity assumption, grammatical analyses of child language which fall under the principles of UG are preferred. With respect to this, the continuity hypothesis provides an external evaluation criterion. Using this as a basis, Pinker (1984) shows that early child language can be described by the category inventory and rule types employed in the analysis of adult language. He clarifies that ad-hoc solutions, which could for example come from limited sets of data, can in this way be avoided. In addition, a grammatical analysis which concurs with the principles of UG is easily extendable. Analyses working with arbitrary categories and principles, such as the previous attempts at computer simulation of language acquisition, fail if one tries to apply them to greater domains of grammatical phenomena (for this cf. Pinker 1979).

Grammatical theories contain a number of categories and rule types which are required in describing structurally different human languages. The peculiarities of any particular language are not necessarily perceptible from the types of rules and categories, but from the values of UG parameters individual languages have fixed. The same applies to child language. That early child language differs from adult language does not mean that completely different instruments have to be employed for its description. Rather – because of learnability constraints – those analyses which fall under UG are to be taken in preference.

The next step is to decide which of the partly competing grammatical theories can best account for the grammars accessible to the language learner. There are three approaches in grammatical theory presently under discussion:

(a) Chomsky's Government-Binding (GB) theory (1981)
(b) Bresnan's Lexical Functional Grammar (LFG) (1982)
(c) Gazdar, Klein, Pullum and Sag's Generalized Phrase Structure Grammar (GPSG) (1985)

Pinker (1984) commits himself wholly to LFG, maintaining that LFG is descriptively superior to the other approaches. According to Pinker, the characteristics of structurally differing languages can best be described by means of LFG. Moreover, various grammatical phenomena have been studied in this framework. Lastly, it is said that in language processing models, grammatical competence can be represented in terms of LFG (cf. Ford 1982), whereas for the other two approaches no such evidence has been offered.

Pinker's commitment to LFG in his learnability theory seems to me to be premature and insufficiently motivated. In committing himself he is also subject to the weaknesses of this grammatical theory. Grammatical functions, for example, enter Pinker's theory as undefined notions in syntactic and semantic representations. However, it is arguable whether subject, object and other grammatical functions may even be allowed to count as universal categories at all; cf. Reis's arguments (1982) on the notion of subject in German grammar. Moreover there is only one level of syntactic representation, the near-surface c-structure. It is arguable whether that is sufficient; see Chomsky (1981). In any case arguments are given for two levels of syntactical representation in GB theory. The functional structure, lastly, is an odd mixture of syntactic, semantic and morphological characteristics and categories. It is unclear which grammatical module should be depicted by the f-structure.

It will be clarified in the second and third chapter of the present study that a disproportionate orientation to LFG leads to problems in the analysis of child language. LFG does indeed provide further-reaching insights into *lexical* representations and rules than the other two approaches. On the other hand, LFG has rather little to say about word order and constituent structure. Furthermore, there is language learning data discussed, in particular on the position of the verb in German child language, which does not agree with LFG's predictions. With respect to that, I will mainly be using concepts from GB-theory.

I think that language acquisition researchers do not have to commit themselves blindly to one grammatical theory. Otherwise their results could – as has happened in the past – become obsolete as soon as the theory changes. The alternative certainly cannot be to ignore grammatical theories completely, since these are needed to fulfill the learnability constraints. My strategy in analysing child language will be to pay heed to insights from various grammatical theories and to evaluate possible alternatives on the basis of learnability considerations as much as on the basis of available empirical evidence.

1.3.3 *On the structure of the language acquisition device*

1.3.3.1 In older approaches (cf. e.g. Wexler/Culicover 1980) the idea of a language learner testing hypotheses was discussed. It was assumed that the child has access to an innate mechanism (LAD) consisting of three components:

(a) Characterisation of the *form* of possible grammars, that is, information on the types of grammatical categories and rules.
(b) Characterisation of the *modes of interaction* in possible grammars, that is, information as to how various rules cooperate.
(c) Information about an *evaluation metric*, with which the possible grammars according to (a) and (b) can be evaluated.

The idea was that the child, on the basis of the linguistic input, forms hypotheses regarding the structure of adult language. Due to (a) and (b) these hypotheses are possible grammars and fall under the limits imposed by UG. With the aid of (c) the child choses the grammar most highly valued from the large number of those possible. The evaluation should, among other things, be guided by the number of category symbols: the fewer symbols a grammar rule contains the higher it is valued.

In more recent learnability research, the concept of the hypothesis-testing language learner is criticized. As the structure of the evaluation metric is not more closely defined, it cannot be explained in this model just how systematic developmental sequences occur in language learning. The child obviously does not directly chose the correct structure, but constructs it in a learning process running through a succession of intermediate stages. It remains unclear just why certain hypotheses are acquired and appear systematically before others in language learning.

Moreover, this model cannot guarantee that the child will in the end chose the correct grammar of the respective adult language. The child would need additional information on ungrammatical sentences in order to reject hypotheses accepted in error during a particular developmental stage. It is assumed, however, that children at the early developmental stages are generally *not* corrected with respect to grammatical errors. Pinker (1984) also assumes that only positive evidence is available to the language learner, i.e. information on possible sentences in the appropriate language; negative evidence on the other hand forms no relevant part of the linguistic input. Both the limited amount and the type of linguistic input require a learning mechanism which from the beginning limits the language learner's possibilities more strongly than is the case in the model of hypothesis-testing.

The criticism mentioned above has led to an alternative approach to the LAD, which has become well-known as the *parameter model* of language acquisition (cf. e.g. Hyams 1986). The language learner is no longer said to choose various grammars and compare them with one another. It is instead assumed that the possibilities the child has in constructing possible grammars are constrained by parameterised principles of UG. The parameters represent the limited number of options which are responsible for the grammatical differences between natural languages. The parameters are moreover highly abstract principles which take respective effect on a whole range of grammatical phenomena.

A well-known example is the pro-drop parameter from GB theory (Chomsky 1981:240). This parameter entails a cluster of grammatical phenomena which occur in several languages, e.g. in Italian and Spanish, which do not exist in this form in English or German. These phenomena include, among others, missing subjects (a), free inversion in simple sentences (b), and extraction of the subject from subordinate clauses (c):

(3) a. Pensava ai suoi abiti
"(She) thought of her clothes"
b. Ha telefonato Giovanni
"Giovanni has rung"
c. Chi credi che parlera
"Who do you think will speak"

These phenomena can be derived according to the GB analysis from a single parameter, namely from the fact that the agreement features

> (AGR) count as a possible governor in these languages; this parameter is called pro-drop. The aforementioned features appear in the languages either only together, as for example in Italian, or not at all, as in English. From this it can be concluded that pro-drop forms an option offered in Universal Grammar. This parameter is activated in languages where the phenomena illustrated in (3) occur; in the others it is not. The variation in natural languages can in this way be derived from one single principle (of UG).

Recent approaches in learnability theory assume that during the course of language development the parameters are fixed at the values required by any given language. Positive evidence in the linguistic input is sufficient for this. Such an approach to LAD leads to several specific predictions.

Firstly, grammars which a child contructs during development must be possible options of parameters of Universal Grammar. Otherwise the model would not fall under the continuity assumption.

Secondly, developmental correlations between various grammatical phenomena of child language have to be derivable from UG parameters. Longitudinal studies (cf. e.g. Garman 1979, Clahsen 1982) show that child language acquisition can be characterized as a discontinuous process with separate phases, in which developmental progress is made simultaneously in differing grammatical domains. The parameter model offers a theoretical framework for such observations. One may assume that parameters are fixed or that the previously chosen values of separate parameters are reset and that thereby child grammar can be restructured. The precondition for this is however the evidence that the grammatical phenomena occurring together in development fall under particular parameters of UG.

Thirdly, in fixing parameters, it is required that simple data available to the child from the linguistic input be sufficient (cf. also Baker 1979). Hyams (1984) shows, for example, that the child acquiring English can fix the pro-drop parameter at the required value as soon as s/he finds the pronouns *it* and *there* in the input and categorises them correspondingly. These elements have no real meaning in themselves, but rather serve to fill an empty subject position. The child is in this way able to discover that empty subjects are not permitted in English. Ideally, as in the example mentioned, lexical units and their properties should be sufficient in fixing the parameters at the required values. This at least corresponds with the lexicalist position (see 1.3.1). It has to be shown that by acquiring new lexical material or through changes in the lexical representation of individual elements, restructurings are triggered in child grammar thereby fixing parameters.

In the following chapters I will try to provide evidence for this. Using results from German child language I will argue, that the acquisition of early child grammars can be explained in terms of the parameter model.

1.3.3.2 The parameter model is also a basic element of the LAD in Pinker's learnability theory (1984). He shows, though, that additional assumptions are required. They especially concern the question of how children make use of the material from the linguistic input, which is necessary for fixing UG parameters. Pinker claims that the child exploits correlations between semantic and syntactic categories in the linguistic input. This hypothesis is known as semantic bootstrapping in learnability research; it will be explained in the following example.

Some of the parameters of UG refer to the position of elements in phrase structure rules. The composition of syntactic constituents is determined by universal principles (the X-bar theory). With regard to the elements within syntactic constituents there are various options in natural languages, however, which are controlled by parameterised principles. Since the child is not predisposed to the acquisition of any particular language, it must be assumed that the word order parameters are fixed during the course of learning and that positive evidence is sufficient for this process. In a somewhat idealized picture of the course of development one can imagine that the LAD (by means of X-bar theory) starts to produce phrase structure rules in which the position has not yet been fixed, e.g:

(a) S → NP, VP
(b) NP → (Det), N
(c) VP → NP, V

According to the parameter model, simple sentences are enough to fix the positional parameters; (4) should for example be sufficient to fix the parameters in rules (a) to (c) at the values required by German:

(4) Der Junge wirft Steine
(=The boy throws stones.)

The result of the development would be PS-rules (without commas) which correspond with the target German grammar.

The *objections* Pinker puts forward (1984:37f.) have to do with the categorization of the linguistic input by the child. He indicates that the positional parameters can only be fixed if the child already knows the linguistic features of the categories which occur in the PS-rules. The universal knowledge of the categories in question which is provided by X-bar principles is however not sufficient because the child not only has to know what nouns, verbs, heads, etc. are, but in order to set the positional parameters s/he also has to be able to identify the syntactic categories in the linguistic input. There are no universal position-patterns or morphological markings, however, for syntactic categories. Thus, it cannot be assumed that the child knows of such features from the start. On the other hand s/he has to be able to identify the categories in a particular language. Otherwise under certain circumstances positional parameters would be falsely fixed. One could then conceive that the child would reach a categorisation (4*) in German by means of the composition rules (a) to (c) and the input (4):

(4*) $[_{S} [_{VP} [_{NP} [_{N}\text{Der}]] [_{V}\text{Junge}]] [_{NP} [_{N}\text{wirft}] [_{Det}\text{Steine}]]]$

It is completely unclear how the child ever constructs the PS-rules required by German on the basis of (4*).

A solution for this learnability problem is the hypothesis of semantic bootstrapping which began with insights from Grimshaw (1981) and MacNamara (1982) and has been worked out further by Pinker (1984). The basic idea is that the child uses semantic features in order to identify syntactic categories in the input.

An important source of information for the child arises from the fact that s/he can extract the meaning of adults' sentences from the situational context and from the meanings of individual words. It is also helpful that there are strong correlations between semantic categories and syntactic categories in the input offered to the child. Physical objects are here preferably encoded by nouns, actions and states by verbs, definiteness by articles, etc. One assumes that such strong form-function correlations make it possible for the child to identify the syntactic categories of the particular language. Since the semantic information (about physical objects, actions and definiteness) are available to the child in perception, the syntactic categories in (4) can be identified by semantic bootstrapping. Because of semantic bootstrapping (4*) can be ruled out as a possible constituent structure, and the positional parameters can be fixed at the required values.

Semantic bootstrapping is understood as an early learning strategy. This means that grammars constructed by children in the initial phases of language learning comprise syntactic categories which can be interpreted as canonical realisations of semantic notions. Hence, for example, strong correlations are to be found between thematic roles and syntactic functions; Agent-arguments occur preferably as subjects, Theme-arguments as objects, etc. These ideas by and large agree with the empirical results of language acquisition research and on this point similarities with Slobin's approach also arise. It is assumed here, too, that form-function mappings are relevant to the construction of early child grammars. In Pinker's learnability theory, however, semantic bootstrapping only serves as a learning aid for the identification of grammatical categories. In contrast to Slobin, the grammars developed by children comprise the same categories as for adult language.

After the child has identified the elementary syntactic categories with the aid of semantic bootstrapping, a second learning strategy, termed structure-dependent distributional learning by Pinker, takes effect. In (5) e.g. the elements which occur cannot be categorized by means of semantic bootstrapping:

(5) The situation justified extreme means.

In this, no action is expressed by the verb and the nouns do not refer to perceptable physical objects. Furthermore the subject is not an Agent-argument. Pinker conceives that the child in that case falls back on the grammar which s/he has previously built up (by means of semantic bootstrapping). What is decisive is that this grammar contains information on syntactic categories. This makes it possible for the child to investigate the distributional characteristics of those elements in the input which could not be directly analysed. This allows the child to identify the categories in (5).

Summarizing, in Pinker's theory of the language acquisition device three components are assumed:

(i) universal and parameterised principles of UG
(ii) semantic bootstrapping
(iii) structure-dependent distributional learning

Under (i) comes, for example, the information that the subject is a grammatical function, which (a) occurs as the Agent-argument of active predicates, (b) is dominated directly by S, and (c) is an oblique argument in the passive, etc. Thus, there is a cluster of universal and parameterised properties of subjects. We will ignore for a moment possible arguments against the universal status of grammatical functions (see 1.3.2). Here it should simply be illustrated that children exploit such correlations during language learning.

The child starts out by using property (a) in order to construct a preliminary grammar in which the subject occurs in terms of a syntactic function. (ii) serves, as a learning aid in this, along with the Agent-subjects from the input. The grammar established by means of semantic bootstrapping is the precondition for the activation of (iii). This grammar, together with the strategies from (iii) are used by the child in the analysis of material from the input which cannot directly be categorized by semantic bootstrapping. Early child grammars already include syntactic categories; Pinker also counts the subject as one of these. The child is hence now able to identify even those subjects which do not occur in the Agent-function in the input by investigating their distribution. Due to the availability of (i) the child expects that the whole cluster of features (b), (c), ... (n) is valid for the elements identified as subjects. Universal characteristics are as such accessible without further learning. As far as parameterised properties are concerned, the child has to check a narrowly limited number of options in order to fix the value of the appropriate language.

With regard to the general structure of the LAD I am going to orientate myself using Pinker's ideas (1984), without, however, adopting his commitment to LFG as the single theoretical framework for (i). In the following two chapters, selected areas of child grammar will be studied in some detail and the learning mechanisms will be given.

2. Early child grammars

In the two- and three-word utterances of children of about 18 months regularities in word order and in the composition of syntactic constituents can be recognized; in contrast, inflectional elements and grammatical function words, for example articles, auxiliaries, prepositions, conjunctions, are mostly not present in children's utterances.

Brown (1973) was the first to define this earliest stage in grammar acquisition in terms of *M*ean *L*ength of *U*tterance, MLU. Brown measures the MLU in grammatical morphemes, and Stage I is evaluated as: MLU < 1.75. This measurement can in principle be taken independently of the particular language being learnt. However, difficulties arise in highly inflected languages if the MLU is supposed to be measured in grammatical morphemes (see Crystal 1974, Clahsen 1982). For this reason the MLU values in more recent investigations are given instead in terms of the number of words (see for example Slobin, Bever 1982). In any case the MLU provides an independent criterion which makes comparative acquisition studies on the earliest phase of grammatical development possible. Stage I has been described in detail in empirical language acquisition research, and there are numerous investigations from structurally varying languages available.

The aim of this chapter is to show that Stage I of child grammar acquisition can be analysed in the framework of learnability theory. I will be basing my claims mainly on Pinker's approach (1984), but will however suggest expansions and alternatives on several occasions in order to be able to explain the available data. In the empirical section I will be referring to currently available data mainly stemming from my investigations into German child language.

A learnability approach to Stage I has three purposes. It has to (a) provide a descriptively adequate grammar with which the linguistic utterances arising typically in Stage I can be analysed. Additionally, it has to be specified (b) what information the child needs from the linguistic input in order to construct the grammar for Stage I. Finally (c) learning mechanisms have to be formulated which the child can use in acquiring the grammar for Stage I. The general hypotheses for my investigation of (a), (b) and (c) stem from the basic assumptions of learnability theory:

(A) The grammar for Stage I falls within the limits of UG.
(B) Positive evidence from the input of Stage I is sufficient to set the parameters at the appropriate values.
(C) The learning mechanisms which come into play in Stage I fulfill the learnability constraints.

As already mentioned in chapter 1, assumption (A) is disputed in empirical language acquisition research, particularly as far as Stage I is concerned. Some researchers, even those who would otherwise accept learnability theory, such as Felix (1984), argue that no specific knowledge of grammar is expressed by the early two- and multi-word utterances. They view Stage I in language learning in much the same way as the flutterings of a young bird learning to fly, see also Berman (1985). Should this analogy be shown to be correct, assumption (A) would have to be rejected. However for this to occur, strong empirical arguments would have to be produced. On learnability considerations at least, (A) has to be preferred. I will try to show that this assumption is also confirmed by the available empirical evidence. A descriptively adequate analysis of Stage I in German child language will be presented here, which will show itself to be one possible grammar from the numerous options available in UG.

The grammatical features which are found in children's utterances at Stage I, particularly the order and composition of constituents, are described mainly by means of phrase structure rules in grammatical theories. The form taken by these rules is defined by principles of X-bar theory (Jackendoff 1977). This module of UG makes statements about (i) possible syntactic categories, (ii) levels of syntactic representation and (iii) word order. In spite of several different variants in the literature (see also Lightfoot 1979), all of the current grammatical theories regard X-bar theory as a component of UG. In this area a learnability approach need not restrict itself to any special grammatical theory; the chosen variant of the X-bar principles can easily be carried over onto another if this were to be required for theoretical reasons. My own hypothesis is nonetheless that the child constructs a phrase structure grammar at Stage I which falls under the limits of X-bar theory.

Furthermore it has to be determined which information the child needs for the construction of early PS grammars from the linguistic input. Using assumption (B) as a basis, it is to be shown that the grammatical categories occurring in the PS grammar for Stage I can be identified by means of semantic bootstrapping. I think that there are close correlations between form and meaning in the input available to the child at Stage I and want to show that the child is able to identify the categories relevant to the construction of the early PS grammar through semantic bootstrapping. It is additionally to be shown that simple data from the input, preferably information on lexical categories and their characteristics, suffice to establish the word-order parameters in Stage I. This hypothesis is based on the idea that the child's developmental progress in the area of grammar can be traced back to the expansion of the lexicon; this was referred to as the lexical learning hypothesis in paragraph 1.3.1.

Lastly, learning mechanisms used by the child in Stage I in order to construct the early PS grammar should be established. It must be shown in (C) that the suggested mechanisms do not violate the continuity assumption (see 1.3.1). That is, no learning mechanisms should be given which are only valid for Stage I in child language. Instead, the continuity assumption requires that the language learning mechanisms be stationary and direct and not change in the course of development. Hence, the LAD must be available at Stage I. I want to show that the results of the data analysis do not force us to reject these claims.

In addition to that, I assume that, based on the lexicalist position, several of the learning mechanisms cannot be activated at Stage I, because the child has not yet identified the necessary elements in the linguistic input nor categorized them in the lexicon. These include inflectional elements and grammatical function words. On the other hand, learning mechanisms for the position and composition of constituents can take effect at Stage I. It is to be shown that the errors which are typical for Stage I are mainly due to children's limited lexical knowledge rather than to the absence of learning mechanisms.

2.1 Some features of Stage I in German child language

In the following I will briefly sketch the basic elements occurring in the early phase of German child language. The empirical results will be taken from the research summary given in Clahsen (1986). This information provides the empirical basis for the attempt to establish a PS grammar for Stage I.

> Clahsen (1986) suggests a developmental sequence consisting of five phases for early German child language. Each phase has a number of linguistic features. These feature-sets are said to describe the invariant aspects of each phase of acquisition. The developmental sequence's five phases cover the area of child language learning to the age of about 3.5 years, that is from one-word utterances to subordinate clauses in phase V. Within this period of time the children learn the most important syntactic rules and some aspects of German morphology.
> In order to produce a developmental sequence, all the available empirical investigations were examined and linguistic features and developmental sequences were generalised across different studies. It was seen that a descriptive synthesis of this type is possible for the acquisition of syntax as well as for several parts of morphological development. Brown's Stage I (1973) is equivalent to phase II in the developmental sequence suggested here. Thus, I will use the term phase II throughout the following. The examples given in the following sections are taken from Clahsen (1982); the abbreviations "M", "D" and "J" stand for Mathias, Daniel and Julia. When evidence from other sources is used, it is explained at the appropriate place in the text.

The studies on phase II show that children already have access to the most important word classes. As **nominal elements** we find nouns and pronouns. Noun phrases (NPs) can have determiners (Det) or attributive adjectives. Determiners are demonstrative and possessive pronouns.

(1) *diese* tuhl (M.)
(=this chair)

(2) *diese* eis... (M.)
(=this ice cream...)

(3) *meine* auto hoch (M.)
(=My car is driving up.)

(4) *eine* rad (D.)
(=a wheel)

(5) *ein* buch (D.)
(=a book)

In addition to that, in Miller's data (1976) on phase II examples of utterances with the case- and gender-neutral article *de* occur frequently:

(6) da s *de* lala
(=There is the dummy.)

(7) wo s *de* boden
(=Where is the floor?)

Lastly we find NPs consisting of two nouns, for example *titti fell* (=teddy's fur). They serve as a possessive genitive, but are, however, used in phase II without the case marker required in German. **Adverbial elements** occur mostly in the form of simple adverbs, for example locatives (*hier, da* = here, there), and occasionally of prepositional phrases (PP), in which the preposition required in German is usually missing. In this phase of development three types of **verbal elements** occur: – simple verbs (V), e.g. *fahren* (to drive), *gehen* (to go), etc., – predicative adjectives (Adj.) such as in *du böse* (you naughty), and – (separable) prefix verbs (PrV), e.g. *aufsetz* (put on).

A further characteristic of phase II is that the children's utterances consist mainly of so-called content words whilst function words and inflectional elements hardly occur. Moreover, subjects and verbal elements are often left out. Quantitative analyses of the missing elements were carried out in Clahsen (1982). The following serve as illustrative examples of this:

– missing auxiliaries

(8) hase lieb (M.)
('hare sweet')
(=The hare is sweet.)

(9) schinken aufgessen (M.)
('ham eaten up')
(=Purzel has eaten the ham.)

- missing verb

(10) ich sine (D.)
('I orange')
(=D. has got an orange.)

- missing preposition

(11) boden nitter (D.)
('floor snippings')
(=The snippings are on the floor.)

- missing article

(12) tunnel dick (D.)
('tunnel thick')
(=The tunnel is thick.)

- missing subject

(13) licht seh (D.)
('light see')
(D. is looking through the video-camera.)

In most cases, the children's **sentences** in phase II consist of different combinations of two constituents. The following cases can be distinguished:

- **Subject-verb-sentences** contain a verbal element as well as the subject:

(14) ich ziehn (M.)
(=I pull.)

- **Verbless sentences** contain an adverbial element or an object as well as the subject:

(15) Daniel pier (M.)
('Daniel paper')
(=Daniel has got paper.)

(16) diese gleise mama (M.)
('these lines mama')
(=Mama bought these lines.)

- **Subjectless sentences** consist of a verbal element plus an adverbial element or object:

(17) drehen brücke (D.)
('turn bridge')
(=D. is turning the bridge.)

(18) boden bürs (M.)
('floor brush')
(M. is brushing the floor.)

- **Sentences without both subject and verb** contain only adverbial elements and/or objects:

(19) diese leine (D.)
('this alone')
(=D. wants to read the book alone.)

Expanded sentence structures with more complements (in addition to subject and verb) only rarely occur in phase II, but appear typically in the more advanced phases III and IV.

There are numerous empirical studies on word order in phase II. These studies show that children prefer verb-final patterns (see 18). Every type of verbal element occurring can however also be in the first or second position before the complements, such as in (17). This is also true for separable prefix verbs and predicative adjectives which cannot be used in these positions in German. This leads to word order errors, in terms of the target language norm. Quantitative analyses on verb placement (Clahsen 1982) showed that the verb-final pattern covers about 70% of all possible cases. Thus, in phase II verb placement is generally variable, with the verb-final pattern clearly used more often. Moreover there are no positional differences between the different kinds of verbal elements in phase II.

As an illustration let us look briefly at the placement of prefix verbs. In phase II prefix and verb are often not separated; they are instead together, mostly in the order of Pr-V at the end of the sentence (see 20). There are also cases in the data where prefix verbs occur **before** the complements but not before the subject. In these cases the internal order of Pr-V is also found (see 21).

(20) purzel pierkorb *rausräum* (M.)
(The dog Purzel is clearing out the waste paper basket.)

(21) *raus holt* hier (M.)
(M. is getting a brick out of the cupboard.)

Both of the positional patterns for separable prefix verbs in (22) are available to the child, whereby (a) is the variant used the most. Other systematic positional patterns for prefix verbs do not occur in phase II.

(22) a. .... PrV
b. ... PrV ...

In German (22b) is not possible. As a non-finite element, Pr must instead be at the end of the sentence. (22a) occurs in German in subordinate clauses or in modal- and auxiliary-verb constructions, if the prefix verbs are in the infinitive or are participles. The comparison with the adult language shows that prefix verb placement in phase II is still not correct. The children do not yet adhere to the target language norm, and they use positional patterns which do not exist as such in the target language. It is interesting, though, that not all logically possible positional variants occur in the children's utterances. In the data available on phase II (see also Miller 1976) there are for example no instances in which prefix verbs are at the end of the sentence in the order of V-Pr. Rather, only variant (22a) is used if the prefix verbs occurs after the complements. From this it can be concluded that verb placement in phase II is in no way arbitrary. Instead, the child makes a systematic choice from the conceivable possibilities.

Similarly it is found that the subjects in phase II are consistently placed before the verbal elements. Utterances whose subject appears in other positions are very rare in phase II. Other constituents (=complements), however, can also come before the subject. All in all these observations point to the fact that even here specific word order restrictions (for subjects and for verbal elements) are in effect, leading to some patterns being considered by the child as possible patterns and others being rejected from the start. In the following paragraphs it will be shown how the peculiarities of word order and the other characteristics of phase II mentioned can be analysed within the framework of the learnability theory.

2.2 A phrase structure grammar for phase II

One of our hypotheses was that the child – besides other components of grammatical knowledge – already has access in phase II to a PS grammar which falls under the X-bar theory. It must also be shown that the peculiarities of phase II, especially with regard to the composition of syntactic units, can be described by PS rules.

In the following I will begin by sketching a relevant part of the expansion rules and a subset of the children's lexicon. Then the grammar will be explained and applied to the empirical results.

(23) i. $$S \rightarrow NP_{SUBJ'} \begin{Bmatrix} VP \\ P \\ A \\ NP \end{Bmatrix}$$

ii. $$NP \rightarrow (\begin{Bmatrix} N_{POSS} \\ A_{MOD} \\ Q \\ DET \end{Bmatrix}) N$$

iii. $$VP \rightarrow (NP_{OBJ}), (\begin{Bmatrix} P_{ADJUNKT} \\ N_{OBJ2} \\ N_{OBL} \\ N_{ADJUNKT} \end{Bmatrix}), V$$

(24) i. **verbs** (V)
kaufen (to buy) (SUBJ, OBJ)
fahren (to drive) (SUBJ, OBL)
werfen (to throw) (SUBJ, OBJ, OBL)
geben (to give) (SUBJ, OBJ, OBJ2)
fallen (to fall) (SUBJ)

ii. **nouns** (N)
Zug, Tasche (train, bag)
ich, deine, das (I, your, this)

iii. **adjectives** (A)
heil, böse, fertig (uninjured, naughty, ready)

iv. **prepositions** (P)
hier, da, weg (here, there, away)

v. **quantifiers** (Q)
nur, mehr, nein (only, more, no)

vi. **determiners** (DET)
ein, de, diese (one, the, these)

The expansion rules and lexical entries refer to phase II of German grammar acquisition. They are – similar to the rules in Pinker (1984:111) for English child language – mainly noted in the LFG format; this provides the possibility of transferring them into the corresponding components of an adult grammar. The characteristic feature of the LFG notation is that main constituents at the level of c-structure are supplied with function indices representing grammatical functions.

Rules (i) and (iii) digress from the c-structure representation in LFG; here word order has not yet been determined. I will show that the PS-grammar (23) alone is not sufficient, especially in the analysis of verb placement in German child language. In this area additional grammatical principles are in effect, which are to be defined in paragraph 2.4 in terms of the GB-theory. In the meantime, I will pay no attention to verb placement and will concentrate on the composition of syntactic constituents. For this I am going to use the LFG notation. This decision has nothing to do with special theoretical premises, though. As mentioned, PS rules for the composition of syntactic constituents are also used in the other grammatical theories. If another way of writing them is preferred, then the suggested rules can easily be put into another format without changing the basic theoretical assumptions and the given results.

The grammar of (23) and (24) describes the basic types of nominal, adverbial and verbal elements as well as the internal structure of the syntactic constituents occurring in phase II of German child language. Compare the observations from paragraph 2.1 with the corresponding categories in rules (23) and lexical entries (24). The rules (23.i) and (23.iii) only present the dominance relations; the commas used in these rules signal that the order of the elements is not fixed. Rule (23.ii) gives the constituency *and* the linear order of the NP. In 2.1 we saw that the modifying elements (Det) in NPs generally precede the head (=N); hence commas are not needed in (23.ii). However, the position of verbs in the PS rules (23.i) and (23.iii) cannot be fixed. It was seen in 2.1 that adverbials and objects can also come before the subject (see 16), and that verbal elements can also precede complements. In the PS rules (23.i) and (23.iii) commas were introduced allowing for the observed alternatives in position, but closer investigation into this is required, as will be made in paragraph 2.4. Grammars (23) and (24) enable us, however, to describe the composition of syntactic units in phase II of German child language.

Two possible objections to the suggested grammar should be dealt with briefly here. Both concern the descriptive adequacy of PS grammars for phase II of early child language. The first objection comes from the observed subject/object asymmetries in the NP expansions of phase II. It was found that animate pronouns and proper nouns are preferred as subjects, whilst objects are mainly inanimate NPs and pronouns (see Miller 1976). Such differences in animacy cannot be described by grammar (23). This was one of the reasons which caused researchers in the seventies (see Bowerman 1973, Miller 1976) to analyse early child language with semantic categories and relations. In particular the preference for the case grammar approach can be seen as underlying these observations.

The second objection is that sentence patterns can be derived from grammar (23) which do not occur in the data available for phase II. It was found that the children's utterances in phase II had not more than two, and at the very most three constituents. Grammar (23) can also produce longer sentences, from which it has been concluded that PS grammars are generally unsuitable for describing early child language.

I think that the objections are unfounded and that the conclusions in both cases are not appropriate.

The animacy differences for subjects and objects in the children's utterances are quantitatively preferred tendencies and not absolute restrictions which would mean that syntactic categories have to be omitted. In no way do children in phase II exclusively use sentences with an animate subject and inanimate object. Instead, numerous instances can be found in which the animacy features are spread differently, e.g.:

(25) blätter dran (M.)
('leaves on')
(M. shows H. a sieve on which there are leaves.)

(26) schaukel putt (M.)
('swing bust')
(M. points at the broken swing.)

(27) setzen mann (D.)
('sit man')
(D. puts the man down.)

(28) hol hund (M.)
('fetch dog')
(M. fetches the dog.)

Examples of this type occur frequently in the data. They show that grammatical functions cannot always be put down to semantic features, here to the differences in animacy. Quantitative analyses carried out by Pinker (1984:131ff.) on English child language demonstrate that not only pronouns and proper nouns but also full NPs with possessive or demonstrative pronouns occur as subjects. Additionally, there is just a tendency here towards short subjects, not however a clear restriction towards short subjects which would be valid without exception.

This indicates that the quantitative tendencies observed in phase II have little to do with the basic grammatical competence of the children, but are rather due to external factors. For example, the fact that mainly animate subjects occur could simply be because the children in phase II mostly use verbs of action which are subcategorised for animate subjects. On top of that pragmatic factors probably play a role, too. In phase II, the subject often has Topic-function (see Bates, MacWhinney 1979). Topic elements usually have a more limited lexical content than rhematic elements. So, it is to be expected that – simply for pragmatic reasons – pronominal subjects occur more often than pronominal objects. These observations should make it clear that the children in phase II do not use all the structural patterns available to them to the same extent. External factors arising from the children's communicative intentions and realm of experience ensure instead that a specific number of the structures possible in principle are used in preference.

In a similar way the limitations on the length of utterances at phase II can be accounted for. Note that a PS grammar produces sentences in adult language which are in principle of unlimited length, but that in reality extremely long sentences are rarely found. External factors are also responsible for this, mainly the limited capacity of the short-term memory. Factors of this type are all the more valid for children in the early phases of development and lead to the children's linguistic utterances in phase II consisting mostly of only two constituents, where contextual deletions can also occur. Again plausible external reasons can be given for the peculiarity observed in phase II, whilst the actual grammatical competence can be represented by means of PS rules. Therefore, I will stick to the grammar suggested in (23) and (24) to describe the constituency of syntactic units in phase II of German child language.

2.3 Learnability considerations on syntactic categorisation

At the core of the following discussion are questions as to (i) which learning mechanisms the child uses and (ii) which information it needs from the input in order to construct the syntactic categories and the PS rules of grammar (23). On the basis of the continuity hypothesis, it should be shown (concerning (i)) that principles of X-bar theory are available even at the earliest stage of development. I think that these principles serve the child as mechanisms for learning the syntactic units and the levels of projection in grammar (23). In addition, they are relevant to word order, as analysed more closely in paragraph 2.4. The basic hypothesis for (ii) is that the categories in (23) can be determined by means of semantic bootstrapping. It should be shown that the child makes use of form-function relations in the linguistic input in order to identify the necessary categories (see 2.0).

The standard example of syntactic categorisation in phase II can be demonstrated with the following simple example (cf. Pinker 1984:68ff.):

(29) Der Hund beißt die Katze
(The dog bites the cat)

The first thing the child has to do is determine the lexical categories of the words in (29). For this purpose, the child uses semantic information from the input analysed. The elements *Hund* and *Katze* in (29) stand for living things and can be identified as nouns (N) by means of semantic bootstrapping. The word *beißt* expresses an action and is categorised as a verb (V). Both articles mark definite expressions and can, on the basis of this semantic information, be defined as determiners (Det). Hence (30) arises as a first transitional step:

(30)

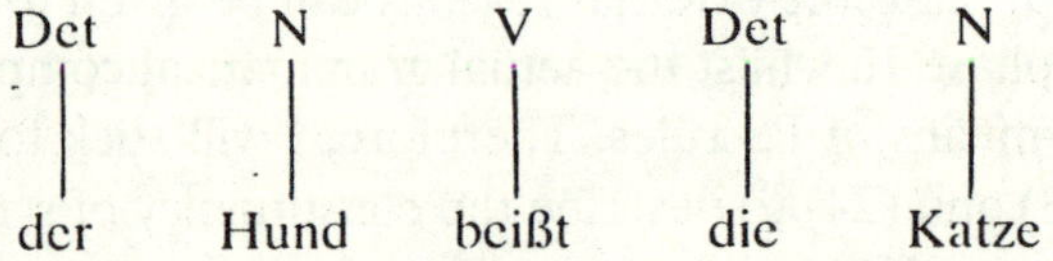

The next step is the construction of a syntactic constituent structure. For this purpose, the child makes use of principles of X-bar theory. Among other things, these principles make sure that every major lexical category is projected onto a maximal category; in accordance with the LFG, I assume two levels of syntactic projection here. Also required is the expansion of the maximal projection of the verb ($=V^2$) to S (cf. Bresnan 1982). These principles result in the following categorisation of the example given:

(31)

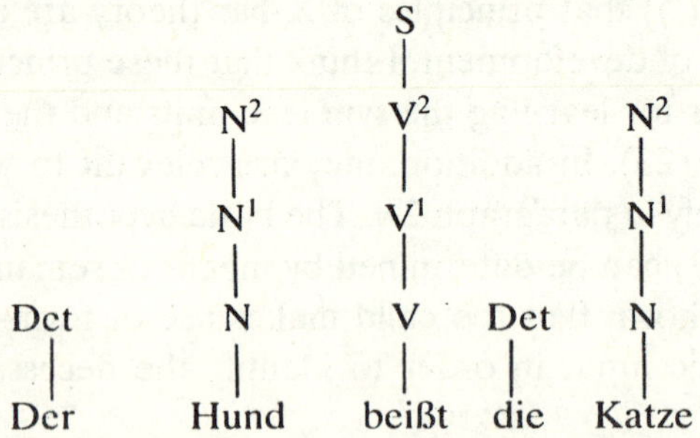

At this point, semantic bootstrapping is used once again. Example (29) has an Agent-argument and a Theme-argument. Subject and object can be identified on the basis of this semantic information. In addition to that, X-bar principles make sure that (i) arguments are treated as sisters of the lexical head category X^0, (ii) specifiers, e.g. Det, as sisters of X^1 and (iii) the subject as a daughter of S. We thus get the full syntactic representation for example (29):

(32)

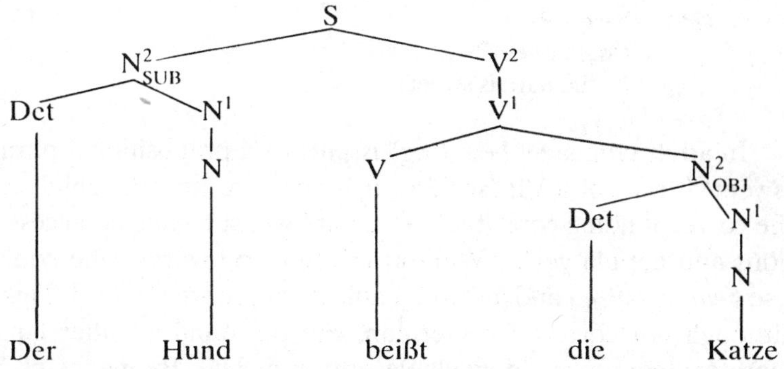

The example illustrates how the child identifies grammatical categories by means of semantic bootstrapping and how s/he, equipped with X-bar principles, constructs phrase structure trees. Instead of building up configuration (32), these mechanisms can be used to construct an elementary PS grammar in a completely analogous way. Without fixed word order, it takes the following form:

(33)
a. $S \rightarrow N^2_{SUB}, V^2$
b. $N^2 \rightarrow Det, N^1$
c. $N^1 \rightarrow N$
d. $V^2 \rightarrow V^1$
e. $V^1 \rightarrow V, N^2_{OBJ}$

Simple positive data such as (29), which can be assumed to occur frequently in the child's language input, suffice for the construction of this grammar. The rules in (33) are used by the child in its further development as a means for the analysis of linguistic elements which cannot be directly identified on the basis of semantic bootstrapping.

The proposed analysis can be applied to standard cases, but some of the peculiarities found in phase II do however require additional considerations. In the following I will look into two learnability problems in phase II.

The first problem is linked to the fact that function words are generally not available in the earliest phase of grammatical development. Let us look at the following examples:

(34) sitzen bein (D.)
('sit leg')
(D. would like to sit on his mother's leg.)

(35) hase lieb (M.)
('hare sweet')
(=the hare is sweet)

In adult language, *bein* (leg) is part of a prepositional phrase and *lieb* (sweet) is part of a VP (see 36). It is not clear how the child can construct the corresponding constituent structure whilst having no access to prepositions and copula verbs. Without the function words, s/he could also analyse *bein* as NP_{OBJ} and *lieb* as an adjectival phrase under S. This possibility, although not correct for German, can be found in other languages and therefore counts as an available option of UG. By means of X-bar principles alone, it is therefore impossible for the child to determine just which constituent structure, (36) or (37), s/he has to employ for his respective language:

(36) a. [$_S$ NP [$_{VP}$ V [$_{PP}$ P **NP**]]]
b. [$_S$ NP [$_{VP}$ V **AP**]]

(37) a. [$_S$ NP [$_{VP}$ V **NP**]]
b. [$_S$ NP **AP**]

If the child learning German in phase II were to accept (37) as a syntactic representation of (34) and (35) then it would have to get negative evidence from the linguistic input in order to be able, later in its development, to reject the PS rules which are ungrammatical for German. However, according to our previous assumptions, explicit corrections of grammatical errors do not form a relevant part of the linguistic input.

Pinker (1984:103ff.) suggests a solution to this learnability problem. He calls the elements in bold type in (36) and (37) orphans because the child cannot clearly define the mothers of these elements without having access to function words. It is possible that PP is the mother of NP, as in (36a), or that VP is the mother of NP, as in (37a). The mother of AP could either be the VP (36b) or S (37b). What is important is that the child is able to identify the predecessing node of the orphans, even without function words. *Bein*'s predecessor is the VP and *lieb*'s is the S-node. Pinker thinks that the orphans are taken temporarily into the custody of the predecessing node in phase II. This analysis is recognised as preliminary until the child can identify function words in the input and hence the respective mothers of the orphans.

For the examples (34) and (35) the child chooses structures (37) in phase II, and the elements in bold type are then preliminary categorisations (=orphans). In Pinker's analysis these elements are annotated with question-marks. During the further course of development the child learning German finds prepositions and the copula in the linguistic input. These elements enable the child to open new structural domains between the dominating nodes and the former orphans. The X-bar principles mentioned above will be applied for the construction of these domains. They allow the child to treat the preposition as the head of the PP and the copula as the head of the VP. The preliminary categorisations of phase II can, on the basis of such positive evidence, be replaced by the analysis (36) which is correct for German.

An additional problem concerns the projection levels which were assumed for the standard case in (33). Up until now, I have presupposed that each major lexical category is transferred into a maximal projection in the syntax. Thereby we would however produce branching levels for phase II, for which there is no empirical evidence in the data. Thus for example no complements of adjectives can be found in phase II (*zufrieden* **mit etwas** (content with something), *stolz* **auf etwas** (proud of something)), nor modifying elements of adjectives (**sehr** *lieb* (very sweet)). There are no indications that the PS rules in phase II already produce Adj-phrases as syntactic units, and the case is similar for prepositions. In phase II intransitive prepositions, mainly adverbs, are almost exclusively to be found. The assumption of a prepositional **phrase** in the syntax would be inappropriate because it would lead to a structure which branches even more than is actually demonstrated in the data.

Moreover, if the learning mechanism were to transform every lexical category into a maximal projection, then no positions for non-maximal constituents could be defined in the PS rules. Such positions are, however, necessary in the syntax of natural languages. Verb movement in German requires for example a syntactic position for the finite verb, that is for a non-maximal constituent. As the syntax has to determine this position, the learning mechanisms cannot simply expand each category in the lexicon into a maximal projection.

Pinker (1984:112) suggests a solution to this problem. He argues that the learning mechanisms for PS rules should only expand the lexical categories to the extent that the arguments occurring and the modifying elements can be inserted into the configuration. The example (38) is analysed for phase II as in (39a), and not, as in adult language, (39b):

(38) Das Buch liegt hier
(The book is here)

(39) a. $[_S \text{NP} [_{VP} \text{V P}]]$
b. $[_S \text{NP} [_{VP} \text{V} [_{PP} \text{P}]]]$

In UG, both options (39a) and (39b) are offered, but the child must choose an option even though there is no direct positive evidence in phase II as to which of the two possibilities is correct for German. Choices of this kind which are limited by universal factors will be recognised as preliminary. Pinker's hypothesis is that the child initially accepts non-maximal constituents. The child is said to stick to (39a) in phase II and to induce the rule (i) VP ⟶ V ?P?. As soon as the child can identify full prepositional phrases in the input, then it has access to a further option of expanding verb phrases, (ii) VP ⟶ V PP. The child finds that, in the positions in German where the lexical category P occurs in the syntax, the maximal projection PP is also possible. The preliminary categorisation (i) can therefore be relinquished in favour of the rule (ii) required by German. This solution is justified by the empirical results for phase II. No branching levels are to be assumed which cannot be shown in the data, and the non-maximal elements in phase II can be expanded to maximal projections as long as the child finds suitable indications for this in the linguistic input. The solution suggested ensures that the PS rules of phase II can be transferred to the grammar of the respective adult language and that there is sufficient positive evidence for this in the input.

Both of the problems discussed and the analyses suggested for them illustrate basic principles of learnability theory. In both cases the starting point involved characteristics of syntactic composition which are not universally defined in natural languages and for which UG offers a limited number of possible options. Learnablity considerations were required in order to explain how the child constucts the constituent structure required for any given language, without having to rely on negative evidence. Principles of X-bar theory alone were not enough to solve these problems.

The analyses suggested made use of one central element of learnability theory, the so-called **uniqueness principle** (cf. Wexler 1981, Pinker

1984). It says that the child assumes one of the possible options from parameterised UG principles as being correct as long as s/he has positive evidence that s/he should choose a different option in the particular language. I shall be making further use of this principle especially with regard to the acquisition of morphology. With respect to syntactic composition, the uniqueness principle and the remaining learning mechanisms ensure that the child constructs a PS grammar with particular categorisations as early as phase II. This grammar is still incomplete in terms of the target language norm and it does contain several preliminary categorisations (orphans). Basically however, the early child grammar can be transferred to the corresponding adult grammar on the basis of positive data only.

The restructuring of the early PS grammar is triggered by lexical development. According to the analysis suggested for both of the learnability problems discussed above, the child is able to make the correct choices for German as soon as s/he has identified function words (prepositions, auxiliary verbs) in the input. This result is consistent with the idea that the language acquisition device itself does not alter during development and that progress in the children's grammar is due to lexical development.

2.4 Parameter theory and the acquisition of word order

This paragraph deals with word order in phase II of German child language. Starting out from the observations made in paragraph 2.1, a descriptively adequate analysis of the available word order data (which can be shown consistent with the theoretically motivated learnability conditions) must be provided. Moreover, learning mechanisms have to be formulated for the acquisition of word order, and the information required from the linguistic input has to be given. Firstly, I will show that the mechanisms in Pinker (1984) are not sufficient for the acquisition of word order. Then I will suggest an alternative analysis which makes use of elements of GB-theory (cf. Chomsky 1981 and paragraph 1.3.2).

2.4.1 *Pinker's analysis*

Pinker (1984), in his analysis of word order in early child language, makes exclusive use of elements from PS grammars. His analysis is carried out within the framework of Lexical-Functional Grammar (LFG), which assumes one level of syntactic representation, the so-called c-structure (see 1.3.2), and describes the variations in word order by means of PS rules. The word order analysis suggested by Pinker simply uses the usual conventions of PS rules, among other things, Kleene's star, brackets, etc. Word order in configurational languages such as English can be described using these conventions. Similarly, Pinker is able to analyse so-called non-configurational languages which have an extremely free word order; Pinker illustrates this with the example of Warlpiri. He shows that the characteristic word order freedom of NP-arguments can be described with the conventions of PS rules.

The problems in Pinker's analysis become clear if one wants to apply it to word order in German child language. A clear typological classification is not possible for German as far as word order is concerned. German word order is more free than English, for example, but it does not have the freedom of word order which is characteristic for non-configurational languages. Hence, in German, the position of NP-arguments is used to mark grammatical relations in cases in which morphological means of expression do not permit a definite decision. Here, I shall be looking at a simple example from German child language in order to demonstrate that Pinker's analysis in this area is insufficient.

The child learning German is confronted with, among other things, the following data in the input:

(40) a. ... der Junge den Hund füttert
(the boy the dog feeds)
b. ... den Hund der Junge füttert
c. Der Junge füttert den Hund
d. Den Hund füttert der Junge
e. Füttert der Junge den Hund

The categories and grammatical functions can be identified in these instances by means of semantic bootstrapping, and the following PS rules can be produced by the mechanisms for syntactic composition:

(41) a. $S \rightarrow NP_{SUBJ}\ NP_{OBJ}\ V$
b. $S \rightarrow NP_{OBJ}\ NP_{SUBJ}\ V$
c. $S \rightarrow NP_{SUBJ}\ V\ NP_{OBJ}$
d. $S \rightarrow NP_{OBJ}\ V\ NP_{SUBJ}$
e. $S \rightarrow V\ NP_{SUBJ}\ NP_{OBJ}$

On the basis of (41), one would predict an almost complete freedom of word order for German child language in phase II. As is clear from the examples with subjects and objects, it should be possible for any constituent to appear before as well as after the verb. The freedom of word order is only restricted by the structure *[V NP_{OBJ} NP_{SUBJ}] because the child does not find the corresponding data in the input (40). The available data (see 2.1) show that that analysis cannot be correct. As early as phase II there are word order restrictions in German child language, for example upon verbal elements and upon the subject, and these restrictions cannot be learnt with Pinker's conventions, and they cannot be described with the PS rules (23i) and (23iii). Therefore additional analyses are required for word order, which will be dealt with in the next paragraph.

The problems in Pinker's analysis of word order can be traced back to the fact that he, as required by LFG, only allows for one level of syntactic representation and is thereby forced to formulate mechanisms for the acquisition of word order, which can only apply to surface structures. Pinker treats all of the order patterns which appear in the input or which are used by the child the same. We found in 2.1, however, that some variants can be seen as dominant patterns and are used frequently by the child, whilst others only occur very infrequently in the input and in the children's utterances. It was also seen that the subject precedes the verbal elements in phase II, but that objects can occur pre- or postverbally. This asymmetry indicates that word order in the early phase of the acquisition of grammar is a means of marking grammatical relations. Pinker's analysis does not account for these observations.

2.4.2 *An alternative solution within GB-theory*

2.4.2.1 The alternative solution which I am suggesting for word order acquisition is based upon elements from GB-theory. Two syntactic levels will be assumed, (i) the underlying or deep structure (=D-structure) in which grammatical relations and canonical order patterns are represented and (ii) the syntactic surface structure (=S-structure) which arises by applying transformations on D-structure representations. Not all of the word order variants are treated the same, but there is differentiation between canonical patterns on the one hand and derived variants on the other. The empirical results show that a differentiation of this type is required in any analysis of word order acquisition in phase II.

A further element which I make use of in analysing word order are parameterised principles of UG. For phase II, I will refer particularly to the directionality parameter (cf. for example Travis 1984) and to Kratzer's INFL/V-parameter (1984).

The directionality parameter controls the constituent-internal word order. Within maximal projections of the lexical categories (N, V, A and P) it permits the options (42):

(42) a. $_{XP}[... X^0]$
b. $_{XP}[X^0 ...]$

The INFL/V-parameter is related to the morphological component of the lexicon and makes it possible to describe the links between the position and the inflection of verbs. Kratzer (1984) shows that natural languages differ in the way in which they categorise inflected verbs in the lexicon. The parameter creates two options:

(43) a. $_{INFL}$[V INFL]
b. $_{V}$[V INFL]

Differences in verb position from language to language can be traced back to the chosen value of this (morphological) parameter. Kratzer shows that option (43a) should be taken for German whilst the parameter in English, for example, is fixed at (43b). The categorisation depends among other things upon the semantic content of the inflections. If there are "strong" affixes which have their own meanings, for example agreement inflections, then (43a) would be chosen, whilst "weak" affixes, for example infinitives, which do not have specific meanings are categorised according to (43b).

Most important here are the links with word order. Kratzer shows that the peculiarities of verb position in both languages (English and German) can be derived from the differing parameterisation in the lexicon. In the syntactic components of German Kratzer (1984) assumes a CONFL position which takes over inflected verbs (in main clauses) or subordinating conjunctions (in embedded clauses). Since inflected verbs in the German lexicon are categorised according to (43a) as INFL-elements, in German main clauses all inflected verbs can be found in this position. In English two positions have to be assumed for COMP and INFL (cf. also Platzack

1983). Only modals and auxiliaries which are categorised as INFL-elements because of their semantic characteristics occur in the INFL-position. Simple inflected verbs, however, remain in the VP because of the categorisation (43b) chosen in English. This parameter allows us to explain the links between the position and the inflection of verbs. This also applies to the rule systems which children construct in early phases of grammar acquisition.

2.4.2.2 I assume that the underlying representation in phase II is (44), and that the directionality parameter for the maximal projections N^2 and V^2, which occur in PS grammar (23), has already been fixed and has the value 'final'. Correspondingly PS grammar (23) has to be specified. The observed word order patterns arise from (44) through movement rules.

(44)

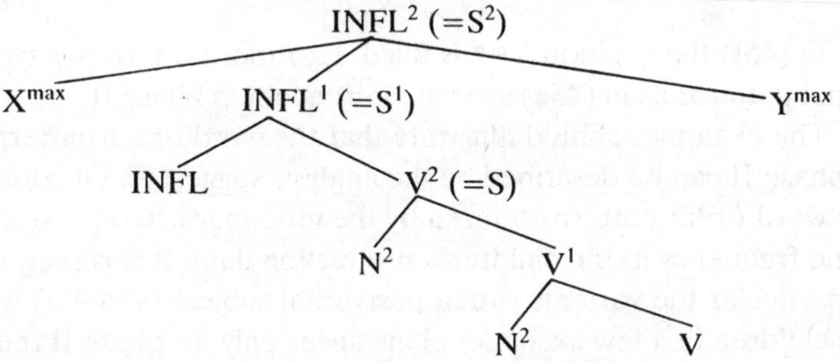

The relevant word order patterns in the data for phase II can be described by the suggested analysis. Let us look at the examples in (45):

(45) a. purzel pierkorb rausräum
(purzel is emptying the wastepaper basket)
b. pierkorb purzel rausräum
c. purzel rausräum pierkorb
d. pierkorb rausräum purzel
e. rausräum purzel pierkorb
f. rausräum pierkorb purzel

Utterances of this type are of course not very frequent in phase II, simply because they have three constituents. In phase II the children use utterances with two constituents far more frequently. Nonetheless examples like (20) can be found and the grammar for phase II must be able to provide the appropriate structures. The examples in (45) make it easier to illustrate the various word order patterns than those with two constituents. That the latter occur more often in the data has nothing to do with the child's grammar directly but more with external factors, including the limited capacity of short-term memory (see 2.2).

If the positions X^{max} and INFL remain empty then the sentence pattern $N_{SUBJ}XV$, as in example (20), occurs which is given here as (45a). If the X^{max} position (for topicalisations) is filled, (45b) arises. If the syntactic INFL position is filled then we have (45c) or (45d), whereby the latter only occurs very rarely. In case X^{max} remains empty and INFL is filled, then (45e) arises. In German the Y^{max} position is needed mainly for extrapositions, such as those in (46); cf. also Lenerz (1985):

(46) Der Mittelstürmer spielt ab auf den linken Flügel
(the striker is playing over towards the left wing)

In (45f) the position Y^{max} is filled. Extrapositions of this type like verb-initial patterns as in (45e) are very infrequent in phase II.

The examples should illustrate that the word order patterns occurring in phase II can be described by the analysis suggested. Of course not all of the word order patterns offered by the grammar are represented with the same frequency in the children's production data. It was seen that (cf. 2.1) in particular the variants with a postverbal subject (45d-45f) were used by the children in a few exceptional instances only. In phase II the patterns in which the subject appears in front of the verbal element are clearly preferred. I think that functional aspects are responsible for this asymmetry in the use of order patterns for the subject. In phase II the position of the arguments in relation to the verb has a discriminatory function: subjects are preverbal, objects can be post- or preverbal (cf. Clahsen 1986a). From this it follows that sentences with verb-initial patterns and other cases with postverbal subjects are rarely found in phase II. Thus the children make very different use of the grammatically possible word order patterns. There are obviously surface structure restrictions in phase II, due to the discriminatory function of word order among other things, which have the effect that some of the grammatically possible word order patterns are used dominantly whereas others occur only seldom or even not at all.

According to the analysis suggested here, a syntactic INFL-position as the head of INFL[1] is already assumed for phase II. There are several indications for this in the data available. Thus the children use verb inflections even in early two- and multi-word utterances, particularly *-t* and *-n*, which are added to the verb stems. A detailed analysis of the acquisition of inflection follows in the next chapter. At this point it is only relevant to say that the verbs marked with *-t* in phase II appear for the most part in either the first or second position (cf. also Mills 1985). In addition to that, some instances of modal verbs can also be found in phase II (cf. Clahsen 1982, Tab. 7-9). The evidence is somewhat sparse, however it can be seen that the modals almost only occur in the front verb position. Modals do have meanings, which make them classic candidates for the INFL-position (cf. Steele et al. 1981). The order preferences for modals (and those marked with *-t*) indicate that in phase II the syntactic component already offers the positions required for verb placement, especially the syntactic INFL-position. Yet in phase II, not all inflected verbs can be placed in this position, as is required in German, because the child does not have access to the inventory of verb inflections, which is required to fix the INFL-parameter at the appropriate value for German. Verbs which are categorised in the lexicon according to (43b) remain in the VP and cannot be placed in the front INFL-position in configuration (44). In this way the verb-final patterns which are typical for phase II arise.

2.4.2.3 The word order patterns for (separable) *prefix verbs* can also be described by the analysis suggested. In phase II examples (20) and (21) from paragraph 2.1, repeated here as (47), are characteristic:

(47) a. purzel pierkorb [$_{P}$raus $_{V}$räum]
b. [$_{P}$raus $_{V}$holt] hier

In (47a) the prefix verb is in the V-position of (44), and the word structure of the prefix verb is described as in (48a). In (47b) the prefix verb occurs entirely in the syntactic INFL-position of (44); it has the representation shown in (48b).

(48) a.

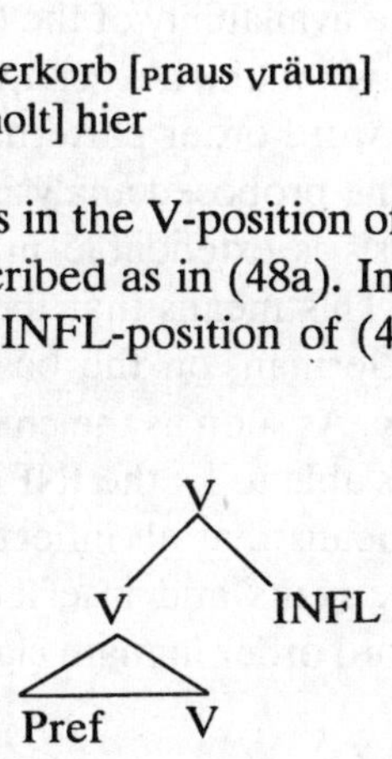

b.

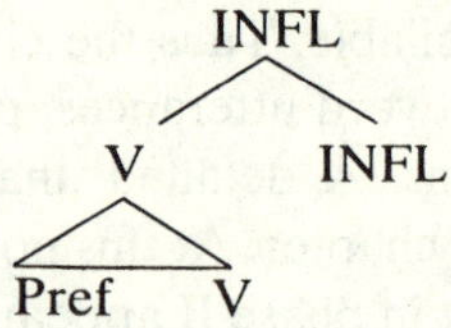

In this way order patterns which are not possible in German can also arise. It is crucial that the children at phase II have not yet recognised the argument status of most prefixes. They do not treat prefix verbs as lexicalised syntagmas, as is required in German, where the prefix has word status and belongs to the subcategorisation frame of the verb (cf. Wunderlich 1985). The required $INFL^1$-substructure for prefix verbs (see 49) can therefore not yet be induced in phase II:

(49)

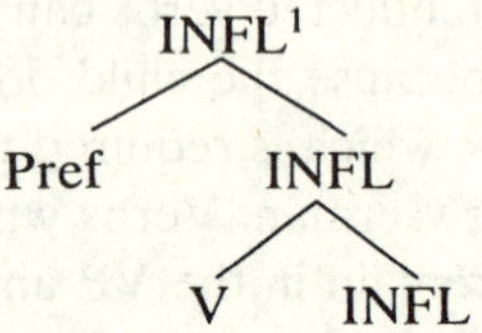

Instead the children tend to categorise separable prefix verbs by means of semantic bootstrapping as V^0/$INFL^0$ elements, as in (48). The order patterns in phase II are therefore identical to those of simple verbs. In the further course of development, especially in phase IV, a restructuring of this initial system takes place, and (48) is rejected in favour of (49). An important trigger for this is the availability of the (subject-verb) agreement system. I shall return to this point in the next chapter.

In sum we found that the word order patterns which occur in phase II can be described in terms of the proposed analysis. It must also be pointed out that the suggested analysis is extendable in the sense this notion is meant in learnability theory. This means that the child is able to acquire the correct word order for German, on the basis of configuration (44), through positive evidence only. As soon as the child has access to the paradigm for verb inflection s/he is able to fix the INFL-parameter at the value needed for German, which means that all inflected verbs can be derived from the lexicon as INFL-elements and inserted into the syntax in the INFL-position. Hereby the word order in main clauses is correct.

2.4.2.4 Word order in *embedded clauses* can be acquired through expanding the child's lexicon. As soon as subordinating conjunctions (COMP) are categorised, the child can recognise that they are in complementary distribution with the finite verb. Hence, the so-called COMP/INFL parameter (cf. Platzack 1983) can be fixed at the value for German.

> Platzack (1983) carried out a comparative study on word order in English, Swedish, Icelandic and German. He suggests that these languages differ with regard to the distribution of COMP and INFL. In English both are separate nodes in the syntax, COMP being the position for conjunctions and INFL for auxiliaries and modals. The parameterisation in German and Swedish is different. Platzack assumes that conjunctions and inflected verbs are simply two surface forms of the same syntactic constituent; he calls it CONFL in order to indicate that it shows the characteristics of both COMP *and* INFL. With the aid of this parameter Platzack is able to describe the similarities and differences between the languages investigated. The analysis is further supported by recent investigations into linguistic change (cf. Lenerz 1985).

The result of fixing the COMP/INFL parameter is that the INFL-position from (44) is associated with the position for subordinating conjunctions and is categorised as CONFL. Moreover, within INFL^1, a final position for the head of the phrase is created, which results in representation (50):

(50)

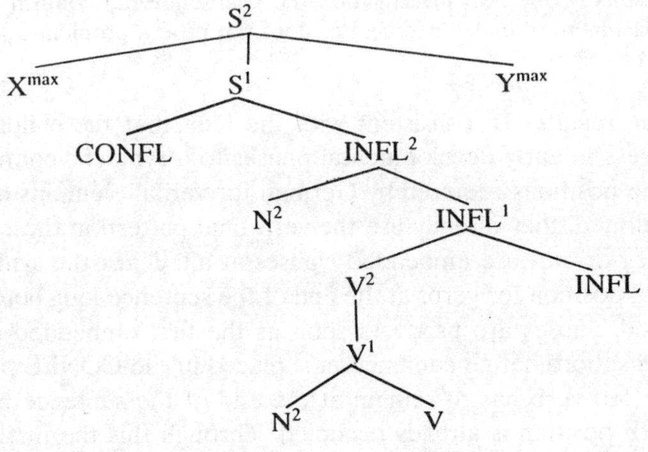

In embedded clauses, the CONFL-position is occupied by subordinating conjunctions; finite verbs therefore have to stay in the INFL-position at the end of the sentence. In main clauses finite verbs are put into the CONFL-position whereby a trace is left behind in the underlying position. With this the development of verb placement is completed; it now matches the standards of adult language in main and embedded clauses.

Subordinating conjunctions first occur in phase V of grammatical development in German child language (cf. Clahsen 1986). In this regard, it is crucial that in all of the available data on the acquisition of German, *no verb placement errors within embedded clauses* occur. At first, this observation seems to be surprising because one would expect that verb placement in embedded clauses, which normally deviates from the position of the verb in main clauses in German, would pose a problem for the children. All of the empirical data available show however that this prediction is wrong.

> Grimm (1973) quotes for example 69 embedded clauses in which verb placement is always correct. Stern/Stern (1928) and Scupin/Scupin (1907) did not find any verb placement errors in their early embedded sentences either (cf. also Mills 1985). Park (1976) reports an imitation test in which children quite successfully corrected verb placement errors in given embedded clauses and put the verbs at the end of the respective sentences. In the material quoted by Ramge (1976:163-166) there are no instances of verb placement errors either. Lastly the results of my own investigation (cf. Clahsen 1982) confirm that verb placement in embedded clauses does not pose a problem for the children.

These results are consistent with the idea that the children already have access in early developmental phases to a syntactic configuration in which the positions required by German for verbal elements are present. As mentioned, they already use the verb final pattern in the early phases when they do not use embedded clauses at all. Thus, the syntax offers a structural position for verbs at the end of the sentence long before the first embedded clauses are used. As soon as the first embedded clauses are used, the subordinating conjunction is placed in the CONFL-position and the inflected verb has to remain at the end of the sentence because the front verb position is already occupied. Through this the final verb position can be specified for the finite verb. The analysis suggests that verb placement in embedded clauses need not be learnt in the usual sense of the word. Instead, the order is correct as soon as the child (in phase V) has access to the lexical prerequisites, here subordinating conjunctions, needed for the fixing of the relevant parameter. All in all the suggested analysis fulfills the requirements of extendability. Given the configuration assumed for phase II, verb placement in German including that of the embedded clause can be acquired on the basis of simple, positive data. Progress in the child's grammar was, in accordance with the lexicalist position, traced back mainly to expansions of the child's lexicon.

2.4.2.5 In the following I will describe which mechanisms and which information from the linguistic input the child needs in order to construct the suggested syntactic representations. I shall be concentrating on the question as to how the syntactic positions for verbal elements are created. Based on the continuity hypothesis, I assume that all the principles of Universal Grammar are available from the start for this. With regard to the acquisition of verb placement the following elements of UG are particularly relevant:

(51) a. *X-bar theory*
$X^2 \rightarrow$ Spec X^1, X^1
$X^1 \rightarrow$ ... X ...

b. *Move alpha* (the configurational matrix, Koster 1984)

c. *Theory of government*

X governs to the left / right, where X=V,P, ...

d. *Theory of predication*
A sentence consists at least of a subject and a predicate (cf. Williams 1981).

I shall also assume that the child is confronted with the following word order data in the linguistic input:

(52) a. an alternation INFL ... / ... INFL
b. an alternation ... XV/... VX ...
c. XVS patterns
d. dominantly SUBJ+PRED-patterns

d. dominantly SUBJ+PRED-patterns
e. [Spec N^1 N^1] - **zwei** *kleine Jungen*
(*two little boys*)
[Spec A^1 A^1] - **sehr** *schöne Mädchen*
(*very pretty girls*)
f. often Mod ... Inf

Even in phase II the child is said to be able to differentiate between inflected and non-inflected verbal elements in the linguistic input. The former are categorised in the lexicon as INFL-elements, the latter as V-elements. The data on phase II show that the children do not yet have access to the complete agreement paradigm and make errors in choosing the required verb inflections. However, even in phase II, an inventory of verb inflections can be found as well as word order asymmetries which are dependent upon the morphological form of the verb (see also Ch. 3). These observations indicate that INFL- and V-elements belong to the available input categorised by children in phase II. Based on this, there are two conceivable analyses of (52a):

(53) a. INFL^1

INFL.........

b. INFL^1

.........INFL

In both cases principles of X-bar theory ensure that INFL is the head of INFL^1 (cf. Kratzer 1984). According to (51c) however, the child must choose one of the options in (53) and for this the input (52f) is relevant. By means of semantic bootstrapping the child can categorise modal verbs easily due to their meaning as INFL-elements. As a result of input (52f) INFL^1 is head-initial as in (53a). In this way the syntactic INFL-position is created as part of the constituent structure of phase II.

It has also been suggested that in phase II the child takes the following underlying structure for S (=V^2 in 44):

(54) NP_{SUBJ} VP_{PRED}

For the construction of (54), (51d) and the structures (52d) and (52e) from the linguistic input are the relevant factors. The constituent structure is universally given by (51d), the order of the elements is to be extracted from the input, directly from (52d) and indirectly from (52e), if it is assumed that (i) the subject is a specifier (cf. Travis 1984) and that (ii) children generalise over different X-bar categories when positioning specifiers.

Finally, it was assumed in the analysis suggested for phase II that the VP is head final at the level of underlying structure. Crucial for the acquisition of that are (51c) and (52b) in the input as well as the assumption that the verbal elements in structures such as ... VX ... occur in the syntactic INFL-position.

As already mentioned the assumption of a syntactic INFL-position is independently motivated. In addition to that, it is required for several different reasons that the word order parameter within the VP must be fixed at the value head final. (51c) requires that a given lexical category may not govern to the left on one occasion and to the right on the next. Only on the basis of input (52b) both structures would be possible, (i) $_{VP}$[V ...] and (ii) $_{VP}$[... V]. (51c) forces the child though to fix one of the two possible structures as being the underlying representation. If the order parameter were to have been fixed at the value head initial within the VP, then movement rules for several of the stuctures in the input would have to be assumed, which would not fall under UG principles; in XVS structures, for example, the movement of the subject to the right would be necessary, a rule which does not fulfill the conditions of the configurational matrix. By means of a head final VP and a syntactic INFL-position, on the other hand, all the structures of phase II can be derived.

A further reason making the choice of option (ii) more favourable is that the child in this case can generalise with regard to the position of the head element across different X-bar categories (cf. Felix 1984). It has been shown for example that NPs occur head finally throughout phase II. Choosing (ii) makes it possible for the child to fix the order parameters at the value head final in the VP too.

In phase V the child identifies subordinating conjunctions and fixes the COMP/INFL-parameter at the value particular to German. Through this, representation (50) arises with its head final INFL-position within INFL[1]. The finite verb has to stay in its basic position in embedded clauses because the CONFL-position is already filled with lexical material. In main clauses on the other hand, a movement rule has to be used to bring the finite verb into the CONFL-position. This rule falls under UG principles. Its acquisition is possible because of the availability of (51b).

> I shall be referring to the idea of a so-called configurational matrix as suggested by Koster (1984:29ff.), in order to specify structural conditions by which an antecedent *a* is linked to another element *b*. The configurational matrix is also valid for movement rules, because in GB-theory it is assumed that the element which is moved leaves a trace behind in its basic position and is co-indexed with this position. The configurational matrix contains among other things the characteristics of prominence and locality. Koster conceives prominence to be that both the elements *a* and *b* fall under the c-command relation. The relation between *a* and *b* is local only when there is not more than one bounding node between them. For further technical details see Koster's analysis (1984).

The movement rule for placing the finite verb in German is consistent with the conditions of the configurational matrix. The CONFL-position takes over the moved element; the movement is therefore prominent and local in the sense of Koster (1984).

Herewith I close the discussion of early child grammars. The results agree with the central assumptions and hypotheses of learnability theory. The analysis suggests that UG principles are in effect even in the initial phases of grammatical development; the continuity hypothesis can to this extent be maintained. Furthermore it has been shown that the child, starting from the analysis suggested for phase II, can only learn the correct grammar on the basis of simple positive data from the linguistic input. The lexical learning hypothesis can be confirmed through this. The analyses carried out up until now have concentrated mainly on the composition of syntactic constituents and on word order. In the following chapter it will be shown how characteristics of inflectional morphology are integrated into the child's grammar and whether learnability theory also makes correct predictions for this.

3. The grammar of a three year-old

At the age of about three, there is a clear turning point in the development of grammar. We find that the values for the Mean Length of Utterance (MLU) suddenly shoot up. Children now have access to grammatical function words and several morphological paradigms. It looks as if a qualitative change away from the early grammatical systems takes place at the age of approximately three years (cf. also Garman 1979:200ff.).

A three year-old's grammar and its acquisition are analysed here in the framework of learnability theory. This means that three problems have to be solved: (a) a descriptively adequate grammar has to be produced, (b) the information required by the child from the linguistic input in order to construct the grammar has to be provided and (c) the learning mechanisms s/he uses for that have to be specified. The basic hypotheses for the investigation correspond to those of the previous chapter (see 2.0). I suggest that the grammar developed by a three year-old also (i) falls under the principles of UG, and can be acquired (ii) on the basis of positive linguistic data from the input, and (iii) with the help of mechanisms, which fulfill the learnability conditions. In particular, I want to maintain the continuity hypothesis and the lexical learning hypothesis. It will be shown that no qualitatively new learning mechanisms are needed for the developments observed. Instead, it will be argued that the changes in various areas of child grammar are triggered by the expansion of the child's lexical knowledge. With respect to that, learnability theory also provides an explanation for the observed developmental correlations in child grammar acquisition.

3.1 Some features of phase IV in German child language

The linguistic developments occurring at the age of three were defined in Clahsen (1986) as phase IV of grammar acquisition. The most important characteristics of this phase are described briefly in the following.

As mentioned previously early child grammars are here called phase II of grammar acquisition (see 2.1). After this, at the age of about 2 to 2½ years, there are several developments which exceed the early two-word phase. Now for example, expanded sentence structures with adverbs and complex verbal elements can be seen more often. These developments were defined as phase III of grammar acquisition. In phase III, there are no obvious, qualitative developmental changes; instead the elementary system of phase II is gradually extended. Phase III, therefore, is more a transitional phase of child grammar learning which will not be looked at in detail here.

The most important developments of phase IV concern the levels of sentence and word structure. Word order is now mostly correct, also in structurally complex contexts, for example with separable prefix verbs and verbal groups. To illustrate this, let us look at the following examples from my data:

(1) immer *fällt* die *um* (D.)
('always falls the over')
(D. is trying to build a church.)

(2) das *ist* theo (M.)
('that is theo')
(M. is looking at a picture book.)

(3) ich *hab* ihn *aufsetzt* (M.)
('I have it on put')
(M. has put on a hat.)

(4) jetzt *hast* du sechs (M.)
('now have you six')
(M. is telling his mother that he now has six croissants.)

(5) die eisenbahn *hat* die Julia *puttmach* (M.)
('the railway has Julia break')
(Julia has broken the railway.)

(6) *mach* das denn noch sik? (M.)
('does that then still music?')
(Does that still play music?)

As shown by the examples, the children now have access to the correct word order in main clauses. The finite verbal element appears in main clauses in the second structural position and in yes/no questions at the beginning of the sentence; I call this position of the finite verb 'V2' (verb-second-position). Remarkable is that the acquisition of the correct position of the finite verb takes place within a very short period of time. The values for the use of V2 jump up from about 40% to about 90%. Tables 1 and 2, with the percentages of V2 placement in Daniel's and Mathias's speech, are an illustration of this.

> Both tables show relative frequencies for the use of V2-patterns and agreement markings in phases II, III and IV. Whilst the average values are given for phases II and III, the values are given for phase IV separately for each recording; in these cases, the age of the child is given, in months (1st number) and in weeks (2nd number). An X is inserted if there were no data available for one particular phenomenon, and brackets are used when there were fewer than three instances.
> The information on agreement markings in tables 1 and 2 is relevant in clarifying developmental correlations with the acquisition of verb placement. The percentages show the number of times the verb forms *-Ø*, *-n*, *-t*, *-e* and *-st* correctly mark agreement with the grammatical person and the number of the subject. The *-Ø* values for Mathias show, for example, that in phase II 45% of the stem forms he used were correct; the spoken adult language is taken as the yard-stick here. In the remaining 55% of M.'s utterances in phase II there were errors.

Table 1: *Verb placement and verb inflection / Mathias*

	Phase II	**Phase III**	**35.2**	**36.3**	**37.3**	**39.3**
V2	.32	.30	.54	.64	.97	.97
Ø-correct	.45	.60	.66	.82	.95	.94
n-correct	.48	.77	.80	.80	.87	1.
t-correct	.80	1.	1.	.95	.86	1.
e-correct	(1.)	(.80)	.60	.67	X	1.
st-correct	X	X	X	(.50)	1.	1.

Table 2: *Verb placement and verb inflection / Daniel*

	Phase II	Phase III	35.2	36.3	37.3	39.3
V2	.31	.24	.43	.73	.94	.90
Ø-correct	.62	.65	.93	.91	.98	1.
n-correct	.47	.50	.83	.86	1.	1.
t-correct	(1.)	.71	1.	.95	.83	1.
e-correct	.50	.37	X	.50	X	1.
st-correct	X	X	X	1.	1.	1.

The values plotted for the use of V2-placement show, along with the examples given, that considerable developments take place in child grammar in phase IV. The values for V2 in phase IV advance and at this point the position of the verb in main clauses is mostly correct.

With regard to the *inflectional morphology* phase IV represents a decisive point in the development of grammar. The children now have access to the person and number morphemes for the marking of subject-verb-agreement (ich komm*e*, du komm*st*, er komm*t*, etc. (I come, he come*s*)). The development of the agreement system in German child language has been described in Clahsen (1986a). The developmental sequence suggested in that study was additionally verified using data from other empirical investigations (cf. e.g. Miller 1976). It was also compared with the results which Mills (1985) obtained for her research summary of linguistic diary studies on the acquisition of German. The basic elements of the developmental sequence were confirmed in the data of those studies. I will summarise the most important developmental stages here.

In phase II most verbs appear in the stem (*-Ø*) or the infinitive (*-n*) form. In addition to this, all of the children already use the inflection *-t*. The forms occurring in phase II are not used as agreement markings. Tables 1 and 2 show that only about half of the *-Ø* and *-n* forms are correct. In the remaining instances, overgeneralisations occur:

(7) hier *kann* nicht raus (M.)
('here can not out')
(Whilst looking at a picture book, M. points to three children who are shut up in a room and are not coming out.)

(8) nur pier Julia *neid* (M.)
('only paper Julia cut')
(Julia is only allowed to cut paper.)

(9) ich mach*en* hier (M.)
(I make here.)

(10) fäll*t* um (M.)
(falls over)
(M. wants to jump from the sofa; he stretches out his hand so that his mother will hold on to him.)

Together with the values from tables 1 and 2, these examples illustrate that properties of the grammatical subject do not affect the children's choice of verb inflections in phase II. The analyses carried out in Clahsen (1986a) showed that for all of the subjects which occurred *-Ø* or *-n* and occasionally *-t* were used, regardless of the grammatical person concerned. In phase II, choice of the inflection is more dependent upon semantic factors, such as the semantic transitivity of the sentence. It has been shown for example that the inflection *-t* occurs typically in intransitive sentences; see also the examples from paragraph 1.2.2.

In phase III the inventory of verbal markings is extended; at this stage the children also use *-e* systematically. At first, this form is also overgeneralised:

(11) ich kann*e* drinsitzen (M.)
('I can sit in')
(M. wants to clamber onto the wheelbarrow too.)

(12) du ma auch zeig*e* (J.)
('you me also show')
(J. wants to have the book read out too.)

Most of the overgeneralisations are similar to example (11). Here *-e* is added although German only requires *-Ø*. Obviously children in phase II want to mark finite verbs overtly. The form *-e* is not used as a separate inflection, but – as in spoken German – as a phonetic variant of the stem form. In phase III, there are already some indications that the correct system is being acquired, e.g. the loss of *-n* as the marker for the 3rd person sing. and the extension of the inventory of forms. The values from tables 1 and 2 show, however, that there are still a large number of overgeneralisations and agreement errors in the inflections which the children use.

Another peculiarity of phase III are verb forms which do not exist in the paradigm for the inflection of person and number in German:

(13) a. fels noch nich is*er* putt (D.)
('rock yet not is -he broke')
(The rock is not yet broken.)
b. das is*er* fest (D.)
('that is -he fixed')
c. da is*er* gro*ß*er fisch (D.)
('there is -he big fish')
d. oben is*er* liege (M.)
('above is -he fly')
(M. is pointing to a fly.)
e. Daniel tut*er* immer (M.)
('Daniel does -he always')
(M. says to his mother that D. is throwing toy figures into the toilet.)

Most examples of this type occur in phase III, but not for all children; obviously it is not a necessary step in acquiring the agreement system. The markings on the verbs in the examples in (13) can be called pronominal copies. Hereby, anaphoric pronouns are suffixed to the verb stems. As with other verb inflections, the verb stem and the suffixed element are immediately adjacent, and the pronouns in (13) agree with the subject in terms of person and number. Pronominal copies are mostly used with verbs which in (spoken) German simply need *-Ø*. In phase III the children obviously try to provide verbs with an overt marking. In this way, we can explain the overgeneralisations with *-e* in examples such as (11). Note also that pronominal copies in other languages are possible agreement markings, e.g. in Swahili (cf. Mallinson/Blake 1979:41ff.). By contrast, the verbal inflections in Germanic languages have lost their pronominal status. In phase III the children are not quite sure about the formal status of German agreement markings. In phase IV pronominal copies no longer occur; the agreement system has been acquired by this stage. The examples with pronominal copies indicate developmental correlations between the acquisition of the pronominal system and of the inflection of verbs. It is conceivable that agreement markings develop from anaphoric pronouns (see Givón 1976). However, further investigations need to be carried out as there is as yet not enough data available on pronominal copies.

In phase IV we see that the agreement system of the adult language is basically available. The children now use all of the inflections in the paradigm and they no longer use forms which are not possible in adult language. With regard to the development of agreement, the characteristic feature of phase IV is the acquisition of the inflection *-st*. As shown by the percentages in tables 1 and 2, there are almost no overgeneralisations in the use of *-st*, i.e. this formative is used correctly from the beginning. We also see that the other forms are used as agreement markings. The availability of *-st* is obviously the decisive step in the development of the agreement system (see also Mills 1985).

The results on the placement and the inflection of verbs also help us to see *developmental correlations* between different kinds of surface structure markings. As mentioned, an advance in the acquisition of word order can be seen in phase IV, and the result is that suddenly the position of verbal elements in main clauses is correct, wherever relevant. The availability of the agreement system is decisive here. As long as the children do not have access to agreement, they cannot systematically use V2-placement. As soon as agreement is available, the use of V2 no longer poses a problem for the children. This is reflected in the change in the corresponding percentages. This shows that the position of the verb and its inflection correlate in the development of German child language.

A further feature of phase IV is that grammatical function words are now for the most part explicitly realised by the children. These elements were almost always omitted in the earlier phases, but this changes in phase IV. Interestingly, the actual acquisition of the most important grammatical function words runs parallel. The quantitative analyses from Clahsen (1982) show that the omission of auxiliaries, articles and prepositions decreases clearly in phase IV. These observations are also an indication that phase IV represents a decisive point in the development of grammar.

In other areas of grammar, development is not yet completed i.e. in phase IV, for example, no subordinate clauses are found. The first utterances in which sentences with several clauses can be identified occur typically when the children are about 3.5 years old. These developments and several other phenomena were defined as phase V of the acquisition of German grammar; the details are in Clahsen (1986).

In phase IV the child does not have access to the German case system, either. Instead, we find mainly nominative forms used in structural contexts where accusative or dative forms are necessary in German. Let us look at the following examples:

(14) hab *der* keubeu noch nich auf (D.)
('have the cowboy (Nom.) not yet on')
(D. is saying that he has not yet put on the cowboy hat.)

(15) ich hab jetzt auf *die* hand (M.)
('I have now on the hand'(Nom.))
(M. is pointing to a man he is holding on his hand.)

In both instances, case-neutral markings are used; in (14) the accusative is required and in (15) the dative. The empirical investigations available on the acquisition of the case system in German child language show that in phase IV – apart from the *-s* suffix for the possessive genitive – there are no special markings for the various cases (cf. Clahsen 1984a, Tracy 1984, 1986). Instead, the nominative form is overgeneralised and used in all instances requiring case marking. The inflections for accusative and dative are not learnt until phase V (see also paragraph 6.1.3).

We can maintain that, in syntax and in the lexicon, perceptible linguistic developments take place in phase IV. The children have access at this stage to several elements of inflection, as well as to grammatical function words, and in most instances word order in main sentences is correct. I will analyse these features of phase IV in the following, using learnability theory as a framework.

3.2 Syntactic structures in phase IV

One of the basic results of the observations on phase IV is that verbal elements are almost always correctly placed. Up until now, in order to analyse this observation it was assumed that the child in phase IV learns a number of syntactic rules, including topicalisation and verb-fronting (cf. Roeper 1973, Clahsen 1982) which are not available in the earlier developmental phases. However, analyses of this type do not satisfy the constraints of learnability theory. In particular, they contradict the continuity condition because mechanisms which are only available for the first time in phase IV have to be formulated. This does not agree with the theory of LAD, nor with the assumption that the learning devices are stationary and direct (cf. Chap. 1.3.3). I want to show that an analysis under continuity is possible for the data on word order in phase IV; we do not have to assume alterations in the learning devices.

In my theory, the developments taking place in phase IV do not so much concern the construction of syntactic representations, but have more to do with the categorisation of inflectional elements in the lexicon. No changes are required in the syntactic component of child grammar. As before, the syntactic representation, already suggested for phase II and depicted here in (16), applies (see 44 in Chap. 2):

(16)

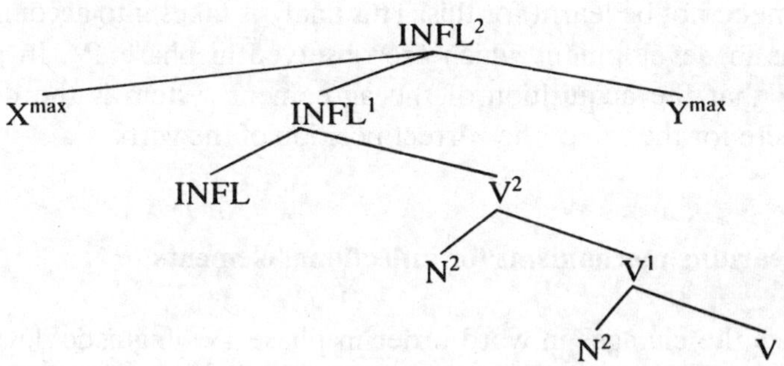

This configuration does not quite correspond to that of German, because (16) does not enable sentence embedding. Nor does it offer positions for COMP or CONFL (cf. Platzack 1983) which could then take on subordinating conjunctions. For this reason embedded clauses cannot be analysed using (16). These limitations correspond to the observation that the children do not use embeddings and conjunctions in phase IV. This also means that no new positions are required for the structures recorded in the data for phase IV. For the placement of verbal elements, the child in phase IV does not have to learn additional syntactic rules or create new positions in the constituent structure; the syntactic representation from phase II is sufficient.

I think that the correct verb position in phase IV results from linguistic developments in the morphological component. Crucial for this is the assumption that the INFL/V parameter in phase IV (see 2.4.2) is fixed at the value appropriate for German; this parameter affects the morphological component of the lexicon. Finite verbs are then categorised according to (17):

(17) $_{\text{INFL}}$[V INFL]

In the next section I will look at which acquisition devices and which information from the input the child needs in order to fix the INFL/V parameter correctly. With respect to this, it is assumed that the linguistic developments made in morphology affect the position of verbs in the children's utterances. The categorisation in (17) causes all finite verbal elements to be produced as INFL-elements in the lexicon and put into the syntactic INFL-position given in configuration (16). Special movement rules need not be learnt for this. This analysis takes into account the correlations in development which are observed in phase IV. In particular it shows that the acquisition of the agreement system is the decisive prerequisite for the use of the correct position of the verb.

3.3 Learning mechanisms for inflectional elements

Besides the changes in word order in phase IV, linguistic development is made in the area of morphology. It has been shown that in German child language the inflectional paradigm for subject-verb-agreement is available in phase IV. It was also made clear that, in all utterances, grammatical function words – such as articles, auxiliaries and prepositions – are used systematically at this stage. I do not think it is coincidental that these changes all happen in child grammar at the same time. The analysis based on learnability theory, which will be introduced in the following, will clarify the developmental correlations between the various morphological phenomena which the children acquire in phase IV. Basically, the analysis orientates itself to the learning devices suggested by Pinker (1984) for the acquisition of elements of inflection.

The decisive similarity between inflections and grammatical function words is that they can only be acquired after the child has systematically compared the formal contrasts occurring in the input, with regard to grammatical dimensions or concepts. The choice of verb inflections in German (*-Ø, -e, -st, -t* and *-n*) depends on the dimensions of person and number (of the subject); the choice of the grammatical function word 'article' in German depends on the dimensions gender, number and case. Semantic bootstrapping is not enough to acquire inflections and grammatical function words. Instead, the child needs structure-dependent, distributional learning devices so that s/he can construct the correct form-function relations. Pinker's (1984) theory on the learning mechanisms in this field starts out with the analysis of the Lexical Functional Grammar (LFG). It is assumed in LFG that the use of elements of inflection and grammatical function words is steered by the establishment of function values which are recorded in the lexical representation of these elements (cf. Kaplan, Bresnan 1982). The entry for the agreement flexive *-s* in English (*Paul dances*) for example, contains the following information:

(18)	-s: V-affix	TENSE	: present
		ASPECT	: imperfective
		SUBJ NUMBER	: singular
		SUBJ PERSON	: 3rd

From this entry and other units in the lexicon, as well as from the syntactic constituent structure, a complex functional representation of the sentence is constructed. All of the function equations from the lexical entries are put into this representation so that agreement with the subject at this level can be carried out.

Pinker (1984:168-174) shows that no reasonable learning devices can be formulated within this system. In particular, he rejects the idea that each inflection in the lexicon has a list of features, by which considerable redundancies arise in the morphological component. Therefore, Pinker suggests a representation of elements of inflection which is slightly different from the LFG-analysis. The basic idea is to use grammatical information coded by means of the inflections or function words as an index to discover the word forms or grammatical morphemes. In this approach, elements of inflection and function words are represented in matrices or paradigms in which the following information is given:

- the *syntactic category* to which the inflection or function word belongs,
- the *grammatical dimension(s)*, analogous to the left side of the functional equations, see (18),
- the *value* of the dimension(s), corresponding to the right side of the functional equations,
- the *phonetic form* of the morpheme or function word.

In this way, we get a specification of the features. Then, elements of inflection and function words are predicates in the lexicon with their own meanings. The representation in the paradigm offers a (secondary) order scheme for these elements. The learning devices required to construct paradigms are formulated in Pinker (1984). The basic elements of this idea are summarised in the following section.

3.3.1 *On the construction of morphological paradigms*

3.3.1.1 Pinker differentiates several kinds of paradigms. To illustrate this, let us look at some (constructed) examples:

(19) a. Category: N

		CASE	
		Nom	*Acc*
NUMBER	*Sg*	daxa	daxb
	Pl	daxc	daxd

b. Category: N

		CASE	
		Nom	*Acc*
NUMBER	*Sg*	-a	-b
	Pl	-c	-d

c. Category: N

		CASE	
		Nom	*Acc*
NUMBER	*Sg*	daxip	daxiq
	Pl	daxjp	daxjq

d. Category: N

		CASE	
		Nom	*Acc*
NUMBER	*Sg*	-ip	-iq
	Pl	-jp	-jq

e. Category: N

CASE		NUMBER	
Nom	*Acc*	*Sg*	*Pl*
-p	-q	-i	-j

Each paradigm has a syntactic category and from this we can see to which word class a particular form refers; affixes also have syntactic categories. The grammatical information linked with inflectional elements is shown in the representations of paradigms as dimensions; these are indicated in the examples in (19) using small capitals. Only a limited number of concepts can be expressed grammatically and come into question as dimensions of paradigms. As well as case and number, these include among others gender, person, tense and aspect. Each dimension can have several values, e.g. the case values 'nominative' and 'accusative', the number values 'singular' and 'plural'; these are in italics in (19). The cells of the paradigm which occur in this way are saturated with the lexical or phonetic form of the inflections or function words.

A general constraint on the construction of paradigms requires that each cell can only have one entry. This is a direct result of the Unique Entry Principle (cf. Pinker 1984 and paragraph 1.3). It ensures that a fixed number of grammatical feature values cannot be coded by two or more forms. In this way syncretisms, which often occur in natural languages, are not excluded. The representation of the paradigm permits the embedding of certain dimensions; hence, the possibility of one form expressing several functions arises. In the paradigm for the article in German, for example, the dimension 'gender' is embedded in 'number'; gender differences are thereby only relevant for the number value 'singular', whilst they are neutral in 'plural'.

Regarding the choice of grammatizable notions, Pinker accepts Slobin's ideas (1985) on Basic Child Grammar. Here, universal (semantic) hierarchies (for more or less easily accessible concepts) are said to govern the choice of those grammatical dimensions which are used by the child to construct morphological paradigms. Dimensions chosen through semantic bootstrapping are used for the construction of paradigms in the early phases in child language. The embedding of certain dimensions within others is also steered by hierarchies like these. Results from Slobin (1985), for example, show that children can choose ASPECT as a grammatical dimension for the inflection of verbs very early on in their development as in Polish and Serbo-Croatian. In contrast, Hungarian children have considerable difficulties to recognise that the definiteness of the object must be chosen as a dimension for the paradigm of verbal affixes. They also have difficulty in inflecting negation words according to the dimensions of tense and person. Observations of this type indicate that the choice of dimensions which can be expressed by grammar is guided by hierarchies of markedness. Hypotheses about the form of hierarchies like these are provided by the results of typological universals research, in particular (Hopper/Thompson 1980, Bybee 1985).

3.3.1.2 In Pinker's acquisition theory for inflectional elements the differentiation between different types of paradigms is important. Elements of regular inflection are represented in adult language by so-called *general* paradigms; (19b) is an example of this. They are linked by word-formation rules with word stems. Elements of irregular inflection, for example irregular verbs, are placed directly into syntactic structures; in the lexicon they are represented in their fully-inflected form as *word-specific* paradigms (see 19a). On top of that, we have to differentiate between one- and multi-dimensional paradigms; (19e) has one-dimensional paradigms, the others are multi-dimensional.

In child grammar acquisition – according to Pinker's hypothesis – developmental differences can be seen between the different kinds of paradigms. He assumes that the child tries to represent the forms categorised in the input as one-dimensional word-specific paradigms. In case the child is forced to do so by extra material from the linguistic input, then the one-dimensional paradigms can be expanded to multi-dimensional, or from the word-specific paradigms, the child can construct general paradigms. The following learning devices can be formulated for this (cf. Pinker 1984: 180f.):

(20) a. One dimension is chosen from a universal hierarchy of grammatizable notions; it is split into relevant values, and a lexical unit is entered in each cell; thus one-dimensional, word-specific paradigms arise.
b. In case a new dimension is accepted for a lexical entry which is already present in a paradigm, a multi-dimensional, word-specific paradigm arises.
c. In case all of the values for a grammatical dimension are occupied by the same form, the entire dimension is eliminated from the paradigm.

It seems plausible to assume that the child initially constructs a matrix for lexical units and, only then, a general paradigm with inflections as cell entries; distributional learning devices are needed to do this. Also, languages vary because they either mark grammatical dimensions by means of regular inflections or they do not. Using (20) as a basis, both possibilities can be acquired without injuring the conditions of learnability. General paradigms can be constructed from word-specific paradigms on the basis of positive evidence from the linguistic input. Mechanisms (21) and (22), which are explained later, serve that purpose. If the child, however, does not find any evidence in the linguistic input, then s/he sticks to the word-specific paradigms assumed at the beginning. If, on the other hand, the child were allowed to construct general paradigms directly – without the detour via (20) – then it could not be explained how s/he is able to construct a word-specific paradigm from these in cases in which this is required in adult language. Negative evidence would be needed in order to recognise that the grammatical dimension concerned was not a case of regular inflection.

Lastly, (20) and the assumptions linked with it are confirmed by the available data on the acquisition of inflection. We find that inflections are first used on a small group of lexical units. Lexical limitations are only lifted at a later stage in development. An example of this is the use of the verbal inflection *-t* in German child language, which is at first only used on a limited number of intransitive verbs; I will be coming back to this phenomenon in my analysis of the agreement system in German child language (see 3.3.2). The important thing here is that observations of this type are in accordance with the idea that the child initially constructs word-specific paradigms.

A further assumption in (20) states that the child first constructs one-dimensional paradigms and only then multi-dimensional paradigms. Regarding (19), it is conceivable that the child constructs a one-dimensional paradigm for both of the elements *daxa* and *daxb* (cf. 19a) identified in the input, with 'case' as a grammatical dimension and "nom", "acc" as values. Further into his/her development, the child also identifies the elements *daxc* and *daxd* in the linguistic input and categorises them with regard to both of the case values. At this point, the Unique Entry Principle comes into effect. It requires that no value is coded by two or more forms. In the example given, it makes sure that the child chooses a further grammatical dimension, in this instance 'number'. Thus, the multi-dimensional paradigm from (19a) arises.

Finally, because of (20c), the children can relinquish temporarily assumed grammatical dimensions as development proceeds. It could be, for example, that the child does not choose 'case' or 'number' from a hierarchy of grammatical dimensions at first, but chooses 'animacy' as the relevant dimension in order to construct a paradigm for the forms in (19a). In the input, *-a* could frequently occur with the feature [+animate] and *-d* often with [-animate]. In a transitional phase, a paradigm with the dimension ANIMACY would then be constructed which would not apply to the adult language in that form. Further into development, the child identifies cases in which *-a* occurs with [-animate] and *-d* with [+animate]. In the paradigms then, the same form can cover both values of the assumed dimension. Mechanism (20c) ensures that in such cases the appropriate dimension is rejected. Examples of the use of (20c) in child language will be analysed in the next paragraph. The empirical results show that in the course of development, children sometimes assume dimensions which are not acceptable in the target language. Mechanism (20c) enables them to reject these dimensions if the target language does not have corresponding means of expression.

3.3.1.3 The next step is the construction of general paradigms. The previously established word-specific paradigms in (19a) and (19c) are the basis for this; the latter corresponds to the agglutinating type, the former to the inflecting. Both types of word-specific paradigms can be constructed in the same way with (20). By contrast, for the construction of general paradigms, Pinker assumes that agglutinating systems are easier to learn than the synthetic forms found typically in inflected languages. This hypothesis tallies with numerous empirical results from language acquisition research. Slobin (1982) finds for example that two year-old Turkish children already have access to the correct case paradigm. On the other hand, German children learn case markings considerably later, when they are about three years old (cf. Clahsen 1984a, Tracy 1986, Meisel 1986). One of the reasons for this difference in development can be seen in the form of the markings. In Turkish, the relations between form and function are clear. In German, though, the case markings arise with gender and number specifications. Russian is similar because there are synthetic forms in which the case marking is done together with the gender and number specifications. The acquisition of this system takes several years. In Russian child language, a phase of development can be seen in which the case markings arise regardless of gender differences (cf. Zakharova 1973). The gender dimension is neutralised during this transitional phase.

Results like this indicate that the child has fewer problems constructing general paradigms with agglutinating forms than with synthetic forms. From this, the following learning devices for the construction of general paradigms can be formulated (cf. Pinker 1984:188-190):

(21) The material which is common to all of the cells in a word-specific paradigm is written in the lexicon and given the feature "stem" or "root".

(22) a. A dimension with corresponding values is chosen from a word-specific paradigm. The common phonetic material (apart from the stem) is written into a one-dimensional, general matrix.

b. In the case of a value not having any common phonetic material, several dimensions are examined at the same time; hence multi-dimensional, general paradigms arise.

(22) is the decisive mechanism. Before this can happen, however, the child must identify the word-stem or, in semitic languages the (consonant) root, in the input and categorise it lexically; (21) serves this purpose. In examples (19a) and (19c), (21) makes sure that *dax* is isolated as the word-stem. Next, (22) can become effective. Using (19c) as a basis and by applying (22a) twice, both of the one-dimensional, general paradigms from (19e) can be constructed. We see here that (22a) is sufficient for the construction of an agglutinating system. That does not apply if the multi-

dimensional paradigm (19b) is to be constructed from (19a), because no common material can be extracted due to standard option (22a). In this instance, the child has to observe several dimensions at once in order to be able to construct a general paradigm, see (22b). One can imagine that a great deal of effort is needed for this process, in comparison to only one grammatical dimension having to be analysed on each occasion. On top of that there is the fact that the amount of direct positive evidence for synthetic forms is altogether smaller. These considerations account for the fact that, on the whole the acquisition of general paradigms with several dimensions causes more problems.

3.3.1.4 After the child has constructed word-specific and general paradigms, there are interrelations between the two. Word-specific paradigms initially contain empty cells for the simple reason that the child does not receive all the elements of irregular inflection in the input at the same time. Thus for example, the matrix for the verb *laufen* ('to run') in the cell (PERSON = 1, NUMBER = Sg, TENSE = Past) could be empty because the corresponding form *lief* has not yet occurred in the linguistic input, or has not been categorised as such. In this instance the empty cell is saturated by the general paradigm. Overgeneralisations occur like this, resulting in the above example in *laufte* ('runed'). Pinker assumes that this kind of cell occupation is temporary; he uses question marks for it, e.g. *?laufte?*. Importantly, this categorisation will only occur in certain limited instances, namely when the child's grammar forces a particular categorisation, although s/he does not have any positive evidence from the input. Elements of irregular inflection for which the child finds direct positive evidence in the linguistic input are accepted into the word-specific paradigm as non-temporary cell occupations. As soon as the child has extracted the word-form *lief* and categorised it as an entry for the cell which is already occupied by *?laufte?*, then the temporary occupation is rejected and the correct irregular verb form remains. The decisive factor is the Unique Entry Principle, by which double occupations in paradigm cells are prevented. The analysis suggested can be summarised in the following mechanism, (cf. Pinker 1984, p.195f.):

(23) Word-specific paradigms compare with general paradigms as follows:

a. Empty cells in word-specific paradigms can be filled by the general paradigm; such cell occupations are classified as temporary.
b. Cell occupations of a word-specific paradigm which are not marked as temporary may not be replaced by the entry of the corresponding cell in the general paradigm.

This analysis of the links between word-specific and general paradigms is in accordance with the conditions of learnability. It shows that the acquisition of elements of regular and irregular inflection, including the acquisition of so-called overgeneralisations which occur in learning, is only possible on the basis of positive evidence. Decisive in the construction of the correct paradigms of the target language is the Unique Entry Principle in conjunction with the corresponding material from the linguistic input. The claim that temporary categorisations which can be rejected afterwards are made in the course of learning inflections does not only apply to the construction of morphological paradigms. Pinker suggests that the child can be forced, either by universal principles or by the structure of his/her grammar, to accept one of the alternatives as correct until positive evidence means that a different categorisation must be chosen in the target language. This phenomenon is seen in several fields of grammar learning, such as in the acquisition of phrase structure rules and in the construction of morphological paradigms; further examples, also for the lexical field, are given in Pinker (1984, Ch.8).

3.3.1.5 A basic insight arising from the suggested approach to the acquisition of inflection is that the child, once s/he has chosen a dimension which can be expressed in grammar, builds up certain expectations with regard to the form inventory of that language. For example, as soon as 'number' is seen as a dimension and *daxa* – from (19a) – has been extracted from the input as a singular form, then the child expects to find alternative forms in the input for the other value of the dimension; in the example, this is for the plural. An important constraint in this context is the *Principle for Limited Paradigm Splitting* (Pinker 1984:202ff.):

(24) In the construction of multi-dimensional paradigms, an extra-chosen dimension is at first only embedded into one of the dimensions already existing in the paradigm.

The principle refers to the construction of paradigms containing syncretisms. In such instances, certain grammatical dimensions are embedded in others; an example of this is the article paradigm in German:

(25)

		NUMBER			
		Sg			*Pl*
		GENDER			
		Masc	*Fem*	*Neut*	
	Nom	der	die	das	die
CASE	*Acc*	den	die	das	die
	Dat	dem	der	dem	den

This representation shows that the differences in gender are only made in the singular, whereas there are differing case forms for both number values. I do not want to go into the development of number and gender markings in German child language here; for this see Mills (1985). Instead the effect of (24) has to be demonstrated here. With regard to the paradigm for article forms in German, (24) is only relevant to differentiate between the various gender forms; however, it cannot be used for the acquisition of the *correct* case markings. It could be that the child initially chooses NUMBER as a grammatical dimension for articles, on the basis of universal hierarchies. Principle (24) takes effect when the child has identified the different (gender) forms of the singular and consequently due to the Unique Entry Principle has to choose an additional grammatical dimension, in this case 'gender'. By means of (24) the splitting of the paradigm with regard to gender takes place only at the singular value, and the child does not have to look for differing values in the plural at the same time. The identical article form *die* does not have to be learnt for each of the three genders. As long as the child does not have positive evidence which forces him/her to employ different forms for the plural, s/he will maintain the limitedly split paradigm. As the child does not find any corresponding article forms in the plural in German, paradigm (25) can be retained. This is different for the case dimension which cannot be inserted into one of the number values, nor into one of the gender values, because the child is confronted with differing article forms for singular and plural.

Several empirical results from language acquisition research support principle (24). In Polish child language for example, we find overgeneralisations for the form of masculine genitive in all genders (cf. Slobin 1985). In German child language there are no occurrences of case differences in the plural forms of articles at first, but for the singular there certainly are (cf. Clahsen 1984a, Tracy 1984). In the early acquisition of cases, in the singular *den* is used in accusative and dative contexts, as well as the nominative form. In the singular therefore, case oppositions can be seen which are based on the values [+nom] and [-nom]. In the plural, however, *die* is used as the only form of the definite article in this developmental phase. In this transitional phase, the dimension 'case' is only present in the singular, because not all of the case forms have been identified. Although the empirical evidence for (24) is still fragmentary at the moment, the observations above still provide initial indications that a child learning inflection acts economically, and at first splits the paradigm only to a limited extent.

3.3.2 *Verb inflection in German child language*

3.3.2.0 In the following I will analyse empirical results on the acquisition of inflections in child language, and I will use the learning mechanisms which I sketched out previously. I will concentrate on phase IV of German child language and in particular on the development of the agreement system.

3.3.2.1 In German, subject-verb-agreement is marked on the finite verb. The term "finite verb" covers the group of verbal forms in which tense, mode, (grammatical) person and number are specified. The markings are suffixes and sometimes occur as stem alternations. As regards their morphological structure, finite verbs in German have two parts: (i) the verb stem, which can also hold derivational morphemes, and (ii) the inflectional forms.

According to the Akademie-grammar (cf. Heidolph et al. 1980:561ff.), the inflectional forms are constructed from three so-called tense roots, as well as from person and number formatives; here I will not go into the subjunctive because there are not any corresponding forms for it in early child language. The present forms are inflected with the basic form, with tense root I, (*leb-t, greif-t, brenn-t*; live-s, grab-s, burn-s). Past forms are made with verb stem II. In weak verbs there is a suffix for the past tense (*leb-te-Ø*; live-d). The past forms of strong verbs are made with ablaut (*griff-Ø*; grabbed). In the so-called mixed inflection, suffixes and stem alternations occur simultaneously, for example in *brann-te-Ø*. The third tense root is needed to construct participles. The person and number formatives are suffixed to tense roots I and II. For the six grammatical persons and both singular and plural, there are five forms available: *-Ø, -e, -(e)st, -(e)t* and *-(e)n*. The ending *-e* (=schwa), for example in *ich spreche*, is not treated as a separate form of inflection, but – as in the spoken language – as a phonetic variant of *-Ø*. Wurzel (1970:25) shows that the *-e* can be phonologically predicted in inflectional endings. Wiese (1986) analyses such cases with the phonological rule schwa-epenthesis.

Affixes have to be assigned grammatical categories in the morphological component of the lexicon. The category chosen for agreement inflections is INFL, which includes AGR(eement) as a relevant feature. If we ignore the subjunctive, then the distribution in German (for the Present) looks like this:

(26) Category: INFL

		NUMBER	
		Sg	*Pl*
	1.	-Ø	-n
PERSON	*2.*	-st	-t
	3.	-t	-n

3.3.2.2 Empirical investigations show that agreement in German child language is marked correctly in phase IV. In the following, the paradigm which children use in phase IV will be described; I will refer to the descriptive results from Clahsen (1986a). Then I will investigate which elements of the above learning mechanisms and which information from the input the child needs to construct the paradigm. In addition to that the transitional stages observed in the acquisition of the agreement system will be analysed, in terms of the approach suggested above.

On the basis of the data available (see 3.1), the general paradigm (27a) can be assumed with respect to subject-verb-agreement (in the Present) in phase IV. In addition, based on the hypothesis that children initially construct paradigms with binary choices, we might predict that the dimension PERSON would first be split into two values; (27b) would then be a precedent to (27a) in the development.

(27) a. Category: INFL

	NUMBER			
	Sg			*Pl*
	PERSON			
1.	*2.*	*3.*		-n
-Ø	-st	-t		

b. Category: INFL

	NUMBER		
	Sg		*Pl*
	PERSON		
[+2.]	*[-2.]*		-n
-st	-t		

In any case, (27b) can not last long because *-t* cannot be associated with the feature values [-2nd pers.] and [+sing.] in German, but is specified for the 3rd person singular. From this, it follows that (27b) has to be filled up with the feature for the 1st person. The transitional phase described in (27b) is not clearly documented in the available data, but it would correspond to the proposed learning mechanisms. (27a) can be confirmed in any event by the available data. This paradigm as well is not yet quite the same as that of the adult language. In the data available on phase IV, there is no evidence for subjects in the second person plural, which are marked by *-t* at the finite verb in German. This could, of course, be the result of the limited amount of data investigated so far. However, it could also have systematic reasons. The principle of limited paradigm splitting (see 24) would ensure that in (27a) and (27b) no differentiation is initially made between the grammatical persons in the plural. Here I will accept (27a) as descriptively adequate for phase IV.

In addition, the following word structure is needed in phase IV in order to link the inflections of the general paradigm (27) with the verb stems:

(28) $_{\text{INFL}}$[V INFL]

Crucially, the INFL-parameter (cf. Kratzer 1984) in phase IV is fixed at the value for German. According to (28), all inflected verbs are produced from the lexicon as INFL-elements and can be put into the syntactic $INFL^0$-position. In this way, we can explain the correct postion of verbs in main clauses in phase IV, without having to accept extra syntactic rules.

Lastly, word-specific paradigms have to be assumed for the elements of irregular inflection, especially for the auxiliaries, to which the children have access in phase IV. They are constructed analogous to the general paradigm (27a); word structure rule (28) cannot be used here. As an example let us look at the inflected forms of the verb *sein* (to be):

(29)

Category: INFL

NUMBER			
Sg			*Pl*
PERSON			
1.	*2.*	*3.*	sind
bin	bist	ist	

In sum, the general paradigm (27a), the word structure pattern (28), and word-specific paradigms like (29) are needed to describe the agreement system in phase IV of German child language.

It is also important that the analysis suggested for phase IV is extendable in the sense of learnability theory. The child can learn the German system, starting out from (27a), (28), and (29), on the basis of positive evidence. As soon as s/he has isolated the verb inflection for the 2nd person plural and categorised it correspondingly, there is a violation of the Unique Entry Principle in the general paradigm (27a), because then there are two entries in the cell marked for the plural. Consequently the initial limited splitting of the paradigm for the singular is retracted and the dimension PERSON is also introduced in the plural.

Similarly, the extension could be conceived with respect to the dimension TENSE. As soon as the child finds past tense forms, e.g. for modal verbs, in the input, particular cells of the previously established paradigm receive several entries at the same time. The Unique Entry Principle makes sure that the child looks for extra grammatical dimensions in such instances. TENSE is chosen as a new dimension and the cells of the current paradigm are split for the values 'present' and 'past'. Next, the mechanisms for constructing general paradigms can become effective. Within the single cells of the word-specific paradigm, the common phonetic material is extracted and written into a one-dimensional, general matrix, see (21) and (22). In this way the stem forms of weak verbs arise, which are classified as tense roots I and II in the Akademie-grammar. As far as I know, it has not yet been investigated whether further development actually takes place like this. However, the important thing is that the analysis for phase IV can be extended in principle to the standard system without violating the conditions of learnability.

Next I will examine the learning mechanisms and the information from the input which the child needs in order to construct the morphological representations suggested for phase IV.

3.3.2.3 We saw that verb inflections are used as early as *phase II*, i.e. the forms *-t, -n* and *-Ø*. These are not used as agreement markings in the early developmental phase. Instead, semantic factors are decisive for the marking chosen by the children; particularly important is the semantic transitivity of the appropriate predicate-argument structure. In analysing the system of the verb inflections in phase II, I will assume that the INFL-parameter has not been fixed at the value for German. Thus, two word-structure patterns for the construction of inflected verbs are used in the morphological component, namely (28) and (30):

(30) $_V$[V INFL]

It depends upon the "strength" of the inflections whether inflected verbs are produced by the lexicon as INFL-elements, due to (28), or as V-elements, due to (30). The difference between strong and weak inflections depends upon their semantic content (cf. Kratzer 1984). I assume that the suffix *-t* is categorised as [+strong] in phase II; an indication for this is that *-t* is used as an encoding of semantic transitivity. The two remaining forms, *-Ø* and *-n*, which occur in phase II, are not linked with specific functions at this developmental stage. The children do not know how "strong" these forms are. In most cases, they are categorised as [-strong] and produced from the lexicon using (30). In this way, we can describe the differences in the position of the verb, which are dependent upon the inflection of the verb. Verbs with the inflection *-t* are INFL-elements because of (28) and can therefore be put into the front verb position in the syntax (see 3.2); verbs occurring in the stem or infinitive form are mainly categorised as V-elements, though; the position of these verbs varies, as we can see from the data; there is, however, a clear preference for the verb-final pattern. The proposed analysis which adopts the INFL-parameter can account for these links between lexical categorisation and syntactic position.

With regard to the choice of *-Ø* and *-n* we cannot give any morphologically describable oppositions in phase II; both forms are obviously used in free variation. In addition, there are differences in the frequency of usage from individual to individual. Some children use the stem forms more often in phase II and others use *-n* as the dominant verb form (cf. Clahsen 1986a: 88f.). No clear oppositions arise between *-Ø* and *-n* on the one hand, and *-t* on the other. The flexive *-t* is used to mark low transitivity, but the stem and infinitive forms are used for both transitive and intransitive argument structures.

Therefore, I assume that *-Ø* and *-n* do not encode specific grammatical dimensions in phase II. *-n* could be considered the default form of verb inflections (=INFL). If no particular functions have to be marked, the affix position is taken by the default form *-n* in word-structure patterns (28) and (30). A second possibility available to the children in phase II, is to put *-t* into the affix position; this can be chosen according to the (above-mentioned) specific conditions. The third and final possibility is that the INFL-position in the word-structure patterns remains unoccupied; in this case, the verb appears in the stem form *-Ø*. In phase II, morphological paradigms do not control whether the INFL-position is filled or is left empty. It is more a matter of possible options which can be chosen in free variation. The individual differences observed in the frequency of usage for *-Ø* and *-n* tally with this analysis.

The system described for phase II can be acquired with the learning mechanisms shown in paragraph 3.3.1. The starting point is that the child identifies various word forms of the same verb, e.g. (31) for the verb *drehen* (to turn):

(31) Category: INFL/V
dreh(en) dreht ((to) turn turns)

The Unique Entry Principle ensures that (31) does not exist for long. Learning mechanism (20) chooses an accessible grammatical dimension for the construction of word-specific paradigms, divides it into relevant values and inserts one word form into each of the cells produced. I suggest that with respect to the dimension chosen in phase II Hopper and Thompson's (1980) notion of semantic transitivity is relevant. In this approach the term transitivity refers to features of argument structures, including the type and number of arguments, the type of the verb, etc. According to Hopper and Thompson, (32a) for example, would be less transitive than (32b), because (32a) among other things does not have an animate Agent:

(32) a. Die Tür geht zu.
(The door is closing.)
b. Ich gehe nach Düsseldorf.
(I'm going to Düsseldorf.)

Results on the use of transitivity markings in child language were shown in paragraph 1.2.2. It was seen that, in the acquisition of structurally different languages, transitivity is one of the earliest concepts in grammar. Slobin (1985) regards transitivity as an element of his universal Basic Child Grammar. While learning German, the child goes through the forms extracted from the linguistic input and looks for transitivity markings. The semantic basis for this is the concept of transitivity in Hopper and Thompson (1980). Using (20) the one-dimensional paradigm (33) is constructed as a transitional step for the word forms in (31):

(33) Category: INFL/V
INTRANSITIVITY

+intrans.	*-intrans.*
dreht	dreh(en)

On the basis of instances such as (32), the child finds frequent confirmation in the input for the equation ... *-t*=[+intrans.], as intransitive verbs occur typically with an inanimate Theme-argument as the subject in the third person singular. This is coded in German with the flexive *-t*. The children find less evidence for the instance ... *-(en)*=[-intrans.], as transitive verbs are found with various grammatical persons. It can therefore be assumed that, in a transitional phase of development, there are several word-specific paradigms similar to (33), in which the cell labelled with the feature [-intrans.] remains unoccupied. These are the starting point for the construction of a general paradigm using mechanisms (21) and (22).

(21) ensures that the material common to all cells receives the label "stem" and is written into the lexicon, e.g. for (33) *dreh*. The different word-specific paradigms are compared using mechanism (22). The dimension "intransitivity" is chosen and the common material within the cells (except for the stem) is written into a general matrix. Note that the child is successful for *-t* but not for *-(en)*, because this form is not linked with [-intrans.] in phase II, nor with any other possible dimension. It is treated like a default-form. The following general paradigm can be constructed for *-t* using the above mechanisms:

(34)

Category: INFL	
INTRANSITIVITY	
+intrans.	*-intrans.*
-t	?

An important element of (34) is that the category is fixed. The child has recognised that the inflection *-t* (as an intransitivity marker) has semantic content. The meaning of *-t* makes it a possible candidate for INFL (cf. Steele 1981). Also *-t* can, on the basis of its semantic content, be categorised as a strong inflection and added to verbal stems according to word-structure pattern (28). By contrast, the default-form *-(en)* does not have any specific semantic content which the children in phase II can see. It is a weak inflection and the corresponding word forms are made using (30). As mentioned, in this way we are also able to explain several peculiarities of the position of the verb in phase II.

3.3.2.4 The construction of (34) leads the child to look for other linguistic markings in the input during further development, so that s/he can fill the cells which are temporarily occupied by "?". With respect to (34), s/he does not find a corresponding form in German. That triggers the reconstruction of (34) and the choice of new dimensions for the paradigms of verbal inflection. Changes in the earliest paradigms, which move the children towards the system reached in phase IV are due to (i) the acquisition of word-specific paradigms for modal and auxiliary verbs, and (ii) the identification of previously unobserved inflections in the linguistic input.

Empirical results show that children in phase III of the acquisition of German have access to auxiliaries (and modal verbs). At this stage in their development, they do not use subordinate clauses. With respect to that, the analysis about auxiliaries in Pinker (1984) does not make the correct predictions. Using LFG as his basis, Pinker treats auxiliaries and modals the same as so-called Raising-verbs, for example *scheinen* (to appear), which are subcategorised for sentential complements. He formulates learning mechanisms with which Raising-verbs and Aux/Mod can be acquired simultaneously. These mechanisms are not descriptively adequate, as we can see from the available data on German. At least, this is true if no further specifications are made, because verbs such as *scheinen* are acquired in phase V, along with other structures for subordinating clauses. Auxiliaries, however, are learnt in phase III.

I assume that auxiliaries are categorised in phase III as INFL-elements and are represented in the lexicon in the form of word-specific paradigms. It is possible that the children use universal form-function relations when they make these categorisations. The meanings, especially those of the modal verbs, indicate that these elements are classic candidates of the INFL category (cf. Steele 1981, Kratzer 1984). The word-specific paradigms required are constructed using mechanism (20). Given the data currently available, it is not yet possible to establish clearly the exact form of these paradigms. We would have to have a larger number of instances with constructions containing auxiliary verbs from phase III. So-called pronominal copies, which are often used – at least by some of the children – in phase III with forms of *sein* (to be) and with modal verbs, are another peculiarity (see the examples under (13) in paragraph 3.1). The grammatical dimensions to be marked with these forms cannot be defined precisely, because examples like this occur rather seldom.

However, we can see that errors in number do not occur for auxiliaries, at least not in the data which are available to me. There are no instances in which, for example the auxiliary *sind* (are) is used with a singular-subject, just the same as there are not any in which *is(t)* is used with a plural-subject. Nor do the instances classified as pronominal copies occur with plural-subjects. These observations indicate that the word-specific paradigms for auxiliaries in phase III have a dimension for 'number'. However, it is not clear whether grammatical person also plays a role; further data are needed in order to check this. These observations tally with the results of typological universals research. On the basis of the hierarchy of grammatical concepts in Bybee (1985), we can expect that children choose the dimension NUMBER *before* the dimension PERSON, if a paradigm for the inflectional forms of verbs is being constructed. These observations lead us to assume that the following paradigm for *sein* (to be) could be established in German child language, whereby the required splitting of the singular-dimension is ignored:

(35) Category: INFL

NUMBER	
Sg	*Pl*
is(t), bin, iser, ises,	sind

Learning mechanisms (22) and (23) ensure that dimensions from word-specific paradigms are linked with the general paradigms assumed. Using (34) and word-specific paradigms such as (35) as a basis, the child tries to establish a general matrix containing NUMBER as a grammatical dimension.

Another trigger for the acquisition of the correct agreement system is that *-st* is identified in the input and categorised as a verbal inflection. There are almost no agreement errors for this inflection. As soon as *-st* occurs, it is reserved for the second person singular. Also, after the appearance of *-st*, the remaining inflections are used correctly in all contexts. Note that *-st* is the only unambiguous form in the paradigm. The availability of this inflection enables the child to recognise the content of agreement markings in German. The child can identify *-st* on the basis of input (36), for example:

(36) a. du dreh*st* das Rad
(you *are* turning the wheel)
b. du dreh*st* dich
(you *are* turning)

S/he then tries to integrate the forms of *drehen* into the word-specific paradigm; (37) can arise as a transitional step:

(37) Category: INFL/V

INTRANSITIVITY	
+intrans.	*-intrans.*
dreht	dreh(en)
drehst	drehst

In this paradigm both values of the grammatical dimension appear in the same verb form. Mechanism (20c) makes sure that INTRANSITIVITY is cancelled from the paradigm and that the child looks for a new grammatical dimension. On the basis of (35) s/he chooses NUMBER as a dimension and constructs a one-dimensional paradigm using (20a); thus for *drehen* we get (38):

(38) Category: INFL

NUMBER	
Sg	*Pl*
dreh(e), drehst, dreht	drehen

In (38), the Unique Entry Principle is still being violated. The child therefore has to choose a further grammatical dimension. On the basis of the content of *-st*, s/he can identify PERSON as a relevant dimension. Mechanism (24) ensures that paradigm (38) is only split to a limited extent, namely within the singular. Through mechanism (20b) a temporary (word-specific) paradigm such as (27b) could perhaps occur, and finally, the paradigm, based on (27a), for *drehen* which is characteristic for phase IV. The corresponding general paradigm is produced by (21) and (22). After this, the children have acquired the crucial properties of the (subject-verb)-agreement system.

Herewith I close Part I of the book. The subject of the analysis up to now has been grammar acquisition in linguistically normal children. No new empirical results were presented, but I used previously available results, mainly from my own investigations into child language, and I interpreted them within the framework of learnability theory. The theoretical framework was developed in Chapter 1 from a summary of the theoretical discussion in language acquisition research. Learnability theory, especially in Pinker's version (1984), showed itself to be the most promising approach for investigating grammar acquisition at the moment.

In Chapter 2 the theoretical approach was applied to analyse early child grammars. I gave syntactic representations, particularly phrase structure rules, with which the grammatical features of early child language can be described. Also, learning mechanisms were formulated with which the grammars constructed by the children can be learnt.

In Chapter 3, I analysed grammars of child language which have developed further. The results show how the acquisition of inflectional features can be dealt with in a learnability approach. The fundamental idea is that inflectional elements and function words in the lexicon are represented in the form of an indexed matrix, in which the grammatical dimensions serve as the index. Learning mechanisms were formulated for the construction of such paradigms and tested against the acquisition of subject-verb agreement in German child language. Several questions have to remain open because the data are limited, especially for the role of so-called pronominal copies and for the forms of the auxiliaries in phase III; the basic empirical results, also those on the course of development, can, however, be accounted for in the framework of the suggested learning mechanisms.

All in all the results of the analysis agree with the assumed theoretical conception of the (child's) language acquisition device. The investigation provides empirical evidence for (i) the continuity hypothesis, (ii) the parameter model of grammar acquisition and (iii) for the hypothesis of lexical learning. In the next part, I will investigate developmental dysphasia and try to show that learnability theory and the assumptions made with it contribute to more precise accounts of child language disorders in the area of grammar.

PART II

DEVELOPMENTAL DYSPHASIA

4. Grammar acquisition and dysphasia (with particular reference to the research situation in West Germany)

The investigation of disorders and delays in the normal acquisition of language was a domain of Psychology, Pedagogy and Medicine in the past. Up to now this field has been almost completely neglected by Linguistics. Those involved in the disciplines concerned with the diagnosis and therapy of linguistically disturbed children complain about the lack of linguistically orientated analyses for language development disorders (see Dannenbauer 1983:7). Thus, it is said, for example, that the available diagnoses and standardised linguistic tests in the literature on logopedagogy and speech therapy are insufficient (cf. Füssenich 1982, Ihssen 1978a, Martens/Schmid 1979, Fried 1982). With regard to the improvement of the diagnostic practise, a linguistic analysis of spontaneous speech is claimed to be the best way to achieve a comprehensive diagnosis which supports specific therapy (Ihssen 1978b:95). It is demanded that Linguistics should provide such methods. Also, how to classify the various forms of language development disorders and how to explain them within the framework of a theory on child language disorders remains ambiguous, cf. Kriz (1984). There are demands for a psycholinguistic approach, orienting itself to the theories of language acquisition and processing (Scholz 1978).

The focus of my studies in the field of child language disorders is *dysphasia*; this notion is used for disorders in the development of the acquisition of grammar. The starting point for my investigations into this was the aim to develop a descriptive linguistic procedure. In Clahsen (1986) such a procedure, the so-called profile analysis, was presented, and this can be used in diagnostic practice with dysphasic children.

In the following investigation, I will basically follow three – closely linked – theoretical questions:

(a) Which form do the grammatical rule systems constructed by children with developmental dysphasia take?

(b) By which principles do the children's grammars change?
(c) With which mechanisms do they develop grammatical rule systems?

The investigation is conceived as a *comparative acquisition study*: the grammatical rules, developmental principles and learning mechanisms of dysphasic children are to be investigated in comparison with those of linguistically normal children. For this, production data, which are generally samples of free speech, were gathered from a combined longitudinal/cross-sectional study. Using a computer-aided linguistic procedure, they were analysed grammatically. The difficulties which dysphasic children have with syntax and morphology will be defined more closely in the framework of theories of child grammar acquisition. I will mainly base my ideas on learnability theory. The general hypothesis for the investigation is that there are narrowly delimited, selective disorders of particular learning mechanisms in dysphasia, while the rest of the acquisition system remains intact. This hypothesis goes against the idea that dysphasic children's learning devices show global deficits, or that such children use deviating strategies of grammar learning.

Another motivation behind my work with child language disorders is an attempt to extend the perspective in language acquisition research. This aims at investigating and comparing language learning under different conditions in order to gain insights into peculiaritites in particular language acquisition types and about possible, general principles of human language learning.

From the investigation into dysphasia we can expect insights into the process of language learning which are not possible solely on the basis of investigations of linguistically normal children. In normal language acquisition the various components of grammatical knowledge largely develop parallel to each other. Correlations in development between morphology and syntax are often difficult to perceive because they are eclipsed by other advances in development. Also, the extent to which each component develops autonomously cannot always be explained clearly. Starting out from the basic hypothesis that selective disorders of particular learning mechanisms occur in dysphasia, the investigation should also contribute to the discovery of correlations in development or autonomous developmental paths in early child language acquisition. Thus, we can show, for example, how far a child develops who has intact devices for the construction of syntactic representations, but whose morphological paradigms are damaged. Hereby, we can obtain insights into the extent to which actual syntax acquisition takes place independent of the development of morphological knowledge.

In the following, I will first present several sets of results from some of the available studies on dysphasia; the focus here will be on studies dealing with dysphasia in German-speaking children. Then I will describe the particular aims and working hypotheses for the empirical investigation.

4.1 Linguistic features

Following Scholz (1983:14), I will use the expression "language development disorders" as a cover term for different forms of developmental disorders and retardations. By the term dysphasia, I refer to abnormal development of language with particular regard to morphology and syntax, but without a dominant primary impairment (Scholz 1978, Dannenbauer 1983). Developmental dysphasia was so termed by Grimm and Kaltenbacher (cf. Wyke 1978), and is characterised by the following general features:

(a) There are clear retardations in linguistic development.
(b) The damage mainly affects the field of morphology and syntax; stammering often occurs, too.
(c) Intelligence is at the normal level.
(d) Impaired hearing or extreme emotional disturbances do not occur.

Dysphasia is, thus, differentiated from other disorders, such as aphasia, oligophrenia, impaired hearing and personality disorders. Dannenbauer (1983) also indicates that dysphasic children do not form a homogenic group, neither in terms of their linguistic behaviour nor with respect to their impaired acquisition and processing. The only common feature is that the children have difficulties in acquiring and using the morphological and syntactic system which other children of their age acquire normally.

Little is known about developmental dysphasia and the linguistic features of dysphasic children. In his research summary, in 1983 Dannenbauer still found that linguistically orientated descriptions of this disorder did not exist (cf. p.7). As a rule the literature defines several so-called degrees for extent of dysphasia. One is usually referred to Liebmann (1901) on this; this description, more than 80 years old, has hardly been changed or extended, even up to the present day. Dannenbauer (1983:93f.) has summarised the linguistic features for dysphasia which are described in the available investigations; in the following I will sketch the most important elements mentioned by Dannenbauer:

(1) a. *Extreme dysphasia*
No spontaneous sentence formation; single words or word aggregates without inflection (structureless groups of words); mainly use of nouns and interjections; word repetitions; all in all "poor" expression.

b. *Medium dysphasia*
Again no spontaneous sentence formation; beginnings of syntactic sentence development; word combinations without inflection; telegraphic-style; lack of self-concept; incorrect use of function words (e.g. conjunctions, prepositions); general criterion: verb in infinitive.

c. *Mild dysphasia*
Spontaneous sentence formation with occasional word order errors; salient inflectional errors; gender confused (in articles); words confused; contaminations.

This classification is not based on systematic analyses of child language data; instead it is a loose compilation of several striking features which any observer can perceive when listening to a dysphasic child. In general the children have obvious difficulties with elements of inflection and grammatical function words, as well as with the construction of constituent structures and use of syntactic rules (word order). All further questions arising from these elementary statements regarding a linguistic description of dysphasia have to remain open. It is unclear, e.g. whether all areas of the system of inflection are affected to the same extent, or whether it is possible that gender errors are only characteristic of (c). It is also unclear *which* errors occur; do the elements really occur in any position or is it possible to establish structures in the children's incorrect utterances, from which we can conclude that they are able to construct syntactic rules? This question can also be posed for the system of inflection, independent of whether the children's utterances are correct in the sense of adult language or not.

Also, the division into so-called degrees of dysphasia is theoretically unfounded and can be rejected by empirical results. Dannenbauer (1983: 94) indicates that the purpose of this classification is not stated explicitly anywhere. For Meixner (1976:21) the degrees correspond to the stages of natural language development, although this is not empirically proven. For other authors, these are general degrees of language disruption. Moreover, Dannenbauer (1983:98ff.) shows by means of examples that the features given for the types of dysphasia do not necessarily correlate with each other. All in all, traditional descriptions of the linguistic features in dysphasia are unsuitable. Decisive disadvantages are that only a few of the features of child language data are looked at in isolation, and that they are measured using adult language as a standard. No attempt is made to identify the child's grammatical rules.

For a long time, language acquisition research has assumed that the child learns a limited number of strategies or rules during language development, with which s/he can produce, in principle, an unlimited set of sentences. The transitional grammars are characterised by different groups of rules acquired by the child during development, until s/he finally has access to the grammar of the target adult language. From this, it follows that in order to make any linguistic analyses of child dysphasia, we have to reconstruct the grammatical systems by which the child is guided as completely as possible, and then compare them with the corresponding grammars of linguistically normal children. In this way, the particular linguistic deficit of a dysphasic child and the stage of language development, which s/he has reached, can be judged (cf. Clahsen 1984b).

Recently, dysphasia has received more attention from several disciplines, and with respect to developmental dysphasia in German-speaking children we also have the results from two larger research projects (Grimm 1983, Kegel 1981, 1985), as well as case studies from speech pedagogists (Bunzel 1978, Grunwald 1982, Dannenbauer 1985), psychologists (Schöler 1985) and psycholinguists (Kerschensteiner/Huber 1976, Stephany 1982). These investigations have definitely contributed to improve our knowledge of the linguistic deficits occurring in dysphasia. However, up to now, investigations have mainly limited themselves to the analysis of single, obvious error types. Grammatical analyses are lacking, in which the children's rule systems are described in a comprehensive and systematic way.

To illustrate this, I will look at several data on the position of verbs, which were investigated with specific reference in the available studies on dysphasia.

In the project headed by Kegel, Günther (1981) investigated retellings of picture book stories by six children with dysphasia. He found that the children '... always use the same sentence pattern *subject-verb-object* ... with the meaning agent-action-goal' (p.47). Günther (1981) and Kegel (1981) on the whole found this observation to be confirmed in imitation tasks.

Completely different results were obtained from the project headed by H. Grimm. Eight dysphasic children between the ages of 3.9 and 4.8 years were investigated in this project, whereby four cross-sections were taken within one year. In Grimm (1983) we see that dysphasic children use the word-order pattern which is typical for subordinate clauses in German, not differentiating between main clauses, interrogatives and subordinate clauses. The linguistic sample investigated has 134 sentences, 112 (=84%) of which have the verb-final pattern. In sentences with topicalised elements, the inversion required in German does not occur, but instead the verbal elements remain at the end of the sentence. Grimm also indicates (1983:174) that separable verbs are not separated, and are not produced in different sentence positions. These results are confirmed by Kaltenbacher/Kany (1985) who have also investigated the position of the verb for the other seven children in Grimm's project.

Thus, while Günther (1981) and Kegel (1981) classify the SVO pattern as characteristic of dysphasia, Grimm (1983:176) regards it as "pure dysphasic language" ('dysphasische Sprache in Reinkultur') if a child mainly uses verb-final patterns in his/her utterances. The only point on which these authors agree is that in dysphasia fundamental deficits in the syntax are present. This conclusion is problematic regarding the contradictory results.

The decisive disadvantage of the available investigations is that they examine verb-placement in isolation from other grammatical phenomena. This point also seems to be the reason for the evident contradictory results. In the previous part of this study, correlations in development were seen between the position and inflection of verbs for L1 acquisition of German. We see that the position of the verb is correct immediately after the acquisition of the (subject-verb-)agreement system. The position of the verb in German requires a differentiation between finite and non-finite verbal elements. With the acquisition of a morphological paradigm for person and number inflections, the notion of finiteness becomes available, and the verb-second constraint in German no longer gives the children any problems.

With this as a basis, dysphasic children's errors in the order of verbs possibly indicate difficulties in constructing morphological paradigms instead, and do not necessarily indicate problems using syntactic rules. The use of the verb-final pattern is then only a secondary effect because the morphological component does not offer the corresponding inflections, and the children are not able to differentiate between finite and non-finite verbs. The data presented by the above mentioned authors is not enough for a reanalysis, though; but, there are links between the inflection and position of verbs in their data:

- The children investigated in the Grimm project do not have access to the subject-verb-agreement paradigm. The verbal elements which occur appear mainly in the stem or infinitive form at the end of the sentence. In isolated instances there are also data for inflected verbs; these appear mostly in second- and first-position (see the following data from Grimm 1983:174):

(2) a. mama leine *bauen*
('mama alone build')
b. die bolidei *hat* das
('the police has that')
c. *hat* mit runterfallen
('has with fallen down')

- In the data presented in Günther's (1981) study, (cf. Hay et al. 1981), the children mostly use the correct inflections and place the finite verb – as required by German – in the second position. In a couple of the instances, incorrect stem or infinitive forms also occur; these appear – as in Grimm's data – at the end of the sentence (see the following examples from "K1"'s retelling of a story, Hay et al., p.109):

(3) a. un dann *spielt* auf n straßen
('and then play on t' streets')
b. un dann n am immer weit *suchen*
('and then n at the always far search')

The crucial feature of the data is that inflected verbs mostly occur at the beginning, in second or initial position, whilst non-inflected verbs appear at the end of the sentence. The principles of word order in German apply in this respect to dysphasia, too. The differences between individual children depend on the availability of the morphological paradigm: Grimm's children use mainly uninflected forms, while the children in Günther's investigations already have access to the person and number inflections. In this respect, the data from Grimm's project agree with the linguistic samples from the dysphasic children I investigated. Günther's data (1981) correspond instead to those from normal children in phase IV of grammar acquisition, at least as regards the order and inflection of verbs (cf. Ch. 3.3). It is unclear whether there is possibly a (milder) type of dysphasia in this instance; because of the limited material, this question cannot be answered. In any case, the observations tally with the hypothesis that there is a selective deficit. It looks as if the children's syntactic representations remain for the most part intact and that – when disorders occur – they happen first and foremost in the morphology. More precise ideas on this will be provided by a linguistic analysis in which the links between morphology and syntax are revealed.

4.2 Psycholinguistic aspects

Little is known about the causes of developmental dysphasia. In earlier investigations brain damage, inborn impairments, mental handicaps as well as vague factors in the educational environment are given as the reason (cf. e.g. Wurst 1973). Ethiological lists of this kind contribute little to an explanation of language development disorders. The fundamental problem with such typologies is that observed linguistic behaviour is linked directly to non-linguistic factors. The relations are purely correlative and there is the danger that features which, purely out of coincidence, go in the same direction in linguistic and non-linguistic behaviour are then linked with each other. Also, there is the fact that such lists can apparently be extended arbitrarily (cf. e.g. the list in Becker/Sovak 1975:108). Finally Crystal (1981) shows that for most of the children who have dysphasia without recognisable organic impairments, no suggestions for therapy can be made from ethiological typologies.

Recently, the investigation of developmental disorders has taken a *psycholinguistic perspective*. Hence, retardations and disorders observed in linguistic development are traced back to deficits in the underlying acquisition and processing mechanisms. Based on this, the second step is to examine the non-linguistic factors responsible for the deficits. A linguistic perspective like this enables a more fundamental understanding of the relations between (i) triggering factors, (ii) underlying acquisition and processing mechanisms and (iii) linguistic behaviour observed. Here, theories of language acquisition and processing are referred to in order to find theoretically based explanations for the observed linguistic disorders. First steps towards a psycholinguistic explanation of developmental dysphasia are provided by Grimm (1983), Kanngießer (1984), Forster (1984), Gopnik (1984) and Schöler (1985), amongst others. Not all of these often very different approaches can be described here. I would therefore like to clarify just some of the controversial questions and will commence with Grimm's explanation (1983).

Grimm (1983) starts with Cromer (1978) and tries to show differences in linguistic processing between linguistically normal and dysphasic children. She assumes that the language of the children without linguistic problems will reveal variable sentence patterns, while that of the children with dysphasia is based on few sentence patterns, especially on the verb-final pattern. Grimm (p.175) then maintains that these differences can be traced back to different kinds of processing strategies. Unimpaired children have access to so-called holistic linguistic processing strategies, by which the child recognises, records and produces larger linguistic units. By contrast, dysphasic children are mainly dependent on analytic strategies, in which each word serves as a single unit of linguistic processing. Grimm (p.177) states that these children construct the verb-final pattern using an analytical strategy 'by which they simply add the new elements which they extract from the linguistic environment to the patterns available'.

The project headed by H. Schöler also tries to reveal deficits in the processing system of dysphasic children. His claims are diametrically opposed to those of Grimm (1983). Schöler (1986) indicates that the utterances of dysphasic children can often be described as reproductions of memorised units. He states that the deficit is that the children can*not* process the sentences analytically. Instead, larger linguistic units are recorded and reproduced as such without the internal structure of these units being clear to the child. Thus, the type of deficit underlying dysphasia is a controversial point: Do the children orientate themselves by holistic processing strategies or by analytical processing strategies? Which of the two positions, Grimm's or Schöler's, is correct cannot be decided definitely. There are several arguments for the plausibility of both positions, even though each position excludes the other. In my opinion, that indicates that the theoretical framework chosen for each is insufficient. Obviously, the type of deficit in dysphasia cannot be defined finely enough using general linguistic processing strategies. As long as the deficit is only investigated in the framework of simple dichotomies (holistic vs. analytical), we cannot make specific predictions nor find evidence to support either position.

Furthermore, the controversy in the available psycholinguistic studies is whether dysphasic children (a) have the same acquisition and processing mechanisms available to them as linguistically normal children, or whether (b) developmental dysphasia is based on qualitatively different language learning and processing operations. Researchers using the parallelism approach (a), (Morehead/Ingram 1973, Johnston/Schery 1976, Menyuk 1978, Homburg 1981, Dannenbauer 1983), refer to the fact that the order of acquisition is not different and that dysphasic children do not develop any bizzare linguistic rule systems. These researchers regard dysphasia simply as a temporal delay in the acquisition of language (retardation hypothesis). In assumption (b), it is claimed that the normal acquisition and processing mechanisms show general deficits which would show up, for example, in the fact that dysphasic children generally use linguistic patterns rigidly and with little flexibility; this would speak for a qualitatively different developmental process (cf. Schöler 1985, Kaltenbacher/Kany 1985).

In my opinion the assumption of parallelism is preferable, at least for heuristic reasons. It explains dysphasia within the framework of linguistically normal children's acquisition and processing mechanisms, as long as the data from the dysphasic children permit this. In this respect, the assumption of parallelism is a constraint on possible attempts at explanation. Understanding this as an heuristic principle prevents general deficits being assumed where specific damage to single learning mechanisms are already sufficient to describe the data. This ensures that only as much damage is assumed as is necessary. Contrary to the authors above, I think, however, that there is definitely not a necessary link between parallelism and retardation. Maybe the temporally delayed acquisition of language is simply one of the possible types of dysphasia. In other dysphasic children there are possibly also qualitative differences from linguistically normal children. According to the assumption of parallelism, one would have to show that there is selective damage to particular learning mechanisms in both cases, and that the rest of the acquisition system remains intact. If this assumption is right, the retardation hypothesis, at least in its most general form has to be rejected.

A psycholinguistic investigation into developmental dysphasia has to reconstruct the acquisition and processing mechanisms by which the children are guided. With the assumption of parallelism as a basis, I want to orientate myself to theories developed in language acquisition research. Recent approaches from learnability theory are important here, cf. Ch. 1.3., as well as Slobin's "operating principles" (OPs) (1973, 1985). I will show that an investigation in this framework contributes to a more fundamental understanding of developmental dysphasia.

4.3 Aims and basic hypotheses

The *first aim* is a grammatical description of the rule systems constructed by children with dysphasia.

My working hypothesis is that these children do not acquire any bizzare systems, but grammars which fall under UG. I assume that the limitations in Pinker's learnability theory (1984) for the construction of child grammars also apply to the rule systems of dysphasic children. Differences between the grammatical systems of linguistically normal and dysphasic children are limited by this hypothesis to two possibilities:

(a) Parameters of UG are not (yet) fixed.
(b) Parameters are fixed at a value possible in UG, but not at that required by German.

I illustrate this hypothesis using the example of the position and inflection of verbs. The so-called INFL/V-parameter formulated by Kratzer (1984) in the framework of GB-theory serves as a theoretical point of reference;

this parameter was introduced in the second chapter (see 2.4), and it refers to the morphological component in the lexicon. Kratzer (1984) shows that languages differ in that they either categorise verbs as in (i) or as in (ii):

(i) $_{\text{INFL}}$[V INFL]
(ii) $_{\text{V}}$[V INFL]

In German, the parameter is fixed at (i), but in English at (ii). As already mentioned in Ch. 2, Kratzer shows that the differences between the two languages in the position of the verb can be traced directly back to the different forms of parametrization in the lexicon.

Let us look at some examples from Wolfgang, one of the dysphasic children in my investigation, whom I will investigate more closely later. W. is, by the length of his utterances, well out of his two-word phase. However, his acquisition of grammar has not kept pace with other developments. W. uses verbs almost only in the stem form and at the end of the sentence; only in occasional instances do modal verbs occur in the second position:

(4) a. du mis ein geb
('you me one give')
(W. wants a sign; mis=mich – Acc. form)
b. is auch ein auto fahr
('I also a car drive')
(W. is driving a toy car.)
c. ein titz is bauch
('a seat I need')
(W. needs a seat)
d. wieder baum runterfall
('again tree fall')
(A tree has fallen down.)
e. auto muß rein jetzt
('car must in now')
(W. is trying to put a doll into the car.)

The examples show that W.'s INFL-parameter has not yet been fixed. However, there are – as required by German – already two positions available in his syntax for verbal elements: (i) final V within VP (examples a-d), (ii) initial INFL after the Topic-element (example e). W.'s problem does not affect syntax in the more narrow sense, but rather he does not have access to any verbal inflections and to this extent cannot fix the INFL-parameter. Verbs therefore remain in the VP. Only modal verbs, which are categorised as INFL-elements because of their semantic features, can be placed into the syntactic INFL-position.

The second example comes from a girl (Petra) who, like W., clearly prefers the verb-final pattern, but who has fully acquired the paradigm for (subject-verb-)agreement:

(5) a. und jetzt du wieder schreibst
('and now you again write.')
b. und dann der andere wieder werft
('and then the other again throw.')
c. wie der läuft?
('how t/he runs?')
(= *Wie läuft der?* in adult language.)
d. ich will was spielen
(I want to play something.)

The examples illustrate that P. uses all of the paradigm's verbal inflections correctly and in spite of this – with the exception of modal verbs – chooses the verb-final pattern. The data show that P. has fixed the INFL-parameter at a value which is different from that required by German. I think that P. does not categorise verbs as INFLs but as V-elements. They therefore remain in the VP and cannot be placed in the syntactic INFL-position. Modal verbs, however, are categorised as INFL-elements – as in English – and can occupy the INFL-position in the syntax.

Both of the instances sketched provide initial indications that dysphasic children do not construct bizzare rule systems, but choose options possible under UG. The task of the investigation is to examine whether the described observations can be generalised for a large number of dysphasic children and for other fields of grammatical phenomena.

The *second aim* of the investigation is to describe the sequence of grammar acquisition in dysphasic children and to compare it with the corresponding developmental sequence in linguistically normal children.

In the face of the fact that dysphasic children do not form a homogenic group, (cf. Dannenbauer 1983), we expect various forms of developmental sequences. We see the following different types:

(6) a. general retardation in language learning.
b. temporal delay in particular, mainly morphological-syntactic fields.
c. different sequences of development than in linguistically normal children.

Results from other investigations show that some dysphasic children go through the same sequence of acquisition as linguistically normal children; this development is simply delayed in general (cf. e.g. Johnston, Schery 1976).

In contrast to this, the data from Wolfgang correspond more to type (b). W. has complete access to content words which linguistically normal children only produce in more advanced developmental phases. Grammatical function words and morphological paradigms, also those learnt early on by linguistically normal children, are often missing. In this way, overall development does not correspond to that of linguistically normal children. W.'s rule system for example, does not fit properly into any one phase of normal language acquisition in every respect. However, W.'s system *within* particular structural fields certainly does correspond to systems developed by linguistically normal children. W. has access, for example, to the verb placement system from phase II of normal language learning (cf. Clahsen 1986). The same applies to the children investigated in the Grimm-project. The data for Petra indicate that dysphasic children's developmental sequences can also differ qualitatively from those of linguistically normal children. Developmental correlations between the inflectional form of the verb and its position in the sentence, as seen in linguistically normal children (cf. Ch. 3.2), do not necessarily apply to dysphasic children too. P. makes dominant use of the verb-final pattern, although she already has access to the agreement system. More precise conclusions are, though, only possible through detailed analyses of P.'s data; but the indications here are that the development of the position of the verb is qualitatively different from that of children without language problems.

In order to work out the different types of developmental sequences in dysphasic children empirically, we must also take longitudinal studies of dysphasic children into account. For each instance of observation, a developmental profile is produced according to the procedure in Clahsen (1986). Using these it is possible to describe the developmental sequence and to compare it with the sequence of acquisition in linguistically normal children.

The *third aim* of the investigation is to define the acquisition mechanisms with which dysphasic children construct their grammatical rule systems.

Using the assumption of parallelism (see 4.2) as a basis, my working hypothesis will be that there are selective deficits of particular learning mechanisms in dysphasia. According to this view it is possible, for example, that the learning mechanisms for the construction of morphological paradigms are impaired. This damage affects the morphological component whereby, however, the devices for the acquisition of syntatic representations remain intact. Or, the learning devices for the construction of phrase structure rules are damaged, which means that the positions required in the syntax for certain lexical categories are not provided. In this way, we can get a psycholinguistically-founded typology of the possible types of dysphasia within the theoretical approach which I have selected.

In the data from Wolfgang and Petra, we primarily find difficulties in morphology. As mentioned, W. has access to so-called content words (nouns, verbs, adverbs, etc.), whilst he has problems with the availability of grammatical function words (auxiliaries, articles, etc. as well as bound morphemes). The differentiation between content and function words plays a central role in Slobin's sub-system of OPs for the construction of linguistic units and in Pinker's system of acquisition devices. Content words can be identified in the input by means of the "semantic bootstrapping" strategy, but function words require structure-dependent distributional learning. The child only learns them by systematically comparing various grammatical forms, using a number of grammatical concepts. Slobin and Pinker maintain that function words are represented by paradigms in the lexicon; they give a number of acquisitional devices for the construction of such paradigms. In W. precisely these learning devices are the ones which seem to be damaged. In any case, we can interpret the specific choice which he makes in the acquisition and use of linguistic units in this way.

In P. on the other hand, the damage does not affect the devices for the construction of paradigms or the syntax, because she has access to the complete agreement paradigm and has the required positions in her syntax. Instead, P.'s difficulties can be localised in the word formation component. P. does not seem to have access to the word formation rule by which affixes from general paradigms are suffixed to verb stems. In the framework of Kratzer's analysis (1984), which is based on Chomsky's theory, P. can be said to put affixes – like other lexical categories – straight into S-structure-representations. In this way, verb inflections get into the INFL-position where agreement with the subject is checked. The inflections are then simply placed onto the verbs in the syntax, and not in the morphology. Kratzer (1984) suggests this analysis for languages with weak verb inflections, for example for English. In languages with strong verb inflections, such as German, the flexives are placed onto verb stems in the *word formation component* of the lexicon. If we maintain this analysis, then the only damage which we would have to assume for P., is that she does not have access to the appropriate word formation rule, and consequently places verb inflections straight into syntactic configurations. All of the other abnormalities, in particular with regard to the position of the verb, result from this. In Ch. 7, I will return to this analysis.

The common features between W. and P. are that the damage first and foremost affects the morphological component. The question whether we can generalise this result, that is, whether morphological difficulties are at the core of the damage in dysphasia, can only be answered by investigating a larger number of children. The present study will contribute to this.

4.4 On the design of the empirical investigation

4.4.1 *Selecting the children*

Dysphasia was determined in this investigation as the core of the children's linguistic problems by an independent diagnosis from a logopedagogue or speech therapist. When selecting the children, I orientated myself by the features in Grimm/Kaltenbacher (1982) (cf. Ch. 4.1). In order to ensure that these features were present in the children under study, a case history file was produced in which demographic information, as well as all of the available diagnostic results were entered. This file was completed for each child with the information from the logopedagogue or speech therapist. Thus, the study includes children who have difficulties with the normal acquisition of syntax and morphology, without having hearing impairments, mental handicaps or massive emotional problems.

This investigation is conceived as a comparative acquisition study: dysphasia will be compared with the grammatical rule systems developed by linguistically normal children in early childhood (until about 3.5 years). In order to ensure comparability with this period of development, the *M*ean *L*ength of *U*tterance will serve as an additional criterion for choice.

The calculation of MLU-values was introduced into language acquisition research by Brown (1973). Since then, the use of MLU-values has been controversial. It has been indicated that not all developmental progress can be covered by MLU-values, that the MLU veils individual strengths and weaknesses in particular areas of linguistic development, and that the conventions for calculating MLU-values are still ambiguous (cf. Clahsen 1986). From these objections, we can conclude that MLU-values can only provide a superficial overall impression of the development of grammar (cf. Miller 1976, Slobin/Bever 1982). In order to get precise information about the stage of development qualitative analyses of the forms which the child uses are required. In the investigations presented here, MLU-values are only used to select the children. I calculate an MLU for words, and not – as was the case in earlier investigations – for grammatical morphemes; in this way, I avoid problems in calculating values. Also I will adopt the conventions for calculation in Clahsen (1986).

In the investigation, I only use data from dysphasic children whose MLU is less than 4.0. This enables us to compare dysphasia with the five phases of early child grammar acquisition suggested in the developmental profile in Clahsen (1986). This profile is based on a descriptive synthesis of all of the available empirical results for early child grammar acquisition in German. I think that MLU is better for this purpose than, for example, the age of the child, which also came into consideration as an alternative criterion for selection.

For the second aim of the present study, we must also have access to longitudinal data from the children. In addition, a greater number of children must be investigated with respect to the third aim. In purely longitudinal studies, often only a few children are studied. In cross-sectional studies, a larger sample can be examined, but statements on the sequence of development are hardly possible. In order to comply with both requirements, longitudinal as well as cross-sectional data will be investigated. Moreover, I will only analyse *language production data*. I think that a detailed description of the productive linguistic achievements of a dysphasic child provides fundamental insights into his/her basic grammatical rule system. Here we are not able to investigate comprehension.

The data available is comprised of video and audio recordings which are about 60 mins. long, of spontaneous interactions between the children being investigated and an adult. The data were elicited in a communicative situation which was as unforced as possible. Additionally, it was required that the child be acquainted (i) with the environment in which the recording took place, (ii) with the people participating and (iii) with the play material chosen to create the situation. The recordings were made in the setting of the logopedagogue or speech therapist's room where the children were treated. Video recordings were made in preference, but if in any instance that was not possible for particular reasons, then audio tape recordings were made. We used small portable video systems and cassette recorders with external microphones for the audio-visual recordings. The equipment was set up outside the play area. Apart from the child under investigation, an adult acquainted with the child took part in the sessions. Games which demand linguistic interaction were offered. Picture books were avoided as they strongly limit the child's possibilities of reply.

Table 3 gives an overview of the linguistic samples.

4.4.2 *Analysing the linguistic data*

In this study, only the linguistic data are subject to more detailed investigations; the non-linguistic data serve to provide background information for choosing the children and interpreting the linguistic data. The analysis of the linguistic data covers three steps: (i) transcription, (ii) grammatical analysis and (iii) interpretation.

The linguistic samples were taken mostly in connection with papers written by students who work with me, and they were also *transcribed* by them.

Table 3: *Summary of the children investigated*

Name	Age at recording 1	Period of observation	Number of recordings	MLU at recording 1	Type of recording
Andreas	7.0	1 month	2	1.71	audio
Anja	9.6	14 months	2	1.46	audio
Jonas	6.6	13 months	2	2.76	video
Julia	3.2	1 month	2	1.76	audio
Klaus	4.6	1 month	2	2.00	audio
Markus	4.7	–	1	1.50	video
Patrick	4.5	–	1	2.25	video
Petra	3.8	12 months	3	2.11	audio
Sven	7.4	–	1	2.17	video
Stefan	4.8	–	1	2.31	video
Wolfgang	4.5	–	1	2.84	video

I thank all of the students who took part in our project for their participation and enthusiasm and especially for my being able to use their data for the present investigation. The data on Andreas, Jonas and Sven stem from State Examinations in speech therapy (Full 1984, Dorn/Spencker 1984, Schuurmanns 1986); these transcripts were kindly made available to me for this investigation.

All of the children's linguistic utterances are in the transcript. All of the information needed to understand the child's utterances is noted there, too; this includes (a) general information on the situational context, (b) information on characteristic gestures, for example when a child stretches out his/her arms in a deictic utterance, (c) information on the intonation, for example to identify questions and (d) other speaker's utterances as far as they are relevant to the interpretation of an utterance. Then I checked the transcripts of the linguistic samples which were recorded in our project. The procedure tested in Clahsen (1982a) was used to transcribe the utterances; extracts from the transcripts are in the appendix of this study.

All of the transcripts were then recorded and analysed on a personal computer. The *grammatical analysis* was coded and also recorded on the PC.

The procedure of linguistic profile analysis (Clahsen 1986) was used as the grammatical description. Here, only a few of its basic elements are explained.

Spontaneous language forms the basis of a linguistic profile. All of the child's utterances are subject to a detailed linguistic description. For this, a profile is used in which the linguistic features are arranged according to development. The core of the profile is a developmental sequence consisting of five phases, which describes the acquisitional sequence of basic elements of German grammar in linguistically normal children. Each phase of the developmental profile has a number of linguistic features. These groups of features combine the characteristic, invariant aspects of each developmental phase. In order to produce a developmental profile, all of the empirical investigations available on early child acquisition of German were gathered and any linguistic features and sequences of acquisition which could be generalised were recorded in the profile. The grammatical analysis takes the following areas into account:

(a) *Word and constituent structure*: refers to word classes, e.g. nominal and verbal elements, articles, prepositions, conjunctions, adjectives, etc., and the internal structure of syntactic categories, e.g. of noun and prepositional phrases.
(b) *Inflectional morphology*: case morphology and the inflection of verbs are investigated.
(c) *Sentence structure*: refers to the type and the position of constituents occurring in the children's sentences.
(d) *Semantic relations*: semantic aspects of sentences in early two-word utterances are investigated and the semantic relations between clauses within complex sentence structures.
(e) *Negation*: refers to the type and position of the negation words in the sentence.
(f) *Interrogatives*: the use of wh-pronouns and word order in direct and indirect questions.

The data are fed into the computer in the form of input masks, whereby a mask of 32 fields is available for each utterance. An extract from a mask of this type for one of Wolfgang's utterances looks like this:

NAME	:	wolfgang 1	ADVEL	:	
SENTNUM	:	001	VERBEL	:	120f
SENT	:	du mis ein geb	CONJUNC	:	
NANLSENT	:		CASEFORM	:	
ANALSENT	:	2c	OMIT	:	
QUANTCRIT	:	4	SEMREL	:	
SENTSTRUCT	:	21	NEGATION	:	
NOMELSUB	:	5	QUESTION	:	
NONSUB	:	5, 6	COMPSTRUCT	:	4

The child's utterance is entered in SENT, along with any context comments which are needed. In the other fields, codes which refer to the descriptive categories in the profile analysis in Clahsen (1986) are entered. SENTSTRUCT "21", for example, means the word order pattern *S*(ubject) X(=Variable) *V*(erb).

A completed profile chart provides (i) a detailed description of individual strengths and weaknesses as well as (ii) the possibility of judging the developmental stage a dysphasic child has reached. The last step is to *interprete* the linguistic samples which have been grammatically analysed. Here, computer programmes, which were written using the database system dBASE, can be used to help. Up to now, three types of programmes have been developed:

(a) A programme PROFBOG, with which completed profiles for any number of data can be produced
(b) Programmes for the production of quantitative analyses on separate fields of the grammatical analysis
(c) Menu-steered sort and index programmes (REPORT)

In comparison to analysing data with paper-and-pencil, PROFBOG saves a considerable amount of time and avoids errors in calculation which otherwise easily occur. Programmes of the second type provide qualitative analyses which extend beyond the absolute frequencies in the profile chart. Tables are produced for areas such as argument position, case morphology, the inflection of verbs, etc., in which the number of obligatory contexts is related to the number of forms which actually occur, and factors about the linguistic environment which could be decisive in the choice of linguistic forms are examined. Finally, the data – sorted according to certain areas of grammatical description – are investigated using report programmes. 15 sub-programmes are available in the menu, which can be used to produce reports about the basic elements of grammatical description.

The completed profile charts of all the linguistic samples under study are in the appendix. When I describe the results of the investigation, I will make use of the profiles and the quantitative analyses which were carried out.

4.4.3 *Overview of the data investigated*

In the following, several general features of the linguistic samples under investigation are explained using the upper parts A and B of the profile charts, as well as MLU-values. Table 4 shows the types of utterances which occur.

Firstly, the values in the table are relevant with respect to the *amount of data* which is available for the grammatical analysis. In order to carry out a profile analysis at least 100 grammatically analysable utterances are needed per child. This requirement is met for all of the children – with the exception of Markus; in most instances, there are even between 150 and 200 utterances in each child's linguistic sample. Additionally, table 4 shows that the relative number of utterances which can be grammatically analysed is at least 50% and in most cases over 70% for all of the children – except for Markus.

Markus's linguistic sample was analysed in Clahsen/Mohnhaus (1985). In that study we showed that this child's linguistic problems lie outside the area of grammar. We found, in particular, that there were strongly preconstructed interactional routines between Markus and his parents, for example imitational exercises, which offer the child little opportunity to develop his own behaviour and linguistic abilities. A procedure for grammatical description such as the profile analysis is not suitable to analyse Markus's linguistic sample; it was therefore excluded from any further investigations. In this case, more discourse-orientated procedures have to be used. The available amount of data for the other children is enough to carry out a profile analysis. And the majority of the utterances can be described grammatically. Thus, by using a grammatical analysis, we gain insights into the linguistic problems which are present here.

Table 4: *Utterance types*

	Number of utterances	Grammatically analysable (in %)	Reactive utterances (in %)	Formulaic utterances (in %)	Meaning unclear (in %)
Anja 1	240	59	37	2	14
Anja 2	320	89	48	0	1
Andreas 1	209	72	44	8	3
Andreas 2	246	62	32	15	6
Klaus 1	121	80	47	3	8
Klaus 2	169	86	41	2	2
Julia 1	212	73	56	5	4
Julia 2	303	56	55	4	5
Markus	214	42	34	16	11
Patrick	250	60	42	14	6
Sven	375	60	40	17	8
Stefan	435	50	47	17	8
Jonas 1	254	71	22	17	5
Jonas 2	207	71	39	6	7
Petra 1	105	60	46	9	6
Petra 2	256	71	30	9	4
Petra 3	257	72	29	6	6
Wolfgang	290	68	14	16	5

The first column displays the total number of utterances (the sum of parts A and B of the profiles, without "repetitions") for all of the samples. The relative frequencies in the second column refer to the proportion of utterances from the total which can be analysed grammatically ("ellipses" and "others" from part B). In column three, the number of reactive utterances ("ellipses" and "simple answers") is compared to the total number of utterances. Column four refers to the proportion of formulaic utterances ("stereotypes" and "formalised expressions" from part A). The figures in the last column are the proportion of utterances whose meaning cannot be identified clearly ("incomprehensible" and "ambiguous" from part A).

A further condition for carrying out grammatical analyses is that we understand the meanings of the children's utterances. Otherwise, for example, grammatical categories and functions could not be clearly defined. The last column in table 4 shows that only a small number of the utterances, on the whole fewer than 10%, cannot be analysed further because their meanings, even with information about the context, cannot be identified for sure. The profiles also show that these are mostly utterances or parts of utterances which cannot be understood because of disruptive noises or for other acoustic reasons (see the values for "incomprehensible" in the profiles). In spite of obvious phonological impairments for some of the children, the utterances are generally comprehensible and suitable for grammatical description.

The proportion of reactive utterances averages about a third of the total in the linguistic samples; the number of formulaic utterances averages about 10%. These values do not show any particular abnormalities. Similar frequencies are also found in children without linguistic difficulties (cf. Clahsen 1986:109).

In table 4 we also see individual differences between the children regarding the number of reactive and formulaic utterances. The values for the same children also vary from recording to recording, such as for Andreas and Jonas. The differences between the values obviously do not depend on the child's age; compare the information for Sven and Patrick on the one hand and for Anja 1 and Klaus on the other. I think that we can trace back the main differences between these values to situational conditions. For Sven, for example, the number of reactive and formulaic utterances is above average. The role plays with numerous greeting forms, addresses and question-answer-routines which form a large part of the recording are the reason for this. Similar applies, for example, to Stefan. A glance at the transcript shows that here, too, role plays dominate. In this respect, a comparison between both of Andreas's linguistic samples is revealing. In the first recording the child was playing by himself without saying much. The interviewer then asked a lot of questions, which are responsible for the large number of reactive utterances (cf. Full 1984). In the second linguistic sample, a role play with Punch puppets was carried out; the value for formulaic utterances is correspondingly high. These examples are enough to show that the situational factors and the behaviour of the interviewer are responsible for the extent to which the child uses reactive or formulaic utterances.

Overall, we do not see any abnormalities in the communicational behaviour of the children from the upper part of the profile charts. The number of imitative utterances is minute, on the whole, the utterances are comprehensible and the greater part of each linguistic sample can be analysed grammatically.

One initial – admittedly not very detailed – result concerning the *stage of grammatical development* reached by the children is permitted by the MLU-values. They show that the Mean Length of Utterance is mostly between 2.0 and 3.0; this corresponds with phase III of normal grammar acquisition (cf. Clahsen 1986:74). For Petra, Wolfgang and Jonas, the MLU-values even extend to phase IV, and for Anja and Andreas they correspond to phase II. In spite of individual differences we see that the development of grammar – measured in terms of the Mean Length of Utterance – does not tally with the age of any of the children. The children under investigation are mostly at phase II/III, which linguistically normal children usually reach at the age of 2 to 2.5 years; the children here are, however, much older.

Another common factor is that none of the values for these children is lower than for phase II or higher than phase IV. The observations show that dysphasic children are fully capable of producing utterances with two and more constituents. Their linguistic disorders cannot, therefore, be traced back to a general disability to form sentences. By contrast, hardly any of the children get much further than phase III; this could indicate that the acquisition of grammatical phenomena, which normally takes place in the more advanced phases IV and V, poses problems for them. Both observations are only preliminary, of course, because no direct conclusions can be made from MLU-values about grammatical rule systems. Instead, qualitative grammatical descriptions, such as in the following sections, are required for this.

5. Grammatical units

The first part of the data analysis focuses on the lexical and syntactic units which occur in the children's utterances. I will investigate the types of nominal elements and the structure of noun phrases, the types of adverbial elements and the structure of prepositional phrases as well as the verbal elements and conjunctions which occur. Each analysis provides insights into the lexical representations of the most important word classes, and into the construction of phrase structure rules by children with dysphasia.

5.1 Nominal elements and the structure of the noun phrase

The analysis was carried out with the descriptive categories of the profile analysis; see the appendix. Here, personal pronouns (Pro^P), e.g. *ich, du,* (I, you) etc, as well as other pronouns (Pro^A), e.g. *der, das,* (the) etc. are differentiated from NPs. A noun phrase can contain a determiner (D), e.g. an article, a possessive pronoun, etc. NPs with attributive adjectives are analysed under (Adj N); if there is an article or another determiner occurring in an NP, the NP concerned is recorded again in (DN). Finally, NPs consisting of a noun and an NP, e.g. possessive genitives, are analysed under (N NP), and simple nouns, e.g. proper nouns, under (N).

A summary of the various types of nominal elements and NPs occurring in the children's utterances is given in table 5.

The table shows that all of the children have access to personal and other pronouns and to full NPs. The quantitative distribution of each type of nominal element varies greatly, however. For Patrick, Sven, Stefan and Petra 2/3, pronominal reference dominates, while nominal reference is preferred by the other children. A comparison between Jonas 1 and Jonas 2, as well as between Petra 1 and Petra 2/3, also shows that, in the same child, there are fluctuations in the relative frequencies from one point in the investigation to the next. This type of variation is not at all unusual in

Table 5: *Nominal elements*

	Number of nominal elements	D+N	Adj+N	D+Adj+N	Number of pronouns (in %)	pronom. subject (in %)	Missing article (in %)
Anja 1	84	8	2	0	7	25	73
Anja 2	196	22	10	1	18	34	58
Andreas 1	90	7	5	0	36	46	77
Andreas 2	90	1	3	0	37	28	96
Klaus 1	74	15	3	0	33	35	48
Klaus 2	111	29	5	2	31	33	38
Julia 1	130	8	7	0	6	4	86
Julia 2	184	11	3	0	5	1	75
Patrick	125	18	2	0	54	67	60
Sven	214	25	0	0	51	72	62
Stefan	180	37	3	1	52	90	22
Jonas 1	168	31	10	0	22	28	61
Jonas 2	137	50	0	0	45	54	13
Petra 1	54	23	0	0	22	80	28
Petra 2	151	17	2	3	74	92	44
Petra 3	234	34	3	2	62	86	30
Wolfgang	213	60	1	1	46	64	38

The first four columns contain absolute frequencies, where we see slight differences to the profile charts, because structures of the form D+Adj+N are not given separately, but are included in (DN) and (Adj N) in the profiles. In the fifth column, the proportion of personal and other pronouns is given in relation to the total number of nominal elements. The sixth column refers to the proportion of pronominal subjects in relation to the total number of subjects which occur. The number of omissions of the article in relation to the total number of obligatory contexts is in the last column.

early child language acquisition. Bloom/Lightbown/Hood (1975) and Nelson (1975) showed that there are differences in the use of pronominal and nominal reference in linguistically normal children. In the earliest phase of acquisition, some children use pronouns preferentially while others use nouns in most contexts under the same semantic relations. The fluctuations in the values for pronominal and nominal reference in dysphasic children fully correspond with the variation known in this part of linguistically normal children's development.

In this context, we see from tab. 5 that the number of pronominal subjects varies widely. Stefan and Petra show a preference for pronominal subjects as well as – to a lesser extent – Patrick, Sven, Jonas 2 and Wolfgang, too. However, other kinds of NPs occur as subjects in these children's utterances, and – more importantly – the children prefer pronominal reference, regardless of the NP's grammatical function. In the data on the remaining children, who mostly use nominal reference, pronominal subjects seldom occur. With regard to the frequency for the use of pronouns, there are no obvious subj./obj.-asymmetries in the data.

With respect to the structure of NPs, tab. 5 shows that all of the children use determiners and attributive adjectives. Adjectives in Sven's utterances only occur in predicative function; see the profile analysis in the appendix. We also see that D+Adj+N structures are rare and only occur for few of the children. Also, expansions of the form N NP, in which the NP is extended by a possessor, only occur in three of the examples from Anja 2 as can be seen from the profiles; (see examples (1a) - (1c)). To those, we can add five examples from Klaus and one from Jonas 2, in which the NP is extended by a mass term; in examples of this type we find the structure NP N:

(1) a. *majo papa* hingebra (Anj2:97)
('majo father brought')
(=Mario's father has brought it.)

b. *ana müte?* (Anj2:248)
('ana hat?')
(A. is asking if this is her hat.)

c. *nadi hem* (Anj2:193)
('nadi shirt')
(A. is pointing at the shirt of the doll 'Nadine'.)

d. *soviel tück äpfel* (Jon2:42)
('so many piece apple')
(J. is pointing how many apples he has.)
e. *ein tück n bär* suche (Kla2:74)
('a piece bear look')
(K. is looking for a jigsaw slab of a bear.)
f. *n toßes tücken vorhang* fehlt noch (Kla2:95)
('a big bit curtain missing still')
(=A big part of the curtain is still missing.)

The examples which are included in the following to illustrate the analysis come from the transcripts. The child's name and the number of the recording is on the left of the colon in the brackets after each example, and the number of the utterance in the transcript is on the right.

Altogether expanded NPs like (1) as well as D+Adj+N structures occur very seldom and only in a few of the children under study. Instead, apart from a noun as head, an NP typically contains a determiner or an attributive adjective. Regarding their position within the NP, the examples in (1) show that the modifying elements, i.e. the possessor in (a) to (c) and the mass term in (d) to (f), generally come before the head of the NP. This regularity in the position is confirmed for all the other types of NPs. The transcripts show that all determiners as well as attributive adjectives are placed *before* the noun which they are modifying; errors in the word order within the NP cannot be seen. For this data, we can use the following phrase structure rule:

(2) $NP \rightarrow (\left\{ \begin{matrix} Det \\ Adj \end{matrix} \right\}) N$

The rule in (2) describes the constituency and serialisation of the NPs which occur typically in the utterances of the children being investigated. A PS-rule seems most suitable for this. One of the arguments in its favour is that we do not see any subj./obj.-asymmetries in the use of nominal elements. To describe the data, a rule is needed which offers identical categories for different grammatical functions; PS-rules enable this.

There are indications for extensions of the elementary rule (2), at least for some of the children in the investigation. Some of the longitudinal data available shows that, after a period of time, the system in (2) can be expanded by more complex NPs (D+Adj+N, N NP, NP N), for example in

Anja 2, Klaus 2 and Petra 2. However, in other children (Andreas, Julia), the original system does not change during the period of observation. The use of expanded NPs can be seen as the result of advances in development which reach beyond the elementary form of the NP. We must remember, though, that the data is limited and that extensions are only seen in a few of the children. I therefore use rule (2) to describe the NP. Additional longitudinal studies are required in order to judge the subsequent development.

In order to get more information about the internal structure of the NP, we have to investigate the types of *determiners* occurring and the use of the article. Here, tab. 5 shows that none of the children uses the article in all of its obligatory contexts. Only for Jonas 2 are the articles missing on relatively few occasions. The omissions made by the other children, on the other hand, average at 55%. Thus, we see that articles are a part of the inventory of the child lexicon, but they are mostly omitted, even in an obligatory context. The longitudinal data available also show that the values for missing articles remain relatively stable or that they even increase, such as in Andreas and Petra 2. With the exception of Jonas, there is no advance in development in the data regarding the frequency of use of the article.

Tab. 6 is a summary of all of the determiners in the data. Forms which only occur in one utterance are in parentheses. A star shows that gender and/or number errors occur in the use of that form.

We see from the table that the children use definite articles, indefinite articles and possessive pronouns as determiners, as well as quantifiers and numerals. We only see a slightly extended system in Jonas, because he additionally uses demonstrative pronouns. This observation enables us to complete PS-rule (2) with (3):

(3) $Det = Art, N_{Poss}, Q$

The method for writing the rules is similar to Pinker (1984). Possessive pronouns or – as in Anja 2 – nouns can be placed in the N_{Poss}-position. The N^0 position in (2) can be substituted with personal pronouns, other pronouns or simple nouns.

Table 6: *Types of Determiners*

	Article definite	Article indefinite	Possessive pronouns	Quantifiers Numerals	Demonstrative pronouns
Anja 1	(der)	ein*	mein(e)*		
Anja 2	(der), die, (das), de*	ein(e)*	mein(e)*		
Andreas 1	(das)	(ein)	(unser), (deine)	(zwei), (tausend)	
Andreas 2				(vier)	
Klaus 1	(den)*, (die), (der), das, de*	ein(en)		mehr, zwei	
Klaus 2	der, die de*, den*	ein(en)*		viel, mehr	
Julia 1	(den)	ein(e)*		alle	
Julia 2		ein(e)*	mein*		
Patrick	(der), das	ein(e)*	mein*	noch, viele	
Sven	der, das*	ein	dein*, mein	(viele)	
Stefan	(das)	ein(e)*	euer, mein dein	viel, noch	
Jonas 1	(den), de*	ei(nen)*	mei*	alle, sechs	
Jonas 2	der, die, (de)*	ein(e)	deine, meine	viele, drei	diese*, dieser
Petra 1	de*	ein(e)*	(meine), (sein)*	noch	
Petra 2	das*, (den)	ein*	dein(e), mein*		
Petra 3	der*, die*, das*	ein(e)*	mein*, unser, dein*		
Wolfgang	die*	ein*	mein(e)*	zwei	

The internal structure of NPs which occur typically in dysphasic children are described by (2) and (3). A comparison with the results in Part I shows that this system corresponds exactly with the rules developed by linguistically normal children in the early phase of grammar acquisition (see Ch. 2.2). This observation provides the first indication that the linguistic problems in dysphasia do not affect the construction of the syntactic constituent structure to such a great extent, given that the syntax of the children obviously provides for the required PS-rules. The devices for the acquisition of phrasal composition and constituent-internal word order (see Ch. 2.3) seem to be intact.

The dysphasic children have difficulties with the phenomena of the more advanced phases of normal grammar acquisition. The use of the article in the NP is affected in particular. We saw that, in the data on linguistically normal children, omissions of the article hardly occur in phase IV; the article is then treated as an obligatory grammatical function word (see Ch. 3.1). Mills (1985:172ff.) also found that the acquisition of gender oppositions is completed at this stage. She shows that gender errors occur seldom, and least of all in the use of the definite article. Regarding the use of the articles, none of the dysphasic children in the investigation reached phase IV of normal grammar acquisition. They prefer to omit the articles. Additionally, the lexicon only offers the children a limited number of the article forms which they need, e.g. in Wolfgang only *die* and *ein*. Table 6 shows that most of the children neutralise gender and number oppositions by using *de* and *ein*, and that errors often occur in the use of forms which usually serve as gender markers in German. These tendencies also apply to case markings, which I look at more closely in Ch. 6.1. Let us look at the following examples to illustrate the observations:

(4) a. *die* tint auch ein bauch (Wol:146)
('the child also one need')
(=The child needs one too.)

b. *ein* tür is hab nich (Wol:185)
('a door I have not')
(W. is looking for a door.)

c. un *de* kopfsauger haare komme hei (Jon1:197)
('and the vacuum-cleaner hairs come in')
(=The hairs get into the vacuum-cleaner.)

d. jetz kanne sech aba nit autstege (Jon2:151)
de kamera

('now can self but not turn off the camera')
(The camera cannot turn itself off.)

e. und *de* tild (Kla1:95)
('and the sign')
(=(We need) the sign.)

f. un *das* po letzt (Pet2:79)
('and the bum hurt')
(=her bottom is hurt.)

g. ich *die* lehrer bin (Pet3:194a)
('I the teacher am')

h. und du *der das* schulkind (Pet3:194b)
('and you the the pupil')

i. daβ *der* band da nich da drunterfällt (Pet3:78)
('that the tape there not there fall down')
(P. means that the presents have to be tied tightly so that they do not fall down.)

These examples show, in particular, the problems with the use of the correct gender markers which we see in all of the children's utterances. Differences occur in the way in which the children deal with this deficit. Most of them only have access to a few article forms; they prefer to omit the article. A second trend is that the articles are not left out so frequently, e.g. in Wolfgang, Stefan and Petra 1. The strategy of these children is, instead, to use one or two invariable forms throughout, and thereby to neutralise gender oppositions. In some of the other children, the lexicon does offer different article forms, e.g. in Petra 3, but often errors are made in the choice of article.

In addition, the longitudinal data available show that the inventory of the article forms can be extended during development, without gender oppositions being established. We see this phenomenon most clearly in Petra. Only in the data for Jonas was gender established – simultaneous to the extension of the lexical inventory – as a grammatical dimension, given that at the end of the period of investigation, he uses different article forms more frequently and in most instances correctly. However, in Jonas 2, there are still occasional errors in demonstrative pronouns and also examples of the gender-neutral article *de*.

The observations above show that problems in dealing with gender markers are a very stable feature of dysphasia. Presumably, the same applies to the number oppositions which we see for the article and the noun; we do not have enough data available, though, to investigate number markers systematically. By contrast, all of the children have access to article forms with which to differentiate between definite and indefinite NPs (see table 6). We see no obvious errors in the use of markers for definiteness in the data; see the examples in (4). Therefore, it can be concluded that the children's difficulties only affect some of the – mainly grammatical – coding features of the article, in particular gender (and number); on the other hand, other (semantic) dimensions of the article (definiteness) are available in dysphasia.

Gender and number are not primary features of the article; instead, these features are assigned by the noun in the NP. Moreover, the whole NP has to be checked for gender and number properties. With respect to that, gender and number belong to the phenomenon of grammatical agreement. In the lexicon, articles are represented in morphological paradigms, whereby gender and number occur as grammatical dimensions. It appears that dysphasic children have difficulties in constructing paradigms like these, in particular when they need dimensions for grammatical agreement; the mechanisms for constructing PS-rules (for NPs) are, however, intact.

5.2 Adverbial elements and prepositional phrases

Using the profile charts in the appendix as a basis, I differentiate in the following simple adverbs (Adv) from prepositional phrases (PP). Also, I will summarise the types of prepositions which occur and the frequency of the omissions of the preposition in obligatory contexts. Table 7 provides an overview. The frequencies are based on the values in the profile.

The table shows that all of the children – except Andreas – use PPs and adverbs as adverbial elements. PPs must, therefore, belong to the inventory of the children's grammar. However, the number of PPs is extremely low for all of the children. Mostly they are only used in 10% of the instances; the data for some of the children have only one instance of a PP. We also see from table 7 that prepositions are omitted in most of the obligatory contexts. Only for Petra 2/3 and Jonas 2 are the percentages for the omissions comparatively low. The decrease in the values compared to the beginning of the investigation could be due to advances in development in these children. For the other children, however, there are no

Table 7: *Adverbial elements*

	Number of adverbial elements	PP	full NP	Preposition missing (in %)	Type of preposition
Anja 1	33	1	0	83	(in)
Anja 2	108	11	1	70	mit, an, (in)
Andreas 1	41	0	0	100	
Andreas 2	31	0	0	100	
Klaus 1	20	2	0	50	mit
Klaus 2	36	4	4	55	in, (unter), (von)
Julia 1	13	4	1	42	unter, (mit), (in)
Julia 2	46	17	1	58	unter, mit, neben, ohne, hinter
Patrick	45	1	0	83	(ohne)
Sven	55	3	1	72	(zu), (auf), (nach)
Stefan	77	3	1	84	über, (mit)
Jonas 1	72	0	0	100	
Jonas 2	58	5	4	16	an, (in), (mit)
Petra 1	15	1	0	66	(in)
Petra 2	77	8	0	33	in
Petra 3	102	11	1	0	in, (von)
Wolfgang	94	1	0	80	(auf)

Prepositions which only occur in one example are recorded in brackets. The first column gives the total number of adverbial elements, that is (Adv) plus (P NP). Column two shows the frequency of (P NP) in the profile. The third column gives the number of instances in which the PP has a full NP, made up of a noun *and* a determiner or attributive element. Column four shows the percentages of the omission of prepositions with regard to the total number of obligatory contexts.

changes. The omission of prepositions and the use of adverbs is still preferred. With regard to the internal structure of PPs, table 7 shows that they also occasionally have full NPs, at least in those children for whom we have sufficient evidence. We also find that the preposition within the PP comes before the NP in all of the instances available; the constituent-internal word order of the PPs which occur is, hence, always correct. Let us look at the following examples:

(5) a. das *in die mitte* (Kla2:43)
('that in the middle')
(=That goes in the middle.)
b. einbin *in badewanne* (Jul1:62)
('jump in the bath')
(The hippo has jumped into the bath-tub.)
c. kann nich auto *auf s haus* fahren (Ste:237)
('can not car on the house drive')
(Ste. is building a garage so that the car can go in.)
d. is a mal *an de kamera* piche (Jon2:148)
('is a bit on the camera play')
(J. wants to play with the camera.)
e. du *in popo* hauen (Pet2:54b)
('you in bum hit')
(=You'll get your bum hit.)
f. ... gegeht *in schiff* (Pet3:112a)
('goed in ship')
(P. has gone onto a ship.)
g. is *auf tis* stes (Wol:56)
('I on table put')
(W. wants to put a figure onto the table.)

To describe the observations above, we can make use of a PS-rule, according to which the PPs are expanded. This rule takes the following form, in accordance with Pinker's conventions (1984:96ff.):

(6) PP $\longrightarrow$ P (NP_{OBJ})

The syntactic structure of the adverbial elements which occur can be described with this rule; here, as in Pinker (1984), adverbs are taken as intransitive prepositions (P). Again, we see that there are no deviant PS-rules in dysphasia, because (6) corresponds to the rule constructed by linguistically normal children in the early phase of grammar acquisition (see

Ch. 2.2). The syntax in dysphasia also offers the required positions for inserting prepositions into the constituent structure. The fact that the internal syntactic structure of the PPs available is correct indicates this. The fact that prepositions are mostly missing from the children's utterances should not be traced back to syntactic deficits, but to problems in the lexicon, especially in the categorisation and choice of the correct preposition. There are additional indications of this in the data.

From table 7 it is clear that the children under investigation use (i) a limited number and (ii) a limited class of prepositions. Apart from single instances of *ohne, von* and *mit* (without, of/from and with) which occur sometimes in the data, we mainly find locative prepositions (*in, auf, unter,* etc. – in, on, under). In addition, the children are obviously not sure about the correct choice of preposition. Hence, errors occur, such as those in examples (5d, 5e and 5f). Errors of this type and a preference for locative prepositions are also typical of the development of linguistically normal children.

Mills (1985:200ff.) has reanalysed data from Grimm (1975) and found that locative prepositions are acquired early on and used most frequently. At first, this leads to overgeneralisations; *in* is, for example, also used in tense expressions. This is similar in the acquisition of other languages. Bowerman (1982) shows, for example, that locative prepositions are initially used in English child language for temporal and causal relations. Slobin (1985) mentions that, in the acquisition of Hungarian, the possessive is marked by the locative at first.

From observations of this type Pinker (1984:332f.) concludes that children in the early phases of grammar acquisition prefer to conceptualise the meaning of abstract predicate-argument structures locally – independent of the target language's structure. From this, it follows that locative prepositions are identified using semantic bootstrapping and are categorised in the lexicon as prepositions (Pinker, p.41). That is not possible for other types of prepositions. They are represented in terms of paradigms in the lexicon – similarly to case markers – whereby thematic roles are needed as dimensions. Also, at least where prepositonal objects are concerned, co-occurrence restrictions between the verb and the sub-categorised preposition have to be considered. Using these ideas, Pinker tries to explain the asymmetries seen in the use of prepositions in the early phase of child grammar acquisition.

In dysphasia, lexical units acquired by means of semantic bootstrapping pose fewer problems than the elements to which this strategy cannot be applied. The children prefer locative prepositions, and there are indications that the meanings of abstract argument structures are conceptualised locally. Prepositions which tend to require structure-dependent learning devices, meanwhile, do not occur typically in dysphasia. Consequently, the position provided by the syntax for prepositions generally remains unoccupied in these instances. In other children omissions are seen less often; here, though, errors in the choice of prepositions are found frequently. Finally, on the basis of the longitudinal data available, we do not see any systematic developmental progress in the use of non-locative prepositions. Thus, the data for Petra, for example, show that the limitation on locative prepositions remains even when she no longer omits prepositions. The problems which the children have with non-locative prepositions are a very stable feature of dysphasia which does not seem to be automatically resolved during development.

5.3 Verbal elements

In the following, I will investigate the types of verbal elements which occur in the children's utterances. I will differentiate between simple (transitive and intransitive) verbs and prefix verbs, as well as between auxiliary and modal verbs. The basic result of the analysis will be that not all types of verbal elements are equally accessible in dysphasia. The children have their biggest problems with auxiliary verbs; on the other hand they have no problems in categorising simple verbs and modal verbs.

The investigation uses the categories of the profile analysis. Here, I differentiate between verbal complexes and simple verbs. Separable prefix verbs (Pr V), constructions with modal verbs (Mod, *will ... kommen* 'want ... to come'), copular structures (Cop, *ist ... blau* 'is ... blue') and auxiliary and participle constructions (Aux, *hat ... gemacht* 'has ... made') belong to the former category. The copulae with predicative adjectives or in the so-called equational construction ('Gleichsetzungsnominativ') (*ist ... Bäcker* 'is ... a baker') and forms of *sein* ('to be') occurring with participles count as auxiliaries. The auxiliaries are specific given that they are not predicates, but grammatical function words necessary for the finite realisation of a non-finite predicate (cf. Wunderlich 1985). In addition to the auxiliaries produced by the children, missing elements can also be analysed here. In the following utterances (from linguistically normal children), we see omissions of auxiliaries, for example:

(7) hase lieb
('hare sweet')
(=The hare is sweet.)

(8) schinken aufgessen
('ham eated')
(=(The dog) has eaten all of the ham.)

We cannot make a separate analysis of the omissions of modal verbs because a missing modal verb, even when the interpretation takes the situational context into consideration, can never be reconstructed without doubt.

Table 8 provides a quantitative view of the different verbal elements in the data under investigation.

The table shows that the majority of the verbs used by the children are simple verbs and prefix verbs; auxiliaries on the other hand only seldom occur, and not at all for some of the children. Contrary to auxiliary verbs, modal verbs are, in general, used more frequently and more pervasively. In addition, modal verbs also often occur as simple verbs without a non-finite predicate:

(9) a. *möcht* nen arzkoffer (Kla1:78)
('want a doctor's bag')
(K. wants a doctor's case.)

b. ein metsa *will* (Wol:86)
('a girl want')
(W. wants a girl.)

c. auto *muß* rein detz (Wol:106)
('car must in now')
(W. is putting the doll in the car.)

d. ... *darfe* nit (Jon1:91)
('may not')
(=you mayn't do that.)

Table 8: *Verbal elements*

	simple verbs	sep. prefix verbs	V missing (in %)	modal verb constr.	copula	cop. missing (in %)	auxil-iary constr.	aux. missing (in %)
Anja 1	19	19	20	1	0	0	0	0
Anja 2	68	31	34	1	0	100	0	100
Andreas 1	42	12	26	2	0	100	0	0
Andreas 2	71	23	11	0	0	100	0	0
Klaus 1	17	10	28	0	3	50	0	100
Klaus 2	41	14	35	0	1	66	0	100
Julia 1	22	8	50	1	4	20	2	50
Julia 2	53	7	26	3	3	50	1	0
Patrick	51	12	22	2	4	50	0	0
Sven	90	19	16	5	4	63	0	100
Stefan	64	22	15	2	7	66	1	66
Jonas 1	56	37	25	5	0	100	0	100
Jonas 2	53	20	16	12	1	66	3	25
Petra 1	11	2	38	0	1	0	0	100
Petra 2	67	7	20	8	2	93	0	100
Petra 3	83	4	23	12	4	81	0	100
Wolfgang	83	28	20	0	3	80	0	100

In the table, there are absolute frequencies for each verbal element and percentages for the omissions. The absolute figures are identical to the respective values in the profile charts. To get the percentages, the number of omissions is taken against the total number of obligatory contexts; hence, for example, "Aux missing" = number of omissions of auxiliaries/number of auxiliaries present + number of missing auxiliaries; the calculation of the figures in the two other columns with percentages is analogous to this.

Instances like these are seen in the data for all of the children. They are analysed in table 8 not as (complex) modal verb constructions, but in the first column with the simple verbs. We find that all of the children use modal verbs, but that auxiliaries only occur in isolated instances. A further indication of the difficulties which the children have with auxiliaries can be observed from the percentages of the omissions. Table 8 shows that the auxiliary and the copula are missing in most instances. If there are enough obligatory contexts, then the values are clearly above 50%. In addition, there are no significant differences between the copula and the auxiliary. A Chi-scquare-test, in which the omissions and the use of the copula and the auxiliary are compared, gives a value of $CHI^2_{(0.05,\ f=1)} = 1.85$. This result is definitely below the value required for it to be significant (3.84). Developmental progress in the use of auxiliaries cannot be seen in our longitudinal data. During the period of observation, the percentages of omissions decrease only for Jonas, and the number of auxiliaries used increases a little. Note, however, that the copula and the auxiliary are still barely represented in the data for Jonas 2.

In contrast to the auxiliaries, the verbal elements which occur in phase II of early child grammar acquisition, as well as modal verbs, are available in dysphasia. Column three of table 8 shows that the verb is missing on average in 25% of the contexts where it is required. Thus, simple verbs are present in the majority of the instances. Only the value for Julia 1 deviates from the average. The main reason for this is the situational context. A glance at the transcript in the appendix shows that the results reflect a picture book viewing task and that a large number of the instances are deictic utterances.

Overall, the values for the omission of simple verbs are clearly below those for the auxiliaries. Also we see an advance in development in the use of simple verbs and modal verbs. The data for Petra, for example, show that the number of omissions of simple verbs decreases and that modal verb constructions are used more frequently. However, hardly anything changes in the use of auxiliaries; even at the end of the period of observation, the children still prefer to leave them out. The children's problems with auxiliaries are obviously a characteristic feature of dysphasia which does not simply disappear during development.

Various factors come into question for the analysis of these observations. One possibility would be a *syntactic deficit*. In this case, the syntax would not offer any positions for the auxiliaries produced by the lexicon. This would lead to the auxiliaries being lost during the process of lexical insertion. For some of the children, there are examples from which we could deduce an impairment in the syntax. In these, the auxiliary appears with the non-finite predicate at the end of the sentence, as if the front (syntactic) INFL-position, which is normally occupied by auxiliaries, were not available:

(10) a. auch mama funden *hat* (Jul1:96)
('also mama found has')
((Flecki) has found mama.)
b. Julia zähne füllt *hat* (Jul2:78)
('Julia teeth filled has')
((The dentist) has given Julia fillings.)
c. mei bäuma putt *sind* (Wol:191)
('my trees broke are')
(Wolfgang's trees have fallen over.)

Examples of this type are extremely infrequent in the data as a whole. Apart from the instances in (10), there are only cases for Julia and Petra in which the copula or the auxiliary comes at the end of the sentence (Jul1: 36b, 63, 64b, 66b, 92b; Jul2:52, 153a, 154; Pet3:204a). Otherwise, the auxiliaries always appear in the syntactic INFL-position.

Also, the verbal elements in modal verb constructions are nearly always placed correctly; the modal verb is at the beginning of the sentence and the non-finite predicate at the end. From the numerous examples with modal verb constructions, there are only four instances in which modal verbs appear in the final position (Jul2:51b, Pat:130, Jon1:215, Pet2:165). More precise analyses of the position of the verb are carried out in Ch. 7.1. The above observations show, though, that we can hardly trace the children's problems with auxiliary verbs back to damages in the syntactic constituent structure. The large number of modal verb constructions in which placement is correct shows that the syntax offers the position required for INFL-elements. Also, if we assume a syntactic disorder, that does not explain the asymmetries between modal verbs and auxiliaries, because both are treated as INFL-elements in the syntax.

As an alternative to this I assume that the *lexical representation* of auxiliaries poses difficulties for dysphasic children. In the lexicon auxiliaries have to be categorised as INFL-elements and word-specific paradigms have to be constructed for the different inflectional forms. Both are impaired in dysphasia. Consequently, the forms required in the syntax are not offered during lexical insertion, and the syntactic INFL-position is unoccupied in most instances. The case is different for *sein* (to be) in its locative meaning and for the possessive meaning of *haben* (to have). Instances with the locative form of *sein* and with possessive *haben* can be found in the data of all of the children, even those who do not have access to the auxiliary or the copula and who normally omit *sein* and *haben* as auxiliaries. In dysphasia there are clear differences between both usages. This asymmetry is most easily observed in the data for Anja and Andreas. Auxiliaries are always omitted; but we find *sein* in the locative and *haben* in the possessive meaning:

(11) a. hier nich *war* num (Anj1:5b)
('here not was number')
(A. is looking for a number.)

b. wo *is* arme? (Anj2:199)
('where is arms?')
(A. is looking for the doll's arms.)

c. ich X ein buch *haben* (Anj2:123)
('I X a book have')
(A.wants to have a book.)

d. *hab* schon? (And2:144)
('have already?')
(=Have you already finished the robber?)

We see that the children's lexicon offers the required word forms for auxiliaries, given that there are instances of *sein* and *haben* in the data for every child. Thus, the difficulties in this area are more narrowly confined to categorising these word forms as function words for agreement features. We can assume that locative *sein* and possessive *haben* can be identified using semantic bootstrapping. The same applies to modal verbs. They have independent meanings which make them prototypical candidates for the INFL category (cf. Kratzer 1984).

However, semantic bootstrapping is not enough to categorise *sein* and *haben* as function words for agreement features. For that purpose, the child has to construct a morphological paradigm with grammatical dimensions (person, number) which are supplied from another position (subject) in the clause. Additionally, the child has to consider the co-occurence restrictions between the auxiliary and the non-finite predicate (e.g. participle vs. predicative adjective) and the type of verb: Agent-verbs require *haben* as the auxiliary, Theme-verbs require *sein* (cf. Wunderlich 1985). These limitations cannot be learnt if only semantic bootstrapping is used. The data available show that the children under investigation do not have access to morphological paradigms for auxiliaries. For the children who use auxiliaries at all, only one inflectional variant can be found, without any recognisable formal oppositions. Generally *is* is used, whereby errors sometimes occur:

(12) das *is* puppen? (Sve:16)
('that is dolls?')
(The interviewer has fetched a box of dolls.)

In both of the previous sections there were indications that problems occur when dysphasic children have to deal with phenomena in grammatical agreement. On the other hand, linguistic units which can be identified using semantic bootstrapping are available to these children. The results on the use of verbal elements confirm that.

5.4 Conjunctions

In the following, the use of conjunctions and subordinate clauses in dysphasic children will be investigated. Using the profile analysis as a basis, I will differentiate between co-ordinating and subordinating conjunctions. In linguistically normal children, both typically occur in phase V of grammar learning (cf. Clahsen 1986). Co-ordinating conjunctions connect main clauses; they include e.g. *und, aber, oder*, etc. (and, but, or, etc.). Subordinating conjunctions are elements which introduce a subordinate clause, and they include relative pronouns, complementizers (*daß*, that) and adverbial conjunctions. Table 9 shows the absolute frequencies taken from the profiles. Additionally, all of the conjunctions which occur are listed.

The table shows that co-ordinating conjunctions are present in dysphasia; subordinating conjunctions – with a few exceptions – are not. The latter are only found in Petra 2/3 and in two instances from Klaus 2. Co-ordi-

Table 9: *Conjunctions*

	Number of conjunctions	co-ord.	subord.	Type of conjunction
Anja 1	0	0	0	
Anja 2	2	2	0	und
Andreas 1	1	1	0	
Andreas 2	1	1	0	aber
Klaus 1	18	18	0	und
Klaus 2	33	31	2	und, aber, wo, wenn
Julia 1	4	4	0	und
Julia 2	15	15	0	und, oder
Patrick	1	1	0	und
Sven	2	2	0	und
Stefan	11	11	0	und
Jonas 1	36	36	0	und
Jonas 2	20	20	0	und, aber, oder
Petra 1	6	6	0	und
Petra 2	27	22	5	und, aber, oder weil, warum
Petra 3	37	29	8	und, aber, oder weil, wo, was, daß
Wolfgang	0	0	0	

nating conjunctions occur in nearly all of the children's data, and in some, frequently. The only exception here is Wolfgang, who does not use any conjunctions at all. From the longitudinal data we see an advance in development with regard to the lexical inventory of conjunctions. In the initial samples, *und* (and) is used almost exclusively as a conjunction. Gradually, other conjunctions are added to that, e.g. *aber* (but), as well as *oder* (or), and conjunctions are used more frequently. However, these increases are mainly in the co-ordinating conjunctions. Except for Petra and Klaus, at the end of the investigation there are still no subordinating conjunctions to be found. It seems to be a stable feature of dysphasia that the children restrict themselves to co-ordinating conjunctions.

The profiles in the appendix show that subordinate clauses without conjunctions are seldom used by the children under investigation. From the sentence structure analysis for phase V, we see that there are only six utterances in the whole data which we can interpret as subordinate clauses on the basis of their meaning:

(13) a. yaya zeigen julia *bampen füßen* (Jul2:135b,c)
('yaya show julia stamp feet')
(Y.(=name) is showing J. how to stamp her feet.)
b. julia kann nich telen *das boden* (Jul2:71)
('julia can not tell the floor')
(J. cannot tell what has happened on the floor.)
c. feis i nis *atehe tieche heiße* (Jon1:35)
('know I not other animals called')
(J. does not know what the other animals are called.)
d. un fa chos überleche *barbie anzieche* (Jon1:186,187)
('and Mrs. chos think how barbie dress')
(And Mrs. Jost is thinking about how to dress Barbie.)

Subordinate clauses with conjunctions are – as mentioned – only found in the data for Petra 2/3 and Klaus 2:

(14) a. du sach *was ich malen soll* (Pet3:57a,b)
('you say what I paint should')
(You should tell me what to paint.)
b. jetzt ich auswischen die *weil ich vergessen die schere* (Pet3:200)
('now I sweep out because I forgot the scissors')

c. von weihnachten der gesagt *daß* (Pet3:77,78)
der band da nich da drunterfällt
('from Christmas he said that the tape does not fall down')
d. *wenn paßt* (Kla2:117)
('if fits')
e. *wo s hinpaßt* (Kla2:157)
('where it fits')

In Klaus, subordinate clauses only occur in (14d) and (14e). It is doubtful whether there is an actual subordinate clause configuration here, as the conjunctions are each used just with one other constituent. Petra is the only one of the children in the investigation who has clear access to subordinating conjunctions and different kinds of subordinate clauses. For her, we find instances of complement clauses, relative clauses and adverbial clauses. Also, the conjunctions always occur in the correct position at the beginning of the clause. The placement of the verb in the subordinate clauses is also correct. Example (14b) is the only case in which the verb-final position is not chosen. This instance cannot, however, be counted as an error in the placement of the verb, because in *weil*-(because)-clauses in German, the second position of the finite verb is also permitted (cf. Lenerz 1985). In the other dysphasic children we only find co-ordinating conjunctions and subordinate clauses do not occur, apart from those in (13).

In phase V, linguistically normal children produce complex sentences which consist of several connected clauses and include conjunctions. The investigations available for phase V do not show any developmental sequences which could be generalised for either kind of conjunction. Most of the children start using co-ordinating and subordinating conjunctions at the same time. However, we initially find semantic limitations. Investigations into the acquisition of different languages show that children only express a limited number of semantic relations between both clauses at first; to these belong "addition" with *und* (and), "adversative" with *aber* (but) for example, "causal" with *weil* (because) for example, and "temporal" through *wenn* (when) for example, (cf. Bloom et al., 1980). Similarly, we cannot see any differences between co-ordinating and subordinating conjunctions in Slobin's comparative language acquisition studies (1985). Slobin (p.1219f.) shows that linguistically normal children treat both types of conjunction as so-called connectives, with which a limited number of accessible semantic notions is closely linked.

In dysphasia, the difficulties are not necessarily in the area of establishment of semantic relations between different propositions. As the profiles in the appendix show, most of the sentences with conjunctions can be described using semantic relations which are also used by linguistically normal children in phase V. In some instances there are even relations in the dysphasic children's data which go beyond phase V, e.g. clauses which are linked with *oder* (or). We see the differences between them and linguistically normal children in the way in which they mark these semantic relations. Hence, in dysphasia we find co-ordinating conjunctions almost exclusively. Difficulties in using subordinate clauses and subordinating conjunctions are obviously specific to dysphasia.

In the interpretation of the results different factors must be considered. Firstly, there is no obvious lexical explanation for these difficulties, because subordinating conjunctions are not a homogenic class in the lexicon. Relative and question pronouns, complementizers and adverbial conjunctions, all represented differently in the lexicon, are included in this. It is hardly possible to explain the children's difficulties with subordinating conjunctions in lexical terms. Also, were it a case of a purely lexical deficit, then we would expect subordinate clause structures without conjunctions to be used frequently and without difficulty by the children. However, the data show that this does not apply.

Deficits in the syntactic constituent structure are another possibility. For the representation of subordinate clauses and subordinating conjunctions, there has to be a COMP phrase (CP) in the syntax. After Platzack (1983) we asumed that, *in German*, the features of COMP and INFL are joined in one node, CONFL, which is the head of S^1 (see Ch.2.4). We could imagine that the CP is not available in dysphasia and that the syntactic representation corresponds to those of the earlier phases of child grammar acquisition (see (44) from Ch.2.4.2). In this case, the syntax would not offer the possibility of sentence embedding, nor any positions in which subordinating conjunctions could be inserted. Co-ordination is, on the other hand, possible without a CP. This analysis fits the data described.

There are several possible reasons for the CP not being constructed in dysphasia. An impairment of the learning mechanisms for PS-rules would be an appropriate assumption. However, this is not indicated in the data. Thus, we see that the subordinating conjunctions available occur in the correct position at the beginning of the clause. From the data on Petra, we can conclude that the CP can be constructed as soon as conjunctions are identified in the input. Additionally, there are no errors in the placement of the verb in subordinate clauses. Were there a syntactic impairment, one would expect to find that subordinating conjunctions are offered more frequently by the lexicon and occupy the wrong positions. In fact, placement errors with conjunctions do not arise in the data under investigation.

Alternatively, it could be assumed that dysphasic children have difficulties in segmenting and identifying conjunctions in the input. Subordinating conjunctions have the characteristic features of grammatical function words: they are unstressed, monosyllabic elements of a closed class, perceptually they are not very salient and they hardly have their own intrinsic meaning. They are also hardly used in isolation and mostly appear sentence internally. These features possibly contribute to the fact that dysphasic children have problems in isolating COMP elements from the input. This would mean that the mechanisms which are, in principle, there for the construction of the COMP-phrase would not be able to come into effect. At this point we cannot decide whether problems with segmentation might be responsible for this. In order to be able to determine how conjunctions are processed by dysphasic children, experimental evidence is required which is not available yet.

I will close this chapter with a short summary of the major results. Lexical and syntactic units used by dysphasic children were the subject of this chapter. The structure of noun and prepositional phrases as well as verbal elements and conjunctions were analysed. We saw that the elements of early child grammar (phase II, see Ch. 2.2) are also available in dysphasia. The children under study have problems on the other hand with some of the elements which develop in phases III, IV and V of normal grammar acquisition. These include gender markers on the article, non-locative prepositions, auxiliaries and subordinating conjunctions. Dysphasic children also use other elements from subsequent developmental phases, e.g. co-ordinating conjunctions (phase V). These observations show that dysphasia is not a general retardation in grammar development, but more a selective impairment of specific areas.

To interpret the results of these observations, I assumed that the impairments in dysphasia first and foremost affect how the children deal with grammatical agreement phenomena and the construction of morphological paradigms in the lexicon. By contrast, linguistic units which can be identified using semantic bootstrapping are available in dysphasia. In this way, I attempted to explain the choice of elements available to dysphasic children. Lastly, the suggested analyses show that in dysphasia, no deficits need to be assumed in the construction of constituent structures. Constituent-internal word order is correct and no deviant syntactic projections arise. This result tallies with the hypothesis that there are selective impairments in dysphasia, which mostly take effect in the morphological area.

6. Selected areas of the inflectional system

Case morphology and verb inflection in children with dysphasia are the subjects of the following. The analyses aim to define the impairments which are present in dysphasia more precisely. Person and number inflections on the finite verb, and case markings are instances of grammatical agreement. Their common feature is that the morphological form of the word is determined by other elements in the sentence. The inflection on the finite verb agrees in German with the grammatical person and number of the subject. The morphological form of the finite verb is not a primary feature of the verb as is tense; instead, it is controlled by the person and number features of the subject. Case is also included as an agreement phenomenon (cf. e.g. Lapointe 1985). Case markings are spelt out on NPs, but the NPs get their case features from another constituent within local substructures, mostly from verbs or prepositions. Case is therefore not a primary feature of the marked element, but a secondary one; i.e. it is a syntactically determined feature which marks the role of the NP in the sentence.

The analyses in the previous chapter provide initial indications that dysphasic children have problems with grammatical agreement and with the construction of morphological paradigms. Using this as a basis, we expect that the use of case markings and verb inflections will also be impaired in dysphasia. This prediction is confirmed in the following investigations.

6.1 Case markings

6.1.1 *On the form and function of case markings in German*

In German, case is spelt out on the personal pronouns (*mich-mir*; *dich-dir*; etc.) and on the inflections within NPs. Personal pronouns with case markings are irregular inflections and are represented in the lexicon in word-specific paradigms. In inflections within the NP, case markings occur together with gender and number specifications. These are represented in general paradigms, in which there are different case forms for masc., fem. and neut. as well as for sing. and pl. Of the inflections available in German, only *-(e)n*, *-(e)r*, *-(e)s* and *-em* are relevant for case markings (cf. Wurzel 1970:23). Case marked NPs arise by suffixing in nouns, adjectives, articles, demonstrative and possessive pronouns. In the inflection of the noun there is a difference between strong and weak declension. The weak forms are marked with *-n*. In strong inflection, masculine and neuter in the genitive singular take an *-s*; furthermore, the dative plural is marked with *-n*. These formatives are the only way to recognise case markings on the noun.

The forms of the articles, adjectives and pronouns are more important for the identification of case formatives within NPs. Strong and weak inflection for these word classes must also be differentiated. At this point, we do not need to worry about the genitive, because corresponding markings do not occur for articles and pronouns in the data investigated. The weak forms are formed with *-n*, as in N-inflection. Wurzel (1970:56) gives the following paradigm for the strong inflection of the other cases:

(1)

		NUMBER			
		Sg			*Pl*
		GENDER			
		Masc	*Fem*	*Neut*	
	Nom	-r	-e	-s	-e
CASE	*Acc*	-n	-e	-s	-e
	Dat	-m	-r	-m	-n

The form *-e* is realised as a schwa. This paradigm applies – apart from minor differences which will not be included in this investigation – to articles, as well as to possessive and demonstrative pronouns (Wurzel, p.55). In addition, it applies to attributive adjectives when there is no strongly inflected determiner preceding them within the same NP (*dein miserabler Wein*, 'your terrible wine'); that is, each NP must have at least one expression which is formed with a strong inflection: either the determiner is strong or the attributive adjective, but not both (Wunderlich 1985a).

With respect to their function, case markings in German are categorised as coding devices for grammatical relations. The nominative is used to mark the grammatical subject, the accusative for the direct object and the dative for the so-called indirect object. The case markings also have semantic functions. The dative shows, for example, the thematic roles Recipient or Benefactive, usually the animate receiver of an action or event. The accusative is mostly linked with the thematic role Theme; objects towards which actions or events are aimed are typically coded in the accusative. Only the nominative is not directly linked with a fixed thematic role. The nominative codes the external argument – in prototypical cases, the Agent-argument of the transitive verb.

We will see whether children with dysphasia use case markings in order to differentiate grammatical relations, or whether they use, instead, the semantic functions of case markings. Besides case morphology, word order, prepositions and agreement markers on the finite verb serve to differentiate grammatical relations in German. In Ch. 7.2, I will investigate functional relations between these different coding devices in the systems which dysphasic children develop.

6.1.2 *Case markings in dysphasia*

The analyses are based on the frequencies given in the profiles in the appendix. A few further differences will be introduced. Table 10 contains a quantitative summary of the use of case markings by the children under investigation. The analysis of the acc. and dat. markers is dependent on the syntactic context. The frequencies show how many cases require acc. and dat. forms (see the columns headed "total"), in how many cases acc. and dat. forms are used and in how many cases the child uses case-neutral forms. NPs and pronouns which occur in the nominative count as neutral forms, e.g. *ich bau* **ein** *mast* ('I build a mast'). In table 10 accusative forms which are homonymous with nominatives (*Er kauft* **das** *Auto* 'He is buying the car') are not included because in these cases it cannot be decided whether the unmarked form has been overgeneralised or the accusative is being used correctly; hence, they are excluded from the analysis.

The frequency at which the forms are used in the different contexts can be read from the table. In the case of the frequency for the column "total" being greater than that for the "neutral form" plus "acc. or dat. form", the child uses other forms, e.g. dative forms in contexts requiring

Table 10: *Case markers*

	Accusative contexts			Dative contexts					
	total	Acc. form	Neut. form	total	Dat. form	Neut. form	Genit.	case-marked pronouns	other case-markings
Anja 1	5	0	5	1	0	1	0	0	0
Anja 2	7	1	6	8	5	1	0	3	2
Andreas 1	2	1	0	0	0	0	0	1	0
Andreas 2	2	0	0	3	0	0	0	5	3
Klaus 1	7	2	5	2	0	1	0	0	4
Klaus 2	6	5	1	2	0	1	0	3	3
Julia 1	1	0	1	1	0	0	4	0	1
Julia 2	1	0	1	6	0	5	1	1	0
Patrick	18	15	3	1	0	1	0	10	3
Sven	5	3	2	3	0	3	0	3	2
Stefan	6	0	2	11	6	3	0	12	4
Jonas 1	7	0	7	0	0	0	0	0	1
Jonas 2	8	0	7	5	3	2	0	2	0
Petra 1	4	0	4	1	1	0	0	1	1
Petra 2	2	0	2	9	2	7	0	2	5
Petra 3	11	1	9	7	7	0	0	8	0
Wolfgang	10	0	10	2	0	1	0	1	0

the accusative, or vice versa. In the penultimate column is the number of pronouns marked with acc. and dat. forms. Case markers which could not be categorised are in the last column of tab. 10; to this group belong acc. and dat. markings on the subject and forms where the acc. and the dat. cannot be differentiated, e.g. *uns* and *euch*.

The table shows that all of the children – even if only occasionally – use case markings which differ from the case-neutral form. In some children, we only find the dative form (e.g. Stefan, Petra 1/2), in others only the accusative (e.g. Klaus 1/2, Patrick). Only in the data for Anja 2 and Petra 3 do acc. *and* dat. occur. From the profiles we can also see that genitive markers – except in five instances for Julia – are not used. In the data for Julia, the *-s* suffix of the possessive genitive is used in two – probably not internally-analysed – patterns, which Julia uses more than once in unchanged form:

(2) a. fabian*s* (Jul1:17)
(J. is referring to Fabian's glasses.)
b. ... julia*s* (Jul1:124b)
(J. means that the object belongs to her.)
c. unter unter fabian*s* (Jul2:102b)
('under under fabian's')

There are also structural contexts which require genitive markers; look at the data under N NP in the profile of Anja 2. In these, the case marker which is required is missing. On the basis of the data available it can be seen that dysphasic children do not use genitive markers typically; acc. or dat. forms are offered occasionally, though. We can see from table 10 that none of the children under investigation has access to the case paradigm for German; look at the examples in (3), (4) and (5). In the contexts requiring acc., we mostly find case-neutral markers (3a, 3b) and sometimes also dat. forms (3c, 3d). The case is similar for contexts requiring dat. Here we mostly find case-neutral markers, too, (4a, 4b) and sometimes also acc. forms (4c, 4d). Lastly, there are some data in which acc. or dat. marked forms are used for the subject (see "other case markings" in table 10 and the examples in (5)):

(3) a. aber ich *der* hund spiel (Pet3:133)
(P. is playing the dog.)
b. *der* mann noch mal rausnehmen (Kla2:80)
(=(We) take out the man.)
c. beißen *mir* (And2:98)
(=(The snake) is biting me)
d. ich *dir* hinführen (Ste:203)
(=I am leading you there.)

(4) a. *du* besser helf ich (Pet2:37)
(=I help you better.)
b. is a mal an *de* kamera piche (Jon2:148)
(J. also wants to play with the camera.)
c. wat machen mit *den* tab? (Kla1:43)
(=What shall (we) do with the rod?)
d. du *mis* ein geb (Wol:79)
(=You give me one.)

(5) a. *den* da is delb (Kla1:117)
(K. is pointing at the yellow monkey.)
b. *ihm* kipsbein nachher kommt (Sve:183)
(=He'll get his leg plastered afterwards.)
c. *uns* auch so was (Pet2:134)
(=We've got something like that too.)
d. das *festen* hacker (Pet2:97)
(=That's a hard hacker;
by hacker, P. actually means a horse.)
e. *keinen* bauer hier (Pat:140)
(=There isn't a farmer here.)
f. und hier.ha.den löffel (Jon1:85)
(=And here is the spoon; *ha* is an
exclamation of reinforcement.)

These examples and the frequencies from table 10 illustrate the difficulties which the children have with choosing the correct case form. We cannot see any oppositions between datives and accusatives; the forms required for the genitive are not even offered. Nor is the nominative differentiated from the casus obliqui. For both, the children prefer – as a type of default-strategy – case-neutral markers and sometimes we even find acc. or dat. forms for the subject.

To gain further insights into the children's case system, I will investigate the types of inflections which are used and the pronouns which are marked for case. Table 10 shows that the largest part of the acc. and dat. forms occur in the form of pronouns; case *inflections* within the NP occur much less frequently in the data. Firstly, I will look at the case markings for pronouns.

Most case markings occur in personal pronouns, e.g. *mir* ('to me') (3c), *dir* ('to you') (3d), *mis* ('me') (4d), etc. However, acc. and dat. are not clearly differentiated here, either. One group of children uses dative pronouns (Andreas, Stefan, Jonas, Petra), another uses accusatives. The forms available in each case are overgeneralised. Also, case-neutral personal pronouns can be found in contexts requiring acc. and dat. (see 4a). These observations show that there is no opposition between dative and accusative in pronouns.

Errors in marking subject pronouns are less frequent. It is especially clear from the data that subjects with the thematic role Agent are always marked with the nominative. If, however, other thematic roles occur in the subject function, as in the examples under (5), then case errors arise. These categorisations can be traced back to semantic bootstrapping, as is very clear in examples (5b) and (5c); using semantic bootstrapping, the dative forms can be chosen here due to the thematic roles. Here, the children also use acc. or dat. marked pronouns. There are not many of these instances, but on the basis of the data available, we can establish a bidimensional paradigm for the case markings of personal pronouns, with agentivity as a dimension; a relevant extract for accusative forms is given in (6):

(6) Category: Pro

		AGENTIVITY	
		+agent.	*-agent.*
	1.	ich	mich
PERSON	*2.*	du	dich
	3.	er	ihm

This paradigm, and in particular the assumption of a dimension for agentivity must be verified using broader material. Nevertheless, the errors which occur when choosing the subject pronoun can be accounted for in this way.

Case forms using inflections within NPs and PPs are only seen for a few children in few instances. Two types of markings are found: (i) clitizised forms with prepositions (*im, am* 'in the', 'at the') and (ii) the inflection *-n* on the determiner or attributive adjective. Only for Anja, Jonas and Petra does type (i) sometimes occur. I regard these elements as unanalysed units, because none of the children uses the suffix *-m* without a preposition. Also, the children treat *im* and *am* like prepositions without an article. For Anja, for example, we find *mit*, *in* and *am* as prepositions, whereby *mit* and *in* occur without an article. On the other hand, *an* does not occur as a preposition, and the child uses the invariant form *am*. Forms of type (i) cannot therefore be regarded as separate case formations.

Case markings on the noun are not documented in the data, not even if elements from the N-inflection are required; see the examples in (7). For some children (Anja, Wolfgang) case markings are not even found on the determiner or on the attributive adjective. The other children sometimes use *-n* here. None of the children has acquired the agreement system which is required by German within the NP; at most, the case marker occurs once in the NP, either on the determiner or on the adjective:

(7) a. ... fabian auch reiβen mit *den löwe* (Jul1:78a)
(=F. has torn the sheet of paper with the lion.)
b. und *den doβe* tommel (Kla2:122)
(=and the big drum.)

The rules mentioned above for pronouns also apply to the use of the inflection *-n*. There are no oppositions between the dative and the accusative. The form is used in contexts requiring acc. and dat., leading to case errors (see 4c, 7a). The inflection also occurs in instances in which nominative forms are required, i.e. in so-called equational copula constructions (5d) and in subjects (5e, 5f). As with the pronouns, there are no incorrect case formations with *-n* in Agent-subjects; they only occur if other thematic roles appear in the subject function. This observation agrees with the assumption that the dysphasic children's choice of case is guided by semantic factors, including the agentivity of the arguments involved.

Overall, the results show that dysphasic children have difficulties using case markings. This applies to pronouns and – even more so – to case markers which have to be formed with inflections. The longitudinal data available do not show any advance in development in the case systems of the children under investigation. The only change is that the pronouns which are marked for case are used more frequently at the end of the observation period. Case formations with inflections, on the other hand, only occur in very few instances. More importantly, the rules for the use of case markers do not change. At the end of the observation period, there are still no oppositions between accusatives and datives, case-neutral markers are still overgeneralised, and we find case errors in subjects. These observations indicate that the children's problems with case markers also exist when linguistic development has advanced in other areas.

6.1.3 *A comparison with the acquisition of case morphology in normal children*

In the following, I will sketch the sequence of case development in linguistically normal children. On the basis of this, I will attempt to determine the deficits in dysphasia. Recent empirical investigations into case acquisition in monolingual children who have German as their first language have been carried out by Tracy (1984, 1986) and Clahsen (1984a). The data for the older diary studies were reanalysed by Mills (1985) with respect to the acquisition of case. The development of the case system in bilingual children whose first languages are German and French has been described by Meisel (1986). The results of the different studies tally with the developmental sequence in Clahsen (1984a:14). Only in bilingual children is the differentiation between (Ci) and (Cii) imperceptible. Meisel shows that the children he investigated learned accusative and dative forms at more or less the same time. The sequence has the following developmental stages:

(8) A: no markings
B: case-neutral markings
C: case markings
i: accusative forms
ii: dative forms

In stage (A), which more or less corresponds with phases II and III of grammar acquisition (see Ch. 2), NPs are still unmarked. The children do not have access to the determiner and pronoun system, which is necessary to carry the case markings. In (B) there are only case-neutral forms, which are also overgeneralised onto contexts in which accusatives and datives are required; (B) corresponds with phase IV in the developmental profile (see Ch. 3). In (C) accusative and dative forms appear for the first time. Initially, the accusative is also used in contexts for the dative, (Ci); later dative forms arise too, (Cii).

From this developmental sequence we can see that the acquisition of case morphology in German child language is comparatively late, at the age of about three. The main reason for this is the peculiarities of German case morphology, in particular the syncretisms in the paradigm. Investigations by Slobin (1982) show that Turkish children, for example, have full use of their language's case system by the age of two. Turkish is different from German as it has an agglutinating paradigm with unique form-function relations. Given the learning mechanisms suggested in Ch. 3.3, paradigms of this type can be constructed more easily than paradigms with synthetic forms.

Moreover, in developmental sequence (8) we can see that in German child language there is initially, in (Ci), a binary case system, which contains the nominative and accusative forms. The acc. is overgeneralised onto the contexts requiring dative; however, accusatives do not occur as subjects. From this, we can conclude that the early case system in (Ci) serves for the encoding of grammatical relations: the nominative marks the subject, while the accusative is used for all casus obliqui, that is, for arguments which have a role in the sentence other than that of subject. The possibility for differentiating various types of oblique arguments, which is offered by German in the form of datives (and genitives), is only learned by the children gradually at a later stage.

The children with *dysphasia* have not developed a case system which corresponds to their age. The results illustrate that none of the children in the investigation had acquired the case paradigm which linguistically normal children already have by the age of about 3½ years. Also, the systems evolved in dysphasia cannot be placed into any phase of normal case acquisition. From (8), we see that the children have definitely passed stages (A) and (B) because all of them use case markings. Similar to the system in (Ci), the children in the investigation do have access to a bidimensional paradigm; the forms occurring and the dimensions marked are, however, different from those of linguistically normal children. Dative forms can occur in dysphasia, too, and they are also used for the subject – as is the accusative – if there is no Agent-argument present. Case markers in dysphasia as opposed to those in normal development do not serve to encode grammatical relations; instead they have a semantic function. These observations indicate that specific impairments are present in dysphasia, which obstruct the normal development of the case system.

I trace the difficulties which dysphasic children have in using case markings back to the fact that they cannot interpret phenomena of grammatical agreement and are not able to construct the appropriate morphological paradigms.

The values for the construction of the case paradigm are features which are assigned to the NP or the pronoun under certain structural conditions (government). The case form within the governing category is thereby asymmetrically controlled by the respective governor. Case markings thus belong to the phenomenon of grammatical agreement. The investigation of the case system shows that, in dysphasia, secondary grammatical dimensions which are assigned under asymmetric control cannot be used to construct a morphological paradigm. On the other hand, the grammar of dysphasic children has dimensions which can be identified using semantic bootstrapping. With this strategy, the child can recognise form-function relations between the thematic role of the argument and the visible marker in the input and construct a paradigm with agentivity as the dimension. The case paradigms seen in dysphasia could arise in this way.

The fact that the children decide on the inflection *-n* is also due to their difficulties with agreement phenomena. From the inflections available in German, we saw that only the suffix *-n* is used, although structural contexts occur in which *-m* and *-r* are also required. From the data here, it is clear that the differentiation between strong and weak inflection is neutralised in dysphasia. Only the inflection *-n*, which is categorised as [-strong] in German, is offered here. The elements of strong inflection, for example *-m* and *-r* are, however, not identified as case markers. To acquire the differentiation between strong and weak, the children would have to compare the different word forms of the article and the attributive adjective in the NP with regard to agreement. However, dysphasic children have problems with this. The available data show that there is no case agreement within NPs. The feature [+strong] is not available in the case paradigm and the children use the form which occurs most in the input, *-n*.

The children's problems with grammatical agreement affect pronouns which are marked for case in the same way as case forms with inflections. Also, the data show that personal pronouns which are marked for case occur comparatively frequently; case inflections, on the other hand, occur in few of the utterances. Moreover, the inventory of available pronouns is gradually extended, while there was hardly any advance in development to be seen in the case inflections.

These differences could indicate that the children have deficits in the area of morphology. Obviously the way they use elements of regular inflection is more impaired than their use of irregular inflections. The results on the use of case markings show that word-specific paradigms can be seen in most of the children, but that elements from general paradigms are used very infrequently. There are several possible reasons for this. It could be that in dysphasia the mechanisms for constructing general paradigms are impaired. The elements with the suffix *-n* would then have to stem from word-specific paradigms.

A second factor which could be responsible for the problems which the children have with case inflections are deficits in the area of word formation. Case formations with inflections arise using word formation rules and case marked personal pronouns can be directly inserted from the paradigm into syntactic structures. It is possible that the necessary word formation rules are not available in dysphasia. The differences observed between pronouns and case inflections could be accounted for in this way. Under this account, the forms constructed with *-n* would have to be regarded as entries of word-specific paradigms, for which word formation rules are not required.

Apart from the two factors mentioned above, the formal properties of German case inflections may also be responsible for the problems which the children have in this area. The inflections in German are synthetic forms in which the case marker comes with the gender and number specifications. Moreover, there are syncretisms in the German case paradigm. Linguistically normal children also acquire the German case paradigm comparatively late; the formal properties of German case inflection are also held responsible for this. Maybe the acquisitional problems in dysphasia are simply more serious in this area, without specific deficits in the area of morphology having to be assumed. The children would then try, with the help of the learning mechanisms for inflectional elements (see Ch. 3.3), to give each value of a chosen grammatical dimension a distinct form and, in the categorisation of the input, to look for inflections which have a unique case value. The case inflections of German are, however, difficult to recognise in the input using this mechanism because of the homonymy and the synthetic forms. We can explain the late acquisition of case morphology in linguistically normal children in this way. In dysphasia, there is the added difficulty that the children do not have access to the gender oppositions which are needed for the acquisition of the correct case paradigm. Consequently case inflections are for the most part not present in dysphasic children.

Using the current data, we cannot definitely decide which of these interpretations applies. Morphological deficits are assumed for the first two possibilities; however, they should not only be limited to the case system, but also apply to other areas of morphology. On the other hand, the final proposal suggests that formal features of case morphology are crucial. Using this as a basis, we expect that children with dysphasia can construct other general paradigms and word formation rules. In order to validate this assumption, the inflection of verbs will be investigated in the next paragraph as a second component of inflectional morphology.

6.2 Verb inflection

Apart from tense and modality, subject-verb agreement is marked on the verb in German. From the previous results, we expect that dysphasic children have problems constructing and using the paradigm for subject-verb agreement. The first part of the data analysis checks this hypothesis. In the second part, the function taken on by the verbal inflections in child grammar will be investigated. We will see that inflections of the verb which mark semantic functions are available in dysphasia; the use of agreement markers is, however, impaired.

6.2.1 *On subject-verb agreement in dysphasia*

6.2.1.1 There are five forms for marking subject-verb agreement in German: *-Ø, -e(schwa), -st, -t* and *-n*. The use of these forms is determined by the grammatical person and the number of the subject (see Ch. 3.3.2). The first part of the data analysis deals with the *form* of the verb inflections occurring in the data investigated. The above suffixes are used to describe the data. Apart from these forms, the children sometimes use verb suffixes which could be regarded as pronominal copies; consider the following examples:

(9) a. ich fahr*ich* weg (Sve:67)
('I drive-I away')
(S. is going by car.)
b. ich wei*ßich* nich (Sve:287)
('I do-I not know')
c. hier bin*ich* ich (Ste:37)
('here am-I I')
(The interviewer asks: who's there?)
d. ich polizeitappe hab*ich* (Ste:181)
('I policeman's hat have-I')
(S. has got a policeman's hat.)
e. is ein haus bau*is* (Wol:181)
('I a house build-I')
(W. is building house.)

In these instances, instead of an inflection, a pronoun is suffixed to the verb stem. As for the verbal inflections, there is no intonational pause between the verb stem and the post-verbal pronoun, and the pronoun agrees with the subject. These parallels indicate that pronominal copies are a part of the child's agreement system and have to be included in this analysis.

A quantitative summary of the verb forms which occur is in table 11. Here, two aspects of the use of verbal inflections are investigated: (i) the frequency of usage, given in absolute frequencies for the different forms, and (ii) the number of forms used correctly, in percentages. The values show that, for example, for -Ø in Anja 1, the child uses the stem form in 11 instances, whereby 45% of those are used correctly. The standard by which we judge whether the form is correct or not is *spoken* colloquial German. Thus, for example, the stem forms in (10) are correct because they frequently occur in spoken German:

(10) a. *mach* wieder
('do again')
((I) do it again.)
b. hier ich *reiß*
('here I tear')
(I tear that here.)

Table 11: *Verb inflection – overview*

	Ø	corr. (in %)	e	corr. (in %)	n	corr. (in %)	t	corr. (in %)	st	corr. (in %)	Others
Anja 1	11	45	7	28	19	0	1	100	0	0	0
Anja 2	33	51	8	25	55	16	2	100	0	0	1
Andreas 1	18	66	26	53	2	100	9	88	0	0	0
Andreas 2	19	63	69	66	5	0	1	100	0	0	0
Klaus 1	6	66	4	0	16	68	3	66	0	0	0
Klaus 2	10	90	2	100	22	36	19	89	0	0	1
Julia 1	5	40	1	100	20	50	8	100	0	0	0
Julia 2	14	50	0	0	45	20	3	100	0	0	1
Patrick	25	88	11	81	23	13	9	100	0	0	0
Sven	43	83	6	50	32	28	25	96	1	100	11
Stefan	47	97	1	100	34	47	4	100	0	0	9
Jonas 1	8	62	84	25	1	0	1	100	0	0	2
Jonas 2	10	60	55	9	2	100	2	100	0	0	6
Petra 1	5	100	0	0	7	14	2	50	0	0	0
Petra 2	33	33	0	0	35	11	5	20	3	100	1
Petra 3	33	90	13	100	25	88	24	75	8	87	0
Wolfgang	85	57	6	33	4	0	6	83	0	0	13

In some instances, the children under investigation used forms which cannot be included among the verbal inflections in table 11. These are, among others, pronominal copies (see (9)) and irregular forms of the verb (*sind*). These are registered in the column "others" in table 11 and have to be analysed separately. Sometimes, the verbal forms can be phonetically distorted and can therefore not be identified for sure:

(11) a. *mössa* tür zu (Wol:214)
('must door shut')
(W. wants to shut the door.)
b. *mats* nits (Jon2:51)
(=that doesn't matter.)

Instances of this kind occur extremely infrequently in the overall data; there are only a few instances for Wolfgang and Jonas. These examples are excluded from the analysis of verb inflections and included separately in the column for "others" in table 11.

The table shows that all of the children use *Ø,e,t* and *n* as verbal forms. The forms occurring most frequently are *Ø*/*e* or *n*. The inflection *st* is on the other hand only seen in Petra 2/3 and in one instance in Sven. Pronominal copies also only occur in some of the children: Sven (9 instances), Stefan (5 instances) and Petra 2 and Wolfgang with one instance each. All of the instances with pronominal copies are formed with *ich* ('I'), analogous to the examples given in (9).

Advances in development with regard to the available inventory of verb inflections can only be seen in Petra. While at the start only using *Ø*/*n* and *t*, at the end of the observation she has access to the full inventory of forms, and pronominal copies no longer occur. On the other hand, the other children show no extensions in their use of forms. The inflection *st* is absent in dysphasia, although structural contexts requiring this form on the verb frequently occur in the children's utterances. It is typical for dysphasic children to have access to the form inventory which is characteristic of the early phases II and III of child grammar acquisition; included in this are the stem and infinitive forms, the inflection *-t* and – in some children – also pronominal copies (see Ch. 3.1). However, *st*, which becomes available to linguistically normal children in phase IV, is not used as a verb inflection in dysphasia (the only exception here is Petra). In the previous chapter it became clear that dysphasic children mainly have difficulties with the acquisition of the elements of the later developmental phases IV and V; the elements of the early phases are accessible in dysphasia. The observations on the inflection of verbs confirm this result.

6.2.1.2 The percentages from table 11 show that – apart from Petra – none of the children in the investigation has access to the correct paradigm for person and number inflection on the finite verb. There are differences between the children with regard to the frequency for the usage of different forms. Some, for example Anja, Klaus and Julia, mostly use *n*-forms, other children, for example Wolfgang, Andreas and Jonas mostly *Ø* or *e*. The decisive thing which they have in common, however, is that the dominantly used form occurs for all of the possible grammatical persons and for the singular and plural. Table 11 shows that the percentages for correctness are low for all of the children who often use *n*. The results correspond for the children who use *Ø* or *e* as the dominant form; here, there are no person or number differences, either. As an illustration, let us look at the following examples from Anja and Wolfgang:

(12) a. ich donnerstach sag*en* (Anj2:174)
('I thursday say')
(A. will say on Thursday...)
b. ein block raushol*en* (Anj2:110)
('a block fetch out')
(Are you getting out a block?)
c. majo mann wat*en* (Anj2:103)
('majo man wait')
(Mario is waiting for the man.)
d. montach kon*en* (Anj2:59)
('monday cook')
(On Monday we're cooking.)

(13) a. is auch ein auto *fahr* (Wol:80)
('I too a car drive')
(W. is driving a car too.)
b. du auch ein haus *mach* (Wol:255)
('you too a house make')
(You're making a house too.)
c. uschi hier *wohn*? (Wol:21b)
('uschi here live?')
(Does Uschi live here?)
d. mein baume *fall* (Wol:34)
('my tree fall')
(Wolfgang's trees are falling down.)

Along with the values from table 11, the examples show that the choice of *n* or of *Ø* is not determined by the grammatical person or the number of the subject. Instead, these forms are used with all of the grammatical persons which occur in the data, and with both the singular and plural. They are obviously default-forms, whereby differences from child to child occur with respect to whether *Ø*, *e* or *n* is chosen as the default-form. A further indication of this is that we cannot see any morphologically determined oppositions between these three forms. The differences result, instead, from the frequencies for the usage of the different forms. This observation will be demonstrated here using Anja as an example; see (14) and (15):

(14) a. am montag nich komm*e* ich nich (Anj2:142)
('On Monday not come I not (to school)')
b. dann hier *anzieh* (Anj2:302)
('then here put on')
(A. is dressing the doll.)
c. mach*e* neue hefte? (Anj2:191)
('make new notebooks?')
(Is he making new notebooks?)
d. *hei* markus pütz (Anj2:172)
('name markus pütz')
(His name is M. P.)
e. ... halb sieb wassa rauskomm*e* (Anj2:41)
('half six water come out')
((We) came out of the water at six thirty.)
f. kann*e* ich nich (Anj2:263)
('can I not')
(I can't do that.)
g. *kann* ich nich (Anj2:263)
(as above)
h. kann*e* nich aufmachen (Anj2:289)
('can not open')
(A. cannot undo her shoes.)

(15) a. mo papa bauch nich *arbeit*? (Anj1:135)
('tomorrow papa need not work?')
(Doesn't papa need to go to work tomorrow?)
b. kanne nich aufmach*en* (Anj2:289)
(see 14h)

Overall, Anja uses *Ø* and *e* less often than *n*. The examples show that the choice of *Ø* and *e* is not determined by the person or number of the subject. From (14f) and (14h) we can also see that *e* is used in cases where the stem form would have been enough. (14g) shows that *e* occurs in free variation with *Ø*. These instances indicate that there are no morphological oppositions marked by Ø and *e*. Instead – as in spoken German – they are phonological variants. In contrast to adult German, however, the choice between *n* and *Ø/e* is not steered by a morphological paradigm. This can be seen from the modal verb constructions in which *n* and *Ø/e* are used in free variation on the non-finite part of the verb (see (15)).

Clear differences between *Ø/e* and *n* are only seen in Klaus 2, Patrick, Sven and Stefan. Table 11 shows that these children (i) often use Ø and *n*, but only use *e* infrequently, and that (ii) the percentages for the correctness of Ø are clearly higher than for *n*. The inflection *n* is – as in the other children – used independently of the grammatical person and number of the subject as a default-form. By contrast, the stem form is correct in most instances.

In Klaus 2 and Patrick, however, the values in table 11 mask an important limitation in their use of *Ø/e*. These forms only occur with a small class of verbs in Klaus 2 and Patrick. In Klaus 2, *e* only occurs twice, and in the instances with Ø, seven out of ten are the verbal form *is*. In Patrick, apart from *is* and *hab* (have), some modal verbs occur in the stem form: *kann*, *brauch* and *muß* (can, need and must). In the few cases in which Klaus 2 and Patrick use other verbal elements with Ø there are agreement errors. The same applies to the instances with *e*. In Patrick, five of the nine correct *e*-forms occur on the modal verb *brauchen* (need). There are agreement errors in the other instances (see (16e) and (16f)):

(16) a. *guck* zauba (Kla2:136)
('look magician')
(The magician's looking.)

b. pferd *steh* nich (Pat:55)
('horse stand not')
(The horse is not standing.)

c. ablepper *aussieh* (Pat:99)
('tow-truck look')
(That's what a tow-truck looks like.)

d. *umfall* (Pat:129)
('falls over')
(Something has fallen over.)

e. du auch eine bau*e*? (Pat:190)
('you one build too?')
(Are you building a ramp too?)

f. alles umfall*e* (Pat:53)
('everything falling')

These observations show that *Ø/e* cannot be regarded as elements of a general paradigm of verb inflections in Klaus and Patrick. As in the other children, they are variants of the default-form *n*, which are used regardless of the grammatical person and number of the subject. The agreement errors can be interpreted in this way. In the word-specific paradigms of the irregular verb *sein* (to be) and in some modal verbs, only *Ø*- and *e*-forms occur; agreement errors are less frequent here. The children's use of word-specific paradigms will be investigated more closely at the end of the section.

Sven and Stefan do not have access to the agreement paradigm of German either, because – as shown in table 11 – *n* is taken as the default-form, without recognisable differentiations between person and number. Different from the other children, their stem forms are mostly correct *and are not* limited to a small class of verbs. These observations indicate that the choice of the stem form in their general paradigm is morphologically determined. However, grammatical person is not available as a dimension here either. In Stefan *Ø* occurs almost only in imperatives (see 17a, 17b). Hence the high percentage for the correctness of *Ø*. The choice of the stem form for the imperative can be traced back to semantic bootstrapping. If, though, a subject occurs in the 1st pers. sing., then the verb is marked with the default-form *n* (17c), or Stefan uses a pronominal copy (see 9c, 9d). These observations show that *Ø* is not used to mark subject-verb agreement.

(17) a. *dib* mal mein telefon! (Ste:23)
('give over my telephone!')
b. *deh* euer haus! (Ste:79)
('go your house!')
(Get into your house!)
c. dann ich schlaf*en* (Ste:76)
('then I sleep')

In Sven, the instances with *Ø* are mostly correct, too (see table 11). There are, however, still agreement errors with *Ø* in subjects in the 3rd pers. sing. (see 18a, 18b) and in one case in the 3rd pers. pl. (18c). Also, Sven often uses the default-form *n* (see 18d, 18e) and sometimes pronominal copies (see 9a, 9b) when the context requires *Ø* or *e*:

(18) a. hund da *komm* (Sve:136)
('dog there coming')
(S. is putting the dog in the flat.)
b. der katte *fang* (Sve:255)
('the cat catch')
(S. is pointing to a child catching a cat.)
c. das *is* puppen? (Sve:16)
('that is doll?')
(S. is getting dolls out of the box.)
d. ich auto halt*en* (Sve:288)
('I car stop')
(S. holds a car up while tidying up.)
e. ich das spiel*en* (Sve:244)
('I that play')
(S. is getting a carton out of the toybox.)

The examples show that the child has problems when choosing the forms of inflection. In Sven's general paradigm, we could perhaps assume a dimension NUMBER with the value [+sing.] for *Ø*/*e*, in order to describe the data available. In this way, we could account for the correct forms and the overgeneralisations in (18a) and (18b). Even the use of such a reduced paradigm poses problems to the children, as *Ø* comes with a plural subject in (18c), and *n* – as in the other children – is used as a default-form, even with [+sing.] subjects.

6.2.1.3 From table 11 we can see that, apart from *n* and *Ø*/*e*, the children use the inflection *t*. Although the percentages are high, there are also agreement errors in the use of *t*:

(19) du dann runterfäll*t* (Pet2:34a)
('you then fall')
(Then you will fall down.)

Moreover, the data show oppositions between *t* and the other forms. We see that *t* does not occur in any of the instances on the non-finite element of a modal verb construction; on the other hand, *Ø* and *e* occur here as variants of *n* (see the examples under (15)). The opposition between *t* and the other forms does *not* arise in dysphasia on the basis of agreement features. In fact in the data of the children in the investigation, the inflection *t* occurs typically with intransitive verbs without an Agent-argument, e.g. *wohnen, fehlen, stehen*, etc. (live, miss, stand, etc.). With transitive verbs whose subject is in the 3rd pers. sing. on the other hand, the inflection *t* which is required in German is not used in most cases. This limited use of *t* is hidden by the frequencies in table 11. The instances with *t* will therefore be discussed separately in the next section (6.2.2). I will try to show that the choice of *t* in dysphasia is determined by semantic factors, in particular by the transitivity of the sentence. Similar to phases II and III of normal grammar development, the inflection *t* is not used by dysphasic children as an agreement marker. Instead, the function of *t* – as initially in linguistically normal children – is to characterise argument structures with low semantic transitivity.

6.2.1.4 The next step in the analysis concerns the elements of *irregular inflection*. We want to find out whether the children have access to the paradigms required for these elements, and whether agreement features are chosen as dimensions for this. I will investigate the forms of inflection which occur for the irregular verb *sein* (to be). In most of the utterances, only *is(t)* (3rd pers. sing.) is used as a form of *sein*. There are no indications of a paradigm with morphologically determined oppositions. Different inflectional forms of *sein* are found in Petra 3, Julia 2, Jonas 2, Stefan, Sven, Wolfgang and Klaus 2.

> *Petra 3* is the only child with access to the complete regular agreement paradigm. The forms of *sein* ('to be') are also correct: *bin* (Pet3:194a) for the 1st person sing. and *is* (Pet3:12) for the 3rd person sing.
>
> *Julia 2* uses *bin* in three instances with the subject *Julia*. Here, agreement errors could be given, but note that the child is referring to herself and that she does not have access to the pronoun *ich*. In addition, we have data with *sind*:

(20) a. julia älter *bin* (Jul2:137a)
('julia older am')
(... only when I am older.)

b. mama papa nicht da *sind* (Jul2:153b)
('mama papa not there are')
(M. and P. are not at home.)

Jonas 2 and *Sven* use *bis(t)* twice. Note that *st* is not offered in the general paradigm. Also, in both children there are data with *is*, and for Sven with *sind*; here, agreement errors occur:

(21) a. *is* mir zu (Jon2:62)
('is me to')
(That belongs to me.)
b. du *bisse* hund (Jon2:124)
('you are dog')
(you are the dog.)
c. ... das *bist* du (Sve:36)
('that are you')
d. ... *sind* schön (Sve:55)
('are pretty')
(S. is taking dolls out of the box.)
e. das *is* puppen (Sve:16)
(see 18d)

Stefan uses *bin, is(t)* and *sind* as inflected forms of *sein*. The forms are used correctly. Only the following instance is unclear with regard to agreement, because the first part of the utterance cannot be clearly identified and *tind* is not marked in the plural:

(22) (du un) ich *sind* tind (Ste:282a)
('(you and) I are child')
(S. jumps into the therapist's arms.)

Wolfgang uses *is* and *sind* without recognisable oppositions. Here, there are clear agreement errors:

(23) a. hier zwei bäum *is* (Wol:18)
('here two tree is')
(W. puts two trees onto a tray.)
b. mei bäuma putt *sind* (Wol:191)
('my trees broke are')
(W.'s trees are broken.)

Similarly, *Klaus 2* uses *is* and *sind*. If we take account of the situational context, it becomes clear that Klaus is referring to a piece of jigsaw in the instance with *sind*, i.e. to a subject in the singular:

(24) a. das *sind* (Kla2:105)
('that are')
(K. is pointing at a piece of jigsaw.)

b. n klein n *is* weg (Kla2:145)
('a little a is gone')
(K. is referring to a bouquet of flowers.)

All in all, there are only a few different forms of *sein*. In most cases, this element is omitted. However, there are forms of *sein* in the word-specific paradigm which are not offered by the general paradigm: Jonas 2 and Sven have access to *bis(t)* (2nd pers. sing.), but not to *st*, although there are numerous occasions in the data in which this inflection is required for regular finite verbs. Agreement errors also occur in irregular verbs. The reason why they are found so infrequently, mainly involves the overall lack of utterances with *sein*. Nonetheless, the errors which occur show that the children's problems are not limited to elements of the general paradigm, but also effect irregular verbs. The utterances with pronominal copies are an additional indication of this. For example, Stefan uses a pronominal subject copy in addition to the element *bin* (1st pers. sing.). Obviously, the verbal form is not sufficient and Stefan wants to introduce an additional marker using a pronominal element:

(25) a. hier bin*ich*.ich (Ste:37)
('here amI.I')
b. hier bin*ich*.stefan m. (Ste:65)
('here amI.stefan m')

The decisive property of the verbal element *sein* is that it can only be used as an inflected verb. Apart from the subjunctive forms, there is no verbal stem for *sein* which can occur here as a possible German word; (the subjunctive forms are not present in the early phases because at that time they hardly occur in the input). On the other hand, regularly inflected verbs are complex word forms consisting of the verbal stem and a suffix position (for INFL), whereby the stem can be used without the INFL-position being filled. This option is not possible with the irregular verb *sein*. The child can either leave the entire verbal position unfilled, or s/he can choose an inflected form. The data show that the children prefer omission and that they have problems in choosing the form of the inflection which is required.

6.2.1.5 On the basis of the available data, we can conclude that dysphasic children do not have access to the subject-verb agreement system of German. There is only a limited set of forms in the children's utterances; in particular, they do not recognise *st* as an inflection of the verb. Also, there are some morphological oppositions in German, e.g. *n* against *Ø/e* which are neutralised in dysphasia. The choice between *t* and the other forms is determined by a morphological paradigm. However, agreement features are not chosen in this paradigm. Instead, the inflection *t* encodes semantic features of particular argument structures; this will be investigated more closely in the next section.

These conclusions apply to all of the children except Petra. With regard to subject-verb agreement, Petra is clearly a special case, because, in the third sample, she has definite access to all of the person and number formatives and uses inflections – with a few exceptions – correctly. Table 11 shows that the percentages for correctness in Petra 3 are about 90%. Her system of subject-verb agreement develops in the time between the second and the third recording. In Petra 2 the form *e* is missing, the percentages for correctness are low and there are still pronominal copies (see 26a), which are not possible in German. Most of the errors in Petra 2 arise with subjects in the 2nd pers. sing.; here the child uses *Ø*, *n* and sometimes *t*, (see 26b, 26c, 26d). The required inflection *st* only occurs in three instances with modal verbs (see 26e, 26f):

(26) a. ich wei*ßich* nich (Pet2:1)
('I knowI not')
b. ... du immer fall*en* (Pet2:51b)
('you always fall')
(You are always falling over.)
c. du *sag* (Pet2:183)
('you say')
d. warum du mach*t*? (Pet2:184)
('why you do?')
(Why are you doing that?)
e. will*s* auch (Pet2:121a)
('want also')
(Subj.=du; takes *st* inflection.)
f. du kann*st* fallen (Pet2:123b)
('you can fall')

The observations above show that Petra 2 has not acquired the agreement system. Only in the third recording does Petra's paradigm correspond with that of linguistically normal children; here, *st* is used with other verbal elements (see 27), pronominal copies no longer occur, and the inflections are mostly used correctly:

(27) a. und jetzt du wieder schreib*st* (Pet3:219)
('and now you write again')
b. und du der ... spiel*s* (Pet3:134)
('and you the ... plays')

Moreover, the investigations described in Ch. 3.1 showed that verb placement in linguistically normal children is correct as soon as they have access to the agreement system. This correlation in development does not apply to Petra. As illustrated by the examples in (27), the inflected verb remains, even in Petra 3, in the verb-final position, although she has acquired the agreement paradigm. Verb placement is dealt with more closely in Ch. 7. I will then come back to the peculiarities seen in Petra and try to show that her erroneous verb placement system is not due to syntactic deficits, but to problems in the morphology.

6.2.2 *Functional analyses of the inflection of verbs in dysphasia*

6.2.2.0 In the following, the function of verb inflections which occur in the dysphasic children's utterances will be investigated. Petra's data will be ignored in this analysis, as she was the only child to have access to the correct agreement paradigm. The verb inflections in the other children, however, do not encode subject-verb agreement. The investigation will show which functions are taken on by verb inflections in dysphasia. So far we have the following results on this:

(28) a. Verbal elements occur in the forms *Ø, e, n* and *t*.
b. There is opposition between *t* and the other forms.
c. The inflection *t* is used with intransitive verbs.
d. The inflection *n* is the default-form; variants of *n* are *Ø* and *e*.

6.2.2.1 Additional analyses are required in order to describe the meaning of *t* and its opposition to the remaining forms. In German, this inflection is found on the finite verb and participles. In the data available on dysphasia, utterances with participles only rarely occur. In most cases the auxiliary is missing and there are sometimes errors in the choice of inflection (see 29).

Detailed analyses on this will not be carried out because of the restricted data on participles.

(29) a. die jetzt *gebratet* (Pet3:174)
('it now fried')
(This is now going to be fried.)
b. ich ... einfach *gegeht* in schiff (Pet3:112a)
('I ... simply gone in ship')
(I simply got onto the ship.)

I indicated in the last section that the inflection *t* mainly occurs with intransitive verbs in the data under investigation. To illustrate this observation, examples from all of the children have been grouped together in (30):

(30) a. steh*t* hier (Anj2:129)
('stands here')
(A. is looking for a song in the book.)
b. puttdeh*t* immer (And1:73)
('break always')
(The house always breaks.)
c. ganze menge nochma feh*t* (Kla2:133)
('all number again missing')
(There are still a lot missing.)
d. da yaya wohn*t* (Jul1:163c)
('there yaya (name) lives')
e. geh*t* so eine noch (Pat:9)
('goes such still')
(P. is trying to put two bricks together.)
f. das gehör*t* da (Sve:54)
('that belongs there')
(S. is putting paper into the box.)
g. deh*t* nich mehr (Ste:261)
('goes not more')
(The telephone button does not work any more.)
h. wat hei*t* dat? (Jon2:46)
('what called that?')
(correctly: wa*s* hei*ß*t da*s*?)
i. uschi.geh*t* rein nich (Wol:24)
('uschi.goes not in')
(W. is trying to press down a Lego brick.)

The examples show that the inflection *t* occurs typically in sentences with an intransitive verb. Also, we see that Agent-arguments seldom occur in sentences with *t*. Instead, the children almost always use inanimate subjects, mostly Theme-arguments. These observations indicate that it is not the case that particular arguments are marked, e.g. grammatical subject, but more the features of the whole sentence. I suggest that the inflection *t* in dysphasia has a *characterising function* and that the choice of this inflection is based on the semantic features of the sentence, in particular on semantic transitivity as described in Hopper/Thompson (1980); see also Ch. 1.2.2 and Ch. 3.3.2. In order to check this hypothesis, I will analyse the instances in the data with the inflection *t*, taking account of the criteria defined by Hopper/Thompson (1980) for semantic transitivity.

Hopper and Thompson describe semantic transitivity in terms of a continuum of 10 features. Included in this are the number of arguments, agentivity, animacy, etc. Each feature can take on different values. Accordingly, highly transitive sentences contain arguments which are animate, concrete, countable, definite, etc. and actions which can be described as voluntary, punctual and concrete. In child language, only some of these features can be investigated. The following parameters from the transitivity scale have been taken from Hopper/Thompson (1980:252):

(31)			*High*	*Low*
	a.	Participants	two or more participants	one participant
	b.	Kinesis	action	non-action
	c.	Volitionality	volitional	non-volitional
	d.	Affirmation	affirmative	negative
	e.	Agency	high	low
	f.	Animacy	human, animate	inanimate

Using these criteria, we define whether a sentence is high or low in transitivity:

- ad (a): Normally, the notion of transitivity refers to an action performed by an Agent and directed towards a Theme-argument. For this reason, at least two arguments are needed in a transitive sentence.
- ad (b): "Actions can be transferred from one participant to another, states cannot" (Hopper/Thompson, p.252). For this reason, action

verbs are more transitive than verbs of state.

- ad (c): If an argument is volitional then the effect upon the second argument is more direct, as if the action were not being controlled by one of the arguments involved; sentences of the first type are therefore more transitive.
- ad (d): In negated sentences, the effect of the action is less direct and the transitivity therefore lower than in affirmative sentences (cf. Hopper/Thompson, p.276).
- ad (e): Agent-arguments control the action. Sentences with an Agent are therefore more transitive than sentences without an Agent-argument.
- ad (f): If a sentence has animate arguments, the effect of the action is more direct than with inanimate arguments; they are therefore more transitive (cf. criterion J in Hopper/Thompson, p.253).

The transitivity scale, if it is to be used for describing argument structures, has to be improved. In particular, the redundancies, e.g. between (31b), (31e) and (31f), have to be avoided (cf. Wunderlich 1985). In this investigation, I only use the scale when analysing the inflection *t*. However, a typology of verbal elements cannot be provided only by using the features in Hopper/Thompson's scale.

The quantitative analysis is in table 12. Sentences with the inflection *t* are investigated with respect to the criteria for transitivity (31). The table has percentages giving the proportion of *low* transitivity in terms of (31). If there were fewer than three instances with *t* the percentages are given in brackets.

The table shows that the components of semantic transitivity correlate in most of the children. The sentences containing the inflection *t* find themselves mainly on the same side of the transitivity continuum for the features investigated. The inflection *t* can therefore be regarded as a coding device for low transitivity.

The first column in table 12 shows that *t* is used with intransitive verbs, which are only subcategorised for one argument in most instances. Only for Julia are the values for this low. In Julia 1, they come about because of three instances with the possessive variant of *haben* (to have) (cf. Jul1:98, 106b, 130b) and one instance with the verb *gehören* (to belong) (Jul1:126). Although these verbs have more than one argument, the sentences are, if we take the other criteria into account, not transitive. In Julia 2, there are

Table 12: *Transitivity and the inflection t*

	1 Argument – (in %)	non-action (in %)	non-volitional (in %)	no Agent-arg. (in %)	inanimate argument (in %)
Anja 1	(0)	(0)	(0)	(0)	(100)
Anja 2	(50)	(100)	(100)	(100)	(100)
Andreas 1	88	88	88	88	100
Andreas 2	(100)	(100)	(100)	(100)	(100)
Klaus 1	100	100	100	100	100
Klaus 2	89	84	84	84	100
Julia 1	25	100	100	100	75
Julia 2	33	33	33	33	100
Patrick	88	55	100	100	100
Sven	92	96	100	100	84
Stefan	75	75	100	100	50
Jonas 1	(0)	(0)	(0)	(0)	(100)
Jonas 2	(100)	(50)	(100)	(100)	(100)
Wolfgang	100	83	100	100	100

only three instances with *t* (cf. Jul2:78, 83b, 147b); in one instance (78) *t* occurs on the participle, and in the other two instances on a transitive (83b) and an intransitive verb (147b).

The verbs in the examples in (30) are characteristic of the use of *t*. These examples and the values in the second and third columns in table 12 show that *t* is mainly used with stative and non-action verbs which do not have an Agent-argument. From the fourth and fifth columns we see that the children – with a few notable exceptions – do not refer to animate Agent-arguments in the instances with *t*. Inanimate arguments are more likely to be the subject, instead, most often in the semantic role 'Theme'.

These observations show that semantic features of the whole sentence are coded using the inflection *t*; this is the only way in which we can explain the observed correlations between the features of the transitivity scale. This assumption is also confirmed by pairs like those in (32):

(32) a. fall*t* aber au (And2:97)
('falls but too')
(After something fell over.)
b. tuhl mal *fall* (And2:133)
('chair fall')
(A. is saying that the therapist should drop the chair.)

The examples illustrate that the verb *fallen* (to fall) appears in different morphological forms and that *t* can be seen as a separate inflection. The choice of the stem form in (32b) is not, on the other hand, morphologically determined. Apart from *n, Ø/e* are default-forms of verbs which Andreas uses without perceptible differentiation (see table 11). Moreover, *n* also occurs in imperatives – apart from *Ø/e* – as a variant of the default-form (see And2:55). The verb form in (32b) cannot therefore be regarded as an imperative marking.

The different forms in (32) follow from the features of transitivity. According to these features, sentence (32a) is less transitive than (32b). In (32a) *fallen* (to fall) is used as an intransitive verb of state; the sentence does not have an animate Agent-argument acting voluntarily. In (32b), however, the underlying reading is agentive: An animate argument, the therapist, should carry out an action voluntarily. The difference in transitivity between the two uses of *fallen* is reflected in the inflectional forms of the verbs. For the unmarked, more transitive case, the default-form is used, and for the marked, highly intransitive case, the inflection *t*.

6.2.2.2 The observations on the function of *t* will be linked and combined with the rest of the results. The system characteristic for dysphasia can be described as follows:

(33) a. Through word-formation rules, complex word forms arise which consist of a verb stem, and a position for inflectional elements: [V INFL].
b. There are three possibilities in morphology for filling the INFL-position:

1. It remains empty; in this case the verb appears in its stem form Ø.
2. It is filled by the default-form *n*.
3. It is filled by *t* for low transitivity.

c. There are two possibilities in phonology for the realisation of [V-n]:
1. The suffix is spelt out phonologically; then the verb appears in the form *n*.
2. [V-*n*] is not realised; in this case the verb comes with *e* (schwa).

The system in (33) applies to most of the dysphasic children in the investigation. Only Petra, who has access to the correct agreement paradigm, is an exception. Additional assumptions are required for Sven and Stefan with regard to the use of the stem form (see 6.2.1.2). Overall, however, on the basis of the data available, (33) can be seen as characteristic of the inflection of verbs in dysphasia.

(33) illustrates that the children do not have access to subject-verb agreement in German: *st* is not offered as an inflection, *t* only occurs with a limited group of verbs and the opposition between Ø and *n* is neutralised in dysphasia. Note that option (b1) in (33) is morphologically determined in German. It can be chosen for the 1st pers. sing. and can also be realised by means of schwa as a phonological variant (*ich komm, ich komme* 'I come'). In dysphasia on the other hand, the choice of (b1) is not steered by grammatical features. Options (b1) and (b2) occur in free variation, whereby individual differences can be seen from child to child. For some children, most clearly for Wolfgang, (b1) is the dominant form of realisation for verbal elements; other inflections are hardly offered. Most children however prefer (b2), regardless of grammatical features or other characteristics which come into question as dimensions of paradigms. The inflection *n* can be seen as a default-form of the affix position in (33a). With regard to the phonetic realisation of the inflection *n*, however, individual differences are seen from child to child. While most of the children choose (c1) from (33) for this, Jonas and Andreas use schwa (*e*) in preference to *n*. This form is not a separate inflection, but – as in southern German dialects – a variant of *n*. In order to account for these instances phonologically, Wiese (1986) suggests the rule of schwa-epenthesis.

The suggested analysis shows that we do not have to assume any deviant rules for the inflection of verbs in dysphasia. System (33) corresponds to that of linguistically normal children before phase IV of grammar acquisition.

The children's problems are concentrated on the construction of a paradigm for subject-verb agreement. The grammatical person and number of the subject cannot be used as dimensions to construct a morphological paradigm for the inflection of verbs. Consequently, the children mostly leave the affix position unfilled or use a default-form. In the input, *st* is the only form which exclusively serves to mark subject-verb agreement. Children with dysphasia have problems reconstructing the meaning of *st* in German. This is the reason why the form is not identified as a verbal inflection and why it is not included in a corresponding paradigm.

On the other hand, *t* can be recognised in the input and used as a marker for low transitivity; the same occurs in linguistically normal children's phases II and III. Crucially, *t* – different to *st* – can be categorised on the basis of semantic bootstrapping. Semantic transitivity is one of the earliest categories marked in child language (see Ch.1.2). From this we conclude that the child, in categorising the input, tries to find ways to code transitivity. Intransitive verbs often occur in German with an inanimate Theme-argument as the subject in the 3rd pers. sing., which is marked on the finite verb by the inflection *t*. This part of the input is decisive, in order to consider *t* as a marker for low transitivity. Thus, the marked salient instance, has a morphological marking here; by contrast the more frequent (transitive) instance is not marked. The differences between *t* and *st* in dysphasia show that these children also have access to semantic bootstrapping and that the core problem involves the use of grammatical agreement. This interpretation tallies with the results on the case system in dysphasia.

6.2.2.3 The analysis in Ch. 6.1 showed that the ability to use case *inflections* in dysphasia is more impaired than the use of case-marked pronouns. There were three factors explaining the differences which are observed: (i) deficits in the construction of general paradigms, (ii) word-formation problems and (iii) formal peculiarities in German case morphology. However, on the basis of the results on the case system, we could not make a definite differentiation between these possibilities.

The analyses on the inflection of verbs show that we do not have to assume any general deficits in the area of morphology. From the system described in (33), we see that the children have access to elements of regular inflection which can be represented in a general paradigm. The paradigm does not correspond to that of German, though, because for it to do so, the children would have to choose agreement features as dimensions. Instead, it is the general paradigm which is also constructed by linguistically normal children in the early phases of grammar acquisition (see (34) in Ch. 3.3.2). In addition, the results on the inflection of verbs show that we do not have to assume general deficits in the area of word formation in dysphasia. From the system in (33) we see that the children have access to complex verbal forms which arise from word formation rules (see 33a). The options (i) and (ii) are thus not confirmed by the results on verb inflection. I therefore assume that factor (iii) is decisive and that the children's problems with case inflections can be traced back to formal properties of case morphology in German.

Overall, we can conclude that the learning mechanisms for constructing morphological paradigms (see Ch.3.3.1) are also available in dysphasia, and that semantic bootstrapping is available for the categorisation of the input. The children's decisive deficits affect grammatical agreement. Secondary grammatical features, which are asymmetrically controlled by other elements of the sentence, cannot be used in the construction of a paradigm as grammatical dimensions. These assumptions are confirmed by the results on verb inflection and case morphology.

Petra in the third sample is the only child with access to subject-verb agreement. It is interesting that, at this point, she has not acquired the correct case paradigm for German. Her grammatical system is, in this respect, similar to that of phase IV of the grammar development of linguistically normal children (see Ch.3). From this, we expect that Petra will acquire the case system very soon in her development. We were unable to pursue this matter systematically. The logopedist treating Petra told me that in the meantime Petra has overcome the initial problems of grammar acquisition and that she has reached a level of linguistic development which is appropriate for her age.

7. Word order

The investigations in Ch. 5 showed that the composition of syntactic units and the constituent-internal word order do not pose any obvious problems for dysphasic children. These results indicated that the mechanisms for the construction of a syntactic constituent structure (X-bar theory, cf. Ch. 2.3), are also available in dysphasia. In order to check this hypothesis I will investigate different areas of word order in the following.

Firstly, I will analyse the *position of the verb*. My choice of this area as the main topic of my investigation into word order is based on several reasons. The principles ruling the placement of verbs in German belong to the central core of syntax. They correspond to Koster's (1984) configurational matrix, with which rules of core grammar are defined (cf. Ch. 2.4). In addition, the position of the verb in German is not dependent upon semantic or pragmatic functions; instead, it can only be described in abstract, syntactic structures. At the same time, the main parts of the data available can be analysed for the positioning of the verb; the corresponding principles are required in almost every sentence containing verbal elements. These features make the placement of verbs in German especially suitable as an object for investigation, in order to gain insights into the syntactic representations in dysphasia.

The second part of the analysis deals with *argument order*. I investigate the positions in which subjects and objects occur in the utterances of dysphasic children. The analysis provides information on the function of word order as a means of coding grammatical relations. In addition, its interaction with the morphological marking offered in German, (case and verb inflection) is investigated. I try to show that in dysphasia, word order has a distinguishing function; morphological markings on the other hand, cannot be employed to encode grammatical relations.

Finally, I will investigate the *position of elements of negation*. At the core of this is the position of the negator in relation to the verb. Elements of negation do not form syntactic constituents themselves, but instead are operators whose position in the sentence depends on semantic factors, especially on scope. I will show that the positions in the constituent structure which are needed for negation are also offered in dysphasia.

7.1 Verb placement

There are already several empirical studies on the position of verbs in dysphasia; the general results were summarised in Ch. 4.1. There, we saw differences in the results: whilst Günther (1981) and Kegel (1981) define the *SVO* pattern as characteristic of dysphasia, Grimm (1983) and Kaltenbacher/Kany (1985) think that the verb-*final* pattern is preferred in dysphasia. I suggest that shortcomings in the linguistic data analysis are responsible for the apparent contradictions in the results. The fact that the position of verbs was analysed in the above studies in isolation from other grammatical phenomena proved to be disadvantageous, especially because verb placement was analysed in isolation from the inflectional forms of verbs. The data available from these studies were therefore reexamined, paying attention to the correlations between the position and inflection of verbs. The contradictions in the area of verb placement could be resolved in this way. We saw that, in Günther and Kegel's data, as well as in those from Grimm's project, inflected verbs are mainly at the front, that is in second or initial position, while uninflected verbs are at the end of the sentence.

These observations tally with my hypotheses on dysphasia. From the data of the above authors, we see that the positions required for the verb in the syntactic constituent structure are still present in dysphasia. The damage which occurs in dysphasia largely affects morphology. This leads to verb inflections not being identified and not being represented in morphological paradigms in the lexicon. This also has the consequence that the position provided for the inflected verb often remains unfilled in the syntax, and that verbs – as in Grimm's data (1983) – are mainly placed in the position which is provided for non-finite elements at the end of the sentence. The errors in the position of the verb which are observed in dysphasia are, in this respect, only a secondary effect of the deficits in morphology. Given the available data, damage to the mechanisms for constructing syntactic constituent structure does not have to be assumed.

In order to test this hypothesis, I will analyse the position of verbs in my data. Firstly, I will provide a summary of the positional patterns which occur. Then, correlations between the position and (i) the inflection of verbs as well as (ii) the categorisation of verbal elements in the lexicon will be investigated.

7.1.1 *Overview: V1,V2 and verb-final patterns*

7.1.1.1 The data analysis is carried out using the categories of the profile chart. The first investigation refers to the utterances in which verbal elements in the sentence occur next to one another. Utterances with discontinuous verb placement are analysed separately in paragraph 7.1.3. In the first investigation, a distinction is made between (i) subjects ('Sub'), (ii) verbal elements ('V') and (iii) adverbs, PPs and nominal elements in object function ('Obj'). A verb placement analysis can only be carried out on those utterances in which, as well as 'V', either 'Sub' and/or 'Obj' occur. From this, we get the following distinctions:

(1) *Sentences in which all categories are present:*

a. taxi *kommt* gleich (Sve:81)
('taxi coming soon')

b. das *les* ich (Sve:252)
('that read I')

c. jetzt ich *auswischen* die (Pet3:200a)
('now I wipe out them')

d. ich das *mache* jetzt (Pet3:16)
('I that do now')
(P. is drawing the Fire Brigade.)

e. is auch ein torm *mach* (Wol:135)
('I too a tower make')
(W. is building a toy tower.)

f. ein tenzer is *bauch* (Wol:65)
('a window I need')
(W. needs a window.)

g. *gehn* du jetzt ater (Ste:98)
('go you now theatre')
(The therapist should now playtheatre.)

(2) *Sentences in which the subject is missing*

a. diesa *mötz* nich immer (Wol:104)
('this want not always')
(W. does not want to have the doll.)

b. unahose noch *anzieh* (Anj2:267)
('pants still put on')
(A. is putting pants on the doll.)

(3) *Sentences in which objects or adverbials are missing*

a. wir *spielen* (Ste:312b)
('we play')

b. *wiederdomme* ich (And2:63)
('again come I')
(A. is coming back.)

Instances like these are analysed in terms of the patterns in (4); only instances such as (3a) are not analysed further, as the difference between verb-second and verb-final placement cannot be decided.

(4) a. verb-second : X* V Y* ; cf. 1a, 1b, 1c, 1d, 2a
b. verb-final : X* V ; cf. 1e, 1f, 2b
c. verb-initial : V S (X*) ; cf. 1g, 3b

The next step is to work out which elements appear at X or Y in the verb-second and verb-final patterns. For X*VY* the possibilities are in (5), and for X*V in (6); note that 'Obj' refers to all sorts of non-subjects, i.e. adverbials, PPs and VP-objects.

(5) a. X=Ø, Y='Obj'
laufen immer (Kla1:47)
('run always')
(The animals always run.)

b. X=Obj, Y=Obj (see 2a)
c. X=Sub, Y=Obj (see 1a)
d. X=Obj, Y=Sub (see 1b)
e. X=Obj+Sub, Y=Obj (see 1c)
f. X=Sub+Obj, Y=Obj (see 1d)

(6) a. X=Obj (see 2b)
b. X=Sub+Obj (see 1e)
c. X=Obj+Sub (see 1f)

The quantitative analysis can be taken from table 13. The percentages give the proportion of the particular word order patterns with regard to the total number of utterances; they add up to 100% for each child. Absolute frequencies are given for the different possibilities of verb-second and verb-final patterns. The third column refers, for example, to the pattern Sub+V+Obj. Note that instances (5a) and (5b) are included in the second column of X*VY*, and instances (6a) and (6b) in the second column of X*V. The last column of table 13 gives the proportion of verb-initial patterns in yes/no questions, as required in German.

Table 13: *Verb placement – overview*

	X* V Y*						**X* V**			**V S (X*)**	
	Proportion (in %)	(O/S) Obj	Sub Obj	Obj Sub	O+S Obj	S+O Obj	Proportion (in %)	(Sub) + Obj	Obj + Sub	Proportion (in %)	Yes/no Ques.
Anja 1	16	2	1	1	0	0	84	20	1	0	0
Anja 2	21	8	2	5	2	0	78	61	2	0	0
Andreas 1	30	10	1	0	0	0	61	21	1	8	0
Andreas 2	33	20	0	2	0	0	60	39	0	6	0
Klaus 1	42	5	2	1	0	0	57	11	0	0	0
Klaus 2	42	7	2	7	0	0	52	20	0	5	0
Julia 1	9	0	1	0	0	1	81	15	3	9	0
Julia 2	20	3	5	0	1	1	72	26	9	6	0
Patrick	54	12	9	9	0	0	36	19	1	9	0
Sven	49	4	16	16	0	0	43	30	2	6	1
Stefan	45	15	3	7	0	0	47	23	3	7	1
Jonas 1	31	10	8	3	2	0	60	41	3	8	0
Jonas 2	49	10	8	4	2	1	41	19	2	9	3
Petra 1	18	0	2	0	0	0	81	8	1	0	0
Petra 2	21	3	6	1	0	2	78	39	4	0	0
Petra 3	31	3	6	2	7	3	68	27	20	0	0
Wolfgang	16	6	5	1	1	2	82	49	24	1	0

The table shows that, overall, verb-initial patterns (V1) occur infrequently. Also, this pattern is not – as in German – limited to yes-no questions. Instead, all of the children who use this pattern also use it in declarative sentences. Additionally, the entries under 'Question' in the profile charts (QXY, QXYZ) show that, in yes-no questions, there are other verb placement patterns as well. To illustrate, let us look at the following examples:

(7) a. uschi hier *wohn*? (Wol:21b)
('uschi here live?')
(Does uschi live here?)
b. das *is* puppen? (Sve:16)
('that is dolls?')
(Are they dolls?)
c. du auch eine *baue*? (Pat:190)
('you also one build?')
(Are you building one (a ramp) too?)

These instances and the observations above show that the children do not have special verb placement patterns for questions.

Regarding the use of verb-second patterns (V2) and verb-final patterns (V-F) we also see individual differences. Most of the children prefer V-F; others, for example Sven and Patrick, however, tend to use a variable position for the verb, whereby V2 is used in the greater part of the examples. Grimm's (1983) and Günther's (1981) statements do not apply to the children in this investigation. Not all children with dysphasia use SVX without differentiation, which is Günther's hypothesis. And similarly, it is not true that V-F is typical for all children with dysphasia (cf. Grimm 1983). These observations have to be rejected in their undifferentiated form.

A comparison with normal grammatical development shows that children without linguistic problems, before they acquire the correct position for the verb in phase IV, have similar percentages to those of the dysphasics in table 13. Thus, for example in two of the linguistically normal children analysed in Clahsen (1982), V-F dominates from the start; in both of these children (Daniel and Julia), the number of sentences with V-F in early phases of development is about 80% (cf. Clahsen 1982: tables 23, 24). On the other hand, for example, Mathias's placement of verbs tends to be variable and the number for V-F is clearly smaller (cf. Clahsen 1982, table 22). These observations show that there are differences between the children before phase IV for the frequencies of V2 and V-F usage. This individual variation is also present in dysphasia.

7.1.1.2 Overall, table 13 shows that none of the dysphasic children has reached phase IV. The placement of verbs in dysphasia is, instead, characterised by the features of the early phases II/III: it is on the whole variable, and V-F is preferred by most of the children. V1 occurs seldom. From these observations, I assume that the syntactic representation to which linguistically normal children have access in phases II/III, is present in dysphasia. The configuration suggested for this in Ch. 2.4.2 is repeated here in (8):

(8)

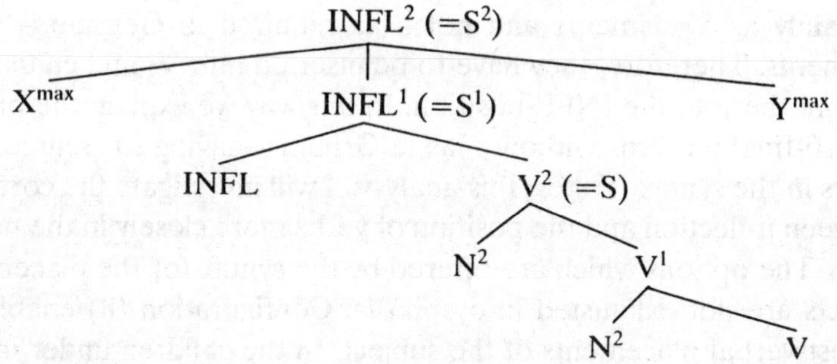

Given configuration (8), the verb-placement patterns which are investigated in table 13 can be reduced to two cases: (i) V-front: the verb appears in the INFL-position; (ii) V-back: the verb appears in the V-position within V^1. The verb-initial patterns are viewed here as being special cases of V-front; in these instances the subject remains in the underlying position within S. The data show that the X^{max} position is either unfilled, e.g. as in (1d, 1e, 1g, 3b), or can be filled by a (topicalised) constituent. Topicalisations occur for all of the children; they are possible for subjects, objects, adverbs and PPs (cf. e.g. 1a, 1b, 1c, 1f, 2a). Similarly, the position Y^{max} at the end of the sentence is provided for extraposed elements. The Y^{max} position is only filled in a few cases (cf. e.g. 1c, 1d). In these instances, the verb remains in the V-position of V^1 and the Y^{max} position at the end of the sentence can – as in German – be filled by one constituent. Instances of this type occasionally occur in Jonas and Petra 2/3; for this, compare the values in the fifth and sixth columns of table 13.

The verb placement patterns in the data for the dysphasic children can be described in terms of the proposed syntactic representation. Damages in the construction of the syntactic constituent structure do not have to be assumed. Crucially, however, the various word order possibilities in (8) are not used to the same extent by dysphasic children. Instead, there are quantitative asymmetries between the various alternatives.

In the placement of verbs, there are instances of V-front and V-back for all of the children, but the verb-final pattern is clearly preferred. In this respect, the results tally with those of Grimm (1983). However, as opposed to Grimm, I assume that the children's problems in morphology are responsible for their preference of the verb-final pattern. Given the results of the last chapter, I think that the lexicon in dysphasia produces verbs mainly as V-elements and not – as required in German – as INFL-elements. Therefore, they have to be inserted into V^1 and cannot be moved from there to the INFL-position. In this way we explain the preference of verb-final patterns without – as in Grimm – having to assume global deficits in the syntax. To test this analysis, I will investigate the correlations between inflection and the position of verbs more closely in the next section.

The options which are offered by the syntax for the placement of subjects are not exhausted in dysphasia. Configuration (8) enables pre- and post-verbal placements of the subject. In the children under investigation, there are instances for both possibilities, but all of the children clearly prefer the position of the subject before the verb; compare here the frequencies from table 13 for Obj+V+Sub and VS(X*) with those of the other columns. Closely linked to this are the asymmetries in the use of topicalisations. The X^{max} position in configuration (8) can be filled with any maximal projection, including the object-NP, the subject and adverbial elements. For all of these, although there are instances in the data, the frequencies of use vary between the children. Often, the X^{max} position is occupied by adverbs, while object-topicalisations such as in (1b) only occur occasionally; objects mostly remain in V^1.

I presume that the preferences in the position of subjects and objects in dysphasia have functional reasons. Given that morphological means of expression, especially case morphology and subject-verb agreement, are for the most part missing in dysphasia, one might think that word order serves to distinguish between grammatical relations. Consequently, the positions for subject and object in dysphasia are to a certain extent fixed and the order variants which are offered by the syntax are not exhausted. To test this claim, the function of word order will be investigated in paragraph 7.2 in connection with other means of encoding grammatical relations.

7.1.2 *Verb placement and verb inflection*

7.1.2.1 In the previous analysis, we saw that verbal elements in dysphasia occur in the V-front or V-back positions, and that most of the children prefer the verb-final pattern. In the following I will investigate the factors upon which the position of the verb depends. With regard to the position of the verb, I consider (i) the morphological form and (ii) the type of the verbal element to be important. The idea of a lexically-driven syntax and the assumption of parallelism underlie this (see Ch. 4.3). I will show that in dysphasia the positions which are available in the syntax for verbs cannot be filled in free variation, but that the way in which they are filled is basically pre-defined by the categorisation of verbal elements in the lexicon. This is the general hypothesis on which I base the two following investigations. Firstly, I will analyse correlations between the morphological form and the position of verbs.

The specific hypotheses on this can be derived from the assumption that the damage in dysphasia affects the morphological component of the lexicon, while the learning mechanisms for the construction of the syntactic constituent structure, semantic bootstrapping, and other components of the language acquisition device remain intact. If these assumptions are basically correct, we can expect that (a) the principles formulated in Kratzer (1984) for developed grammars also apply for dysphasia: verbs with strong inflections are produced by the lexicon as INFL-elements and occur in the V-front position; verbs with weak inflections are categorised as V-elements and occur in the V-back position.

The second hypothesis has to do with the strong/weak distinction in dysphasia. According to Kratzer's analysis (1984), this is dependent in German upon the content of the inflections. Here, the infinitive and participle forms are weak, whereas all agreement inflections are strong. Starting with the assumption that dysphasic children have problems with the phenomenon of agreement, but that semantic bootstrapping is available, we expect that (b) the strong/weak distinction in dysphasia depends upon the *semantic* content of the inflections: those without any specific meaning, in particular the default-form *n* and its variants, are categorised as weak. The verbs linked with these inflections would, according to (a), have to be produced as V-elements and occur in the V-back position. On the other hand, according to (b), verb inflections with specific semantic content, especially the transitivity marker *t*, would have to be marked as [+strong]. Additionally, according to hypothesis (a), verbs with the inflection *t*, would have to be produced by the lexicon as INFL-elements and placed in the corresponding position in configuration (8).

Both the hypotheses (a) and (b) can be checked using the data available. If the expected distribution proves correct, one may conclude that both of the positions which are available for the verb in German, V-front and V-back, are also differentiated in dysphasia, and that we do not have to consider syntactic deficits in this area.

The results of the data analysis are summarised briefly in (9); I explain the details afterwards:

(9)
a. The default-forms of verbs occur for the most part in the V-back position for all of the children.
b. In Julia and Petra, all regular verbs are in the V-back position, regardless of the form of inflection. In the other children, the verbs marked with *t* are at the front; only participles also occur at the end of the sentence.
c. In Sven and Stefan verbs in the stem form (Ø) are at the front. In the other children, they mostly occur in the V-back position.

In most of the children, *n* appears as the default-form, and in some *Ø/e*. These forms show no specific content; they can, for example, be used with all of the grammatical persons (see Ch. 6.2.2). Default-forms are analysed as weak inflections and verbs which occur with these forms are categorised in the lexicon as V-elements. In lexical insertion, they are placed into the V-position of (8) and from there they cannot be moved over V^1.

In Sven and Stefan, INFL=Ø may not be regarded as the default-form. Stefan uses the stem form almost exclusively for imperatives, and Sven uses it mainly with [+sing.]-subjects (cf. Ch. 6.2.1). In both instances, the stem form expresses a specific content and the option INFL=Ø has the feature [+strong]. Verbs in the stem form are categorised in Sven and

Stefan's lexicon as INFL-elements. Consequently, they are inserted into the INFL-position in (8) and always occur in the V-front position. For the remaining children, the choice of the stem form is not morphologically determined; for this reason verbal elements with *Ø* are – like the default-forms – mainly in the V-back position.

Most of the children (except Petra and Julia) prefer the V-front position for verbs marked with the inflection *t*; of the instances with the verbal inflection *t* in these children, of which there are 82 altogether (cf. table 11), there are only 8 instances, i.e. less then 10%, in which verb-final placements occur. This word order preference is also due to the categorisation in the lexicon. In Ch. 6.2.2, I showed that the inflection *t* is a marker for low semantic transitivity. The inflection thus expresses a specific semantic content and therefore has the feature [+strong]. Verbs marked with *t* are categorised in the lexicon as INFL-elements and are inserted into the corresponding position in configuration (8); for this reason, they are mostly placed into the verb-front position. The observations above confirm hypotheses (a) and (b). In particular, the oppositions between the placements of the verbs marked with *t* and those in the default-form show that – also in dysphasia – there are *different* verb positions in the syntax which are filled according to lexical categorisations.

7.1.2.2 With respect to Julia and Petra, we observe an interesting property in this area. In these children there are no obvious oppositions between the positions for default-forms and other inflected verbs. Instead, all types of regularly formed verbs occur dominantly at the end of the sentence. The verb inflection analysis shows that Julia – like most of the other children – has access to *n* as a default-form and to *t* as a marker of semantic transitivity. In contrast to the other children, however, verbs with *t* mostly appear in the V-back position (cf. e.g. Jul1:98, 106b, 126, 163c; Jul2:83b, 147b). Petra has access to the correct paradigm for subject-verb agreement, but, even in the third recording, the verbs occur at the end of the sentence as before (see 10). In Julia and Petra only modal verbs occur in the V-front position (cf. 11):

(10) a. und jetzt du wieder *schreibst* (Pet3:219)
('and now you again write')
b. wie das *geht*? (Pet3:137)
('how that go?') (How does that go?)

c. der immer füsche ehm fische *angelt* (Pet3:96)
('he always fish er fish angles')
(He is always angling fish.)

d. der ich *brate* (Pet3:165)
('the I fry')
(I'll fry that.)

(11) a. Julia *kann* nicht lesen (Jul2:70)
('Julia cannot read')

b. hier *will* ich was malen (Pet3:19)
('here want I to draw something')
(I want to draw something here.)

The instances with modal verbs, which are investigated more closely in the next paragraph, show that we have to assume two different positions for the verb in the syntax for Petra and Julia, as suggested in configuration (8). The problem of these two children has to do with the way in which the positions for the verbs are filled: basically, only modal verbs can be placed into the INFL-position in (8), all of the other inflected verbs remain in the final position. Interestingly, Petra's system is not observed in linguistically normal children. The investigations in Ch. 3 show that verb placement in linguistically normal children is correct as soon as they have access to subject-verb agreement. This correlation in development obviously does not apply to Petra.

In order to analyse Julia and Petra's data, different possibilities come into consideration. I will discuss these briefly in the following:

(12) a. The required movement rule is not available.

b. The strong/weak distinction is neutralised.

c. Verb inflections are not affixed in the morphology, but are directly inserted into the syntactic representation.

Option (12a) could only apply to Petra, but not to Julia, because J. only has access to configuration (8) in which no movement rules are required for verb placement. Petra 3 on the other hand uses subordinate clauses with, for the most part, the correct verb-final placement. In Petra's grammar there is, therefore, the possibility of sentence embedding. For Petra 3's syntax, we can assume the representation which is suggested for phase V of normal grammar acquistion (see Ch. 2.4.2):

(13)

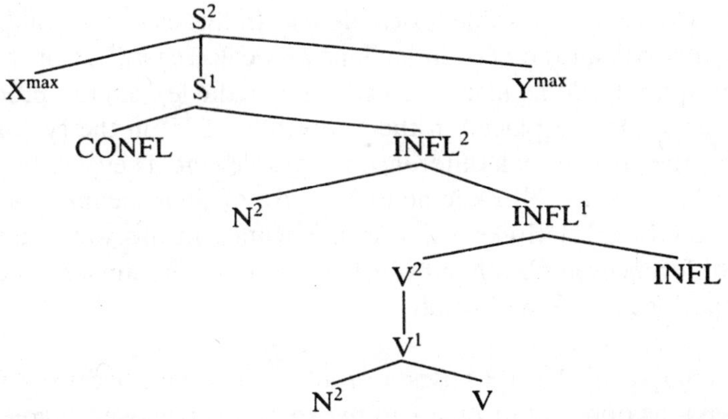

Here, a movement rule (move INFL) is required in German so that the inflected verbs which are inserted into INFL in main clauses are taken to the CONFL-position. We could say that Petra does not have access to this rule. Verbs with inflections for agreement would then fill the INFL-position at the end of the sentence. From here the person and number features of the finite verb can percolate up to $INFL^2$ and there they can be compared and checked against the corresponding features of the subject. In this way, we can explain Petra's correct use of agreement without having to diverge from UG principles.

The problem with this suggestion is, however, the analysis of the *position* of verbs. In order to describe the asymmetries in verb placement, we have to assume – using (13) as a basis – a constraint on the movement rule, by which 'move INFL' is only allowed where INFL is a modal verb. This limitation is completely idiosyncratic and does not correspond to the universal format of movement rules. The format requires that all the movement rules of a particular grammar be variants of the general scheme 'move alpha', where alpha can be fixed onto various projections of X^0. 'Move INFL' corresponds to the universal scheme, but 'move modal verb' does not. Additionally, in (13) there is no longer a difference between modal verbs and other inflected verbs; in (13) both are INFL-elements. Thus, the asymmetries in verb placement which are observed between these elements in Petra's utterances cannot be explained in terms of a syntactic deficit. They indicate, instead, that there are lexical problems, in particular with the categorisation of finite verbs.

(12b) would be a possible lexical deficit. In this case, the children are said to categorise all the verb inflections as weak, regardless of their content. Consequently, all regularly formed verbs in the lexicon are produced as V-elements and are placed in the V-position of V^1 in the syntax. In modal verbs, the strong/weak difference is not relevant. They can be categorised in the lexicon as INFL-elements because of their meaning, and they can fill the CONFL/INFL-position in the syntax. In this way, we can explain the differences in placement which we observe. For Julia's data, this analysis provides the desired result.

The analysis of Petra 3 poses a problem, however, because this child has access – as opposed to Julia – to the correct subject-verb agreement paradigm. According to analysis (12b), we have to assume that all regularly formed finite verbs occur in the V-position in configuration (13); this makes it hard to explain the correct agreement in Petra without a lot of additional assumptions. In Petra – exactly as in German – the diacritical features on the finite verb have to pass over from the level of word structure into the syntax; this is known as percolation (cf. Selkirk 1982). In configuration (13), they have to reach $INFL^2$ so that the agreement features can be compared and checked against the features of the subject. UG principles for percolation have not yet been worked out fully, but, indisputably, percolation is only possible between nodes with the same syntactic features. Diacritical features are thus passed on from N to NP, and from V to VP, but not from the verb to $INFL^1$. If inflected verbs in Petra 3 were to be in the V-position in (13), then the agreement features cannot be projected over V^2, unless the assumption of parallelism were to be rejected and one were to allow the principles of UG to be violated in dysphasia. This conclusion should be avoided here. I want, instead, to try and analyse Petra's data under the assumption of parallelism.

The third possibility for interpreting the data for Petra 3, (12c), corresponds to the analysis suggested by Kratzer (1984) for English. In this analysis, the assumption that fully inflected forms are only produced in the lexicon is partially retracted. Kratzer assumes that verb inflections are inserted directly into the INFL-position of the syntax. Huang (1982) suggests a corresponding analysis for Chinese. Kratzer thinks that the separation of verb and inflection in morphology is a strongly marked option; in any case it is a *possible* solution in natural languages.

Using this as a basis, we can say that Petra does not have access to the word-formation rule which is necessary for suffixing verb inflections from the general paradigm to verb stems. Consequently, inflections have to be directly inserted into the syntax. Petra 3's agreement inflections have the feature [+strong] and are categorised correspondingly as INFL-elements. In (13), they fill the INFL-position at the end of the sentence. From here, the person and number features are passed on to $INFL^2$, and thus ensure correct subject-verb agreement. The movement to CONFL which is required in German would not be employed by Petra in these instances, because there is nothing present in CONFL which, along with the INFL-elements, could result in a possible word. The INFL-elements can, however, be linked (in phonology) with the verbs which are its immediate neighbours in the V-position of V^1. In this way, we can explain the verb-final patterns for finite verbs, with its simultaneous correct agreement. Modal verbs, on the other hand, are represented in the lexicon in word-specific paradigms and can, on the basis of their meanings, be categorised as INFL-elements. They initially fill the INFL-position in (13), without the child having to use word-formation rules for this. From here, they can be moved to CONFL.

Analysis (12c) for Petra 3 is derived from Kratzer's (1984) INFL-parameter, which was chosen as the theoretical framework here. On the basis of the assumption of parallelism, (12c) would be preferable to (12a) and (12b), as then we only have to assume problems with respect to word-formation, and all of the other observed properties in the placement of verbs could be derived from this, without having to assume any other damage. However, in some respects, (12c) is also problematic. Thus, e.g. word-formation deficits have to be employed, for which there is no apparent empirical evidence in the rest of the data. Nor can we find any direct indications in the data that verb inflections – like other lexical units – are directly inserted into the syntax. If (12c) should be maintained, then we would have to try (with the help of experimental techniques) and provide the corresponding evidence, e.g. of difficulties with word-formation.

An alternative to (12c), which possibly corresponds more readily to Petra 3's data, is that not CONFL, but CONMOD is the head of S^1 in configuration (13). This would, in any case, account for Petra's placement of verbs. Subordinating conjunctions and modal verbs occur in the CONMOD position, but simple, inflected verbs cannot. In this interpretation, we do not have to assume any deficits in the syntactic constituent structure, either, because the required head position of S^1 is offered. The lexicon determines which elements fall into this category. Movement rules for verbal elements are not required under this analysis; modal verbs instead, are inserted, like subordinating conjunctions, directly into the CONMOD-position. According to this analysis, Petra 3 has not fixed the COMP/INFL parameter (Platzack 1983) at the appropriate value for German. Additionally, the value chosen by Petra would not belong to the possibilities which are proposed by Platzack. Given semantic bootstrapping it is, however, a perfectly feasible parametrization, which should belong to the options available in UG.

Overall, the peculiarities observed in Petra are marginal compared to the systems of the other children. In any case, in my interpretation of the data we need not assume any deficits in the syntactic constituent structure, neither for Petra, nor for the other children under investigation. The analysis shows that the required configuration is also available in dysphasia, and that the way in which the syntactic positions for verbs are filled is basically determined by lexical categorisations. The children's deficits mainly affect morphology. The analysis shows that the observed facts with regard to verb placement are a consequence of morphological deficits.

7.1.3 *Verb placement and verbal elements*

7.1.3.1 In the following, I will investigate whether verb placement is also dependent upon the type of the verbal element. On the basis of the hypotheses mentioned above (cf. 7.1.2), we expect systematic correlations here. In addition to the analysis in table 10, we must now look at instances with discontinuous verb placement. The total number of (separable) prefix verbs as well as modal and auxiliary constructions are in table 8 (see Ch. 5.3). To analyse discontinuous verb placement, the following distinctions are made (based on the profile charts):

(14) a. *separated verbal prefixes* (V X Pref)
mach das dinges *auf* (Ste:210)
('open the thing')
(The therapist should open the curtain.)

Table 14: *Discontinuous verb placement*

	V X Pref	Mod X Inf	Aux X Part	Cop X Adj	Others
Anja 1	0	1	0	0	0
Anja 2	0	0	0	0	0
Andreas 1	0	1	0	0	0
Andreas 2	0	0	0	0	0
Klaus 1	0	0	0	1	0
Klaus 2	1	0	0	0	0
Julia 1	0	0	0	0	0
Julia 2	0	0	0	0	0
Patrick	0	0	0	0	0
Sven	4	1	0	0	2
Stefan	4	2	1	0	1
Jonas 1	0	0	0	0	0
Jonas 2	0	4	3	0	5
Petra 1	0	0	0	0	0
Petra 2	0	0	0	0	0
Petra 3	0	8	0	0	1
Wolfgang	2	0	0	0	0.

Table 14 contains absolute frequencies. Other types of discontinuous verb placement are included in the last column of the table. Note that in the cases included in table 14, X is always filled by at least one constituent. We find the instances in which verb and prefix or auxiliary and participle are directly next to one another by subtracting the frequencies in table 14 from the corresponding values in table 8.

b. *Modal verb constructions* (Mod X Inf)
hier *will* ich was *malen* (Pet3:19)
(I want to paint something here)
(see 11b)

c. *Auxiliary constructions* (Aux X Part)
hat die kamera allein *tjefieme* (Jon2:128)
('has the camera alone filmed')
(The camera took a picture by itself.)

d. *Copula constructions* (Cop X Adj)
der *s* auch biβchen *lang* (Kla1:23)
('that is also a bit long')
(That's rather long, too.)

The results of the analysis can be summarised as follows; in addition, let us look at the examples from Anja in (16).

(15) a. In *modal verb constructions* Mod is mostly in the V-front position and infinitives remain in the VP; hereby, discontinuous placement of the verb results in some of the children (see table 14). In the whole data, there are only four instances in which Mod appears after the infinitive in the V-back position (Jul2:51b, Pat:130, Jon1:215, Pet2:165).

b. In *copula constructions* the verbal element *sein* (to be) similarly occurs mostly in the V-front position. Table 14 shows that there is only one instance here of discontinuous verb placement (see 14d). In the whole material there are seven instances in which the V-back position is chosen for the copula (Jul1:92b; Jul2:52, 153a, 154; Pet3:194a, 204a; Wol: 191).

c. If an auxiliary verb occurs in *auxiliary constructions*, it mostly comes in the V-front position, whereby discontinuous verb placement arises in four instances altogether (see table 14). Only for Julia are there any instances in which auxiliary verbs come at the end of the sentence, namely three (Jul1: 96, 36b; Jul2:78).

d. Forms of the verb *sein* (to be) with locative meanings (cf. e.g. C16f) mainly occur in the V-front position. In the entire corpus there are only two instances in which a form of the local verb *sein* appears in the V-back position (Jul2:169b, Wol:18).

e. We do not observe any specific verb placement patterns for *prefix verbs*; they occur in both V-front and V-back. The discontinuous placement of prefix verbs occurs, on the whole, infrequently (see table 14).

(16) a. ein *fel* noch (Anj1:1)
('one miss still')
(The number '1' is missing on the dial.)

b. feter *dehn* (Anj1:15)
('harder turn')
(A. is turning the dial more firmly.)

c. ... herr feudmann *weitafahn* majon (Anj2:99)
('herr feudmann further drive majon')
(Mr. F. is driving further on to Marion.)

d. hier auch noch *aufmachen* (Anj2:295)
('here also too open')
(Subj=ich (I))

e. *kann* nich arme (Anj1:195)
('can not arms')
(A. cannot button up the doll's arms.)

f. hier nich *war* num (Anj1:5b)
('here not was num')
(num=Nummer (number))

Examples (16c) and (16d) show that prefix verbs – exactly the same as other regularly formed verbs (cf. 16a, 16b) – can be placed in both verb positions, whereby Anja clearly prefers the verb-final pattern and omits the inflection for the verb. By contrast, modal verbs and forms of *sein* (to be) are in the V-front position (cf. 16e, 16f). Similar observations apply for most of the other children.

At first glance, it seems surprising to find that in dysphasia discontinuous verb placement is mostly correct – at least in modal verb constructions – while in simple verbs, placement 'errors' often occur. We see that – except for one instance (Pet3:8) – all of the utterances with discontinuous verb placement can be described in terms of the proposed syntactic configurations (cf. 8 and 13). This also applies to the instances covered in table 14 under 'Others'; in each of these, one constituent has been extraposed, e.g. as in (17):

(17) *daf* ich jetzt *aufbaue* meine dame? (Jon2:10)
('may I now build up my lady?')

I think that the observed positional regularities can be traced back to the categorisation of verbal elements in the lexicon. Modal verbs are prototypical candidates for the category INFL due to their meanings. Using semantic bootstrapping all of the children are able to identify modals as INFL-elements and place them into the position provided for them in the syntax. The non-finite verbal elements remain in the VP. In this way, discontinuous verb placement arises in modal verb constructions (cf. 15a).

The auxiliary and the copula are omitted in most instances. This was traced back to the children's problems with grammatical agreement (cf. Ch. 5.3). Auxiliaries were analysed as grammatical function words which do not have their own meanings, but are instead lexical fillers of the agreement features. (15b) and (15c) also show that the few auxiliaries which are realised mainly occur in the correct V-front position. This could be due to a variety of factors.

One factor is that in auxiliary and copula constructions the verb position within V^1 is reserved for non-finite verbal elements, and is therefore no longer available for the auxiliary. Thus, the auxiliary is placed into the second verb position. This cannot, however, be the only relevant factor, because then we would also expect the reverse order. Moreover, this factor cannot account for the fact that forms of *sein* (to be), even if they occur without a non-finite verb (cf. 15d), are mostly in the front verb position. I think it is more important that auxiliaries – like the forms of the local verb *sein* – can only be used as inflected verbs. Either, the child simply leaves the entire verbal position unfilled, as happens in most instances, or s/he chooses an inflected form from the word-specific paradigm. Even without the child having access to the correct agreement paradigm, this form can be identified as an inflected verb and is produced by the lexicon as an INFL-element. Consequently, the auxiliaries and forms of *sein* which occur appear mostly in the correct V-front position. In this way, we can analyse the word order regularities in (15).

Exceptions to that can be found mainly in the data for Petra and Julia (cf. 15). Although these children place the modal verbs at the front in most instances, the auxiliaries sometimes are placed at the end of the sentence. This is due to categorisation problems. It appears that the auxiliary and the non-finite element are used as an unstructured verbal cluster, especially by Julia, and that this cluster is inserted into the VP. This is confirmed because the instances of clause-final auxiliaries are limited to a few sentence patterns.

(18) a. auch mama *funden hat* (Jul1:96)
('also mama found has')
(Mama=Subj.)
b. wecki *funden hat* (Jul1:36b)
('wecki found has')
(Flecki has found the cake.)
c. erst julia *älter bin* (Jul2:153a)
('only julia older am')
(Only when J. is older.)
d. erst *älter bin* (Jul2:154)
('only older am')
(see 18c)
e. *fünf bin* (Jul2:52)
('five am')
(I am five)

Also in Petra, both of the instances with clause-final auxiliaries are limited to an identical sentence pattern (Pet3:194a, 204). Otherwise, the auxiliaries are in the V-front position (cf. e.g. Pet3:88). It could be that the children treat at least some of the auxiliary verb constructions just like lexicalised syntagmas. The verbal clusters are then inserted into the VP and the INFL-position remains empty. This could account for the placement of auxiliaries, especially in Julia. Additional investigations are necessary in order to ascertain whether this property can be found in other dysphasic children.

The observations on the placement of verbs show that the children have fewer problems in using modal verbs. In modal verbs there are almost no placement errors, while in auxiliary constructions, at least for Petra and Julia, we find categorisation problems. The reason for this is that modal verbs – different from auxiliaries – have their own meanings. In contrast to auxiliaries, modal verbs can be categorised using semantic bootstrapping. This claim was made in Ch. 5.3 in order to explain the fact that all of the children have access to modal verbs, but that auxiliaries only occur in a few instances. The results on the position of modal and auxiliary verbs tally with this.

7.1.3.2 Finally, I will investigate the position of separable *prefix verbs*. The starting point for this is the analysis suggested by Wunderlich (1985) for German. Prefix verbs are treated here as lexicalised syntagmas, in which the prefix belongs to the subcategorisation of the verb. The prefix is, thus, a fixed argument of the verb in the lexicon, which has the status of a word and is directly adjacent to the verb. An $INFL^1$-structure is induced in the syntax by the joint lexical filling of verb and prefix (cf. Ch. 2.4.2):

(19)

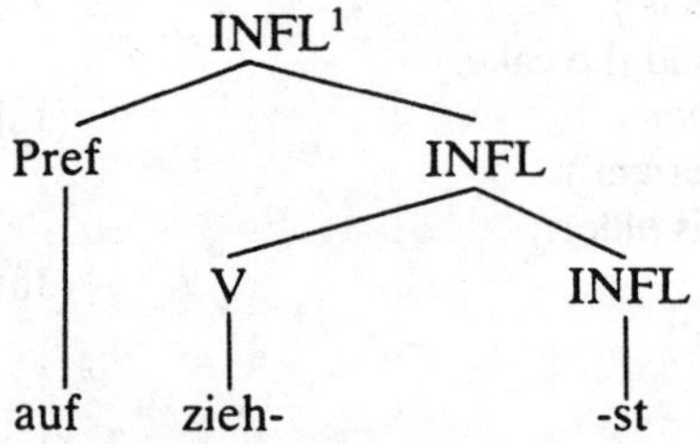

Studies on normal child language show that, at the beginning, the fact that the prefix is an argument has not yet been identified. Using semantic bootstrapping prefix verbs are, instead, categorised as X^0 elements in the lexicon. Consequently, the prefix and the verb are not separated in early developmental phases and are dominantly placed in the V-position at the end of the sentence. The decisive trigger for the re-analysis of prefix verbs is the availability of verb inflection. As soon as the child has access to *st*, for example, s/he can identify the verbal element *ziehst* ('pull' – 2nd pers. sing.) as a syntactic constituent. Consequently, *aufziehen* (to pull up) can no longer be treated as a syntactic island and the earlier categorisation must be rejected in favour of (19). The prefix verbs are then separated correctly. Given this analysis and our basic assumptions on dysphasia, we can derive specific hypotheses on the position of prefix verbs in the data:

(20) a. Dysphasic children classify prefix verbs as lexical categories (V^0 or $INFL^0$) using semantic bootstrapping. For this reason, the prefix will not typically be separated from the verb.

b. Prefix verbs containing strong inflections can induce the required $INFL^1$-substructure in dysphasia, and occur in discontinuous word order.

The data available are suitable for checking these hypotheses, because there are many instances of prefix verbs. Comparing the values for prefix verbs in tables 8 (cf. Ch. 5.3) and 14 shows that, in most of the children, prefix verbs do not occur in discontinuous order. Instead, the elements mostly occur in the order of Pref.+V, i.e., immediately next to one another. They can appear in the V-front and V-back positions, just like simple verbs (cf. 16). From table 14, we see that the verb is only separated from the prefix in a few isolated instances. In most of these instances, it is a verb with the inflection *t* (cf. 21). In Stefan we find discontinuous word order in imperatives as well (cf. 22), and in Wolfgang and Jonas there is a limited number of verbs which occur as V+Pref., where both of these elements are immediately next to one another (cf. 23). Examples such as (23), in which local rearrangements are carried out within the word, only rarely occur in linguistically normal children; overall, instances like these are – as shown by the data – marginal.

(21) a. der *geht* nich *auf* (Sve:72)
('it goes not open')
(It doesn't open.)
b. hier *kommt* das auto so *hin* (Sve:236a)
('here comes the car just in')
(The car goes in here just right.)

(22) a. *gib* mal *her* (Ste:291b)
('give that')
b. *mach* das dinges *auf* (Ste:210)
('make the thing open')
(Open the thing.)

(23) a. ... und de kopfsauger.haaje *komme hei* (Jon1:197)
('and the vacuum cleaner.hairs come in')
(Hair gets into the vacuum cleaner.)
b. uschi.*geht rein* nich (Wol:24)
('uschi.goes in not')
(W. is trying in vain to fix the bits of Lego.)
c. uschi.falte runter (Wol:1)
('uschi.fald down')
(Bits of Lego have fallen down.)

In accordance with hypothesis (20a), the available data show that prefix verbs are treated like syntactic islands from which nothing can be extracted. From this we conclude that semantic bootstrapping is used to categorise prefix verbs in dysphasia. This is preferred by all of the children and many of them even choose it exclusively. Obviously, the children have problems in analysing prefix verbs as syntagmas. Additional evidence for this may be taken from the examples in (24). In these instances the local and directional arguments subcategorised by the verb are realised twice, by an adverbial phrase *and* by the prefix. The examples indicate – just as the results on word order – that the prefix does not have the status of an argument for the children:

(24) a. haus hinfinde nimmer (And2:177)
('house therefind never')
(A. cannot find his way to the house anymore.)
b. einbin in badewanne (Jul1:62)
('jump-in in bathtub')
(The hippo has jumped into the bathtub.)
c. zur tisch hinsetze (Sve:125)
('to the table put on')
(S. is putting a doll onto the table.)

Only in examples such as (21) and (22) the prefix verbs are clearly syntagmas. The decisive factor for this are the inflectional forms of the verb, and this tallies with hypothesis (20b). Inflections which are categorised on the basis of their content as [+strong] ensure that the verbs connected with them are produced as INFL-elements; this applies mainly to the prefix verbs with the transitivity marker *t* and in Stefan – also due to semantic bootstrapping – to imperatives. These verbs are placed into the $INFL^0$-position in the syntax. We thus analyse the discontinuous position of prefix verbs in a similar way to the second position of simple verbs, except that in (21) and (22) the prefix remains in the VP. The data show that strong inflections of the verb enable the child to use the $INFL^1$-structure which is required for prefix verbs. Here the position of verbal elements is again determined by lexical categorisations. Overall, the fact that children with dysphasia hardly ever use the correct discontinuous word order is due, according to the analysis which I suggest, not to deficits in the syntactic constituent structure, but it is a result of morphological problems, in particular in the acquisition of strong verbal inflections. This result tallies with the observations on verb placement.

7.2 Argument order

The following investigates how grammatical relations are coded in dysphasia. I will look at functional aspects of word order and will describe interaction of word order with morphological expressions in child grammar. The focus is on the position of arguments in the utterances of dysphasic children.

In linguistic typology research, it is stressed that all natural languages have a system with which to distinguish between the arguments of the verb in surface structure (cf. Comrie 1981). In *German*, syntactic, morphological and lexical means are offered for this purpose, in particular (i) word order, (ii) case morphology, (iii) person and number inflections on the finite verb and (iv) prepositions. In adult language these means of expression interact in many ways with one another. To illustrate this, let us look at the following examples:

(25) a. Die Frau begrüßt die Tante
The woman greets the aunt
OR: The aunt greets the woman
b. Die Frau begrüß*en* die Tant*en*
The aunts greet the woman
c. Die Frau begrüßt *den* Mann
The woman greets the man

In (25a) and (25b) the grammatical relations cannot be clearly differentiated with case morphology, as the nominative and accusative forms are identical in the feminine. In contrast to this, in (25c) subject and object can be identified because of their case forms. Example (25b) shows that agreement endings also serve to mark grammatical relations. The subject in this case, due to the plural form on the finite verb, is clearly different from the object. The position of the argument is also relevant for marking grammatical relations in German. As the position before the finite verb can be filled with different constituents, including the subject, adverbial elements or the object, sentence (25a) does, in fact, have two meanings. In the unmarked case, however, the subject comes in the first position, so that in (25a) the version Agent = *die Frau* (the woman) is preferred. This shows that argument order also contributes to distinguish between grammatical relations.

For *German child language* the development of coding devices for grammatical relations is described in Clahsen (1984a, 1986a). We saw that word order in the early developmental phases II and III is used to differentiate between the subject and the object. Here, the children have not yet acquired case morphology and only have access to a limited number of verb inflections and prepositions. The arguments are marked by their position. We saw that Agent-arguments occur preverbally throughout (cf. Clahsen 1986a:111f.). In further development, word order becomes grammaticised. In phase IV the children have acquired the correct V2 placement and the topicalisation of objects. Hereby, word order looses a considerable part of its function as a means of distinguishing between grammatical relations since now subjects, as well as objects, occur post- and preverbally. In the next developmental phase, case morphology is introduced as an additional means of encoding grammatical relations.

According to the assumption of parallelism, children with *dysphasia* also have access to a coding system for grammatical relations. The previous results suggest that this should be based mainly on word order; this hypothesis can be tested against the available data.

The initial assumption is that the problems in dysphasia occur mainly in morphology, but not in syntactic constituent structure. The results in the last chapter showed that the children do not have access to morphological means of differentiating between grammatical relations. Subject-verb agreement is typically undeveloped and case morphology has many gaps. Morphological markers are not used to differentiate between the subject and the object; the children concentrate on their semantic function. Moreover, the analysis in Ch. 5.2 showed that most of the children only have local prepositions. Therefore, prepositions cannot be used for the differentiation of grammatical relations, either. In the following, we have to investigate the position of arguments in dysphasia.

As in linguistic typology research, argument order will be analysed in terms of the categories A and P (see Mallinson/Blake 1979, Comrie 1981). They should be regarded as arbitrary symbols whose prototypes are the thematic roles Agent and Patient. In intransitive sentences, we typically only find one argument; I indicate this argument with A for verbs like *lachen* (to laugh) or with P, for example, for *fallen* (to fall). In transitive constructions there are at least two arguments which are categorised with the arbitrary symbols A and P.

Table 15: *Argument order*

	A P V_t	P V_t	A V_t P	V_t P	A V_t	P V_i	A V_i	Others
Anja 1	0	10	0	0	1	1	1	1
Anja 2	5	29	1	4	8	2	8	7
Andreas 1	1	3	1	5	1	8	3	5
Andreas 2	2	22	0	10	2	3	2	6
Klaus 1	1	7	2	2	0	3	0	1
Klaus 2	1	11	0	6	0	11	2	10
Julia 1	5	8	0	0	7	5	1	2
Julia 2	11	7	3	0	6	12	5	8
Patrick	2	16	3	6	1	9	1	16
Sven	10	8	5	0	7	26	9	26
Stefan	13	8	1	12	2	3	1	12
Jonas 1	3	31	4	3	9	14	2	9
Jonas 2	5	4	7	5	6	10	4	16
Petra 1	2	4	1	0	0	1	0	0
Petra 2	7	4	2	2	7	17	22	4
Petra 3	12	5	16	0	4	15	17	11
Wolfgang	20	13	2	3	11	39	1	9

Table 15 provides a summary of the position of arguments in the utterances of the dysphasic children under investigation. In the analysis, all of the utterances which contain a transitive or an intransitive verb, as well as at least one argument (A or P), are included. Instances which cannot be analysed with the given categories are in 'Others'. Transitive constructions in which one of the arguments is missing are analysed in the second, fourth or fifth columns. The table only includes absolute frequencies.

From table 15 we see that the frequencies in the third, fourth and last columns are clearly lower than the values for structures with A in first position and the verb in final position. This observation shows that the sentence schema A<P<V is used dominantly in dysphasia; on average, 70% of the occurring instances have this pattern.

Moreover, there are variants in argument order for all of the children, as can be seen from the column 'Others'. The cases in this column are mainly intransitive constructions of the form V_iP (cf. 26). Instances of this type are found in all of the children. If, on the other hand, the intransitive verb subcategorises an Agent-argument, then the corresponding word order variant V_iA only occurs for Andreas and Jonas in a few instances (cf. And1:79, Jon1:226). In the cases under 'Others' there are seldom any transitive constructions. In these instances, we mostly find the pattern PAV_t, where P is an inanimate argument and A an animate one (cf. 27). Examples of this type are found for Julia, Petra and Wolfgang. Finally, we see that there are transitive constructions with A in postverbal position in a few isolated examples (cf. Anj2:119, Sve:252, Jon1:160, Jon2:81).

(26) a. geht nich so eine (Pat:8)
('goes not so one')
(This doesn't work; P. is trying to fit two bricks together.)
b. kommt dein auto (Sve:134)
('comes your car')
(S. takes the therapist's car and drives it.)

(27) a. ein tür is hab nich (Wol:185)
('a door I have not')
(W. hasn't got a door.)
b. ein titz is bauch (Wol:111)
('a seat I need')
(W. needs a seat.)

The following principles of argument placement can be derived from the observations above:

(28) a. A < V
b. A < P

Deviations from the *'canonical' sentence schema A<P<V* result for the most part through the postverbal position of P in transitive and intransitive

constructions. The position of P in relation to the verb is, thus, not fixed. By contrast, A almost always occurs in a preverbal position. The rule in (28a) corresponds to this observation. (28a) on its own is not sufficient to differentiate the arguments, because it allows the order patterns APV and PAV in transitive sentences. In fact, however, we rarely find object-topicalisations (PAV) in the data. For this reason, the position of A in relation to P is fixed using (28b). In this area we cannot see any developmental progress from the longitudinal data. Rather, the order principles which are described by (28) are still applicable at the end of the period of investigation.

The position of arguments in dysphasia corresponds to the system constructed by linguistically normal children in the early phases II and III. In accordance with our hypothesis, we find that word order is employed as a coding device for differentiating grammatical relations. The fact that there is no developmental progress in this area has to do with the children's problems with morphology. The grammaticalisation of word order and the consequent loss of the distinguishing function of word order are triggered by the acquisition of subject-verb agreement in linguistically normal children (cf. Ch. 3.2). Children with dysphasia have problems dealing with grammatical agreement. For this reason, the conditions which cause a change in the original system in the normal acquisition of grammar do not even arise in dysphasia. Instead, the children stay with their elementary coding system for grammatical relations. It is important that in dysphasia there are no deviant or idiosyncratic rules for the differentiation of arguments; given the system described above, the children have chosen an option which is offered for this purpose in natural languages.

7.3 The position of the negator

The last part of the analysis on word order deals with the position of negation words (NEG) in the utterances of dysphasic children. Our focus is the position of NEG in relation to the verb. I will show that we do not have to assume any damage to the syntactic constituent structure in this area, and that the syntactic positions which are required for NEG are offered in dysphasia.

To analyse the data, I differentiate three types of negation:

(29) a. *Anaphoric negation*: a negative reaction to a previous utterance which is expressed in German by *nein* (no), e.g. *Möchtest du Salz?* **Nein**, *Zucker*. (Would you like salt? No, sugar.)

b. *Constituent negation*: Negation of parts of a sentence, where NEG (=*nicht, kein*, etc.; not, not a) comes before the constituent being negated, e.g. **Nicht ich** *bin gekommen, sondern du*. (Not I came, but you.)

c. *Sentence negation*: Negation of a predicate. *Nicht* (not) occurs as the element of negation.

The surface position of NEG in sentence negation is described within the syntactic configuration which is assumed here for German (cf. (13) in paragraph 7.1.2). Here, NEG occurs in the VP in front of the non-finite verbal element (30); consider the examples in (31).

(30) [... [CONFL... [$_{VP}$ ... NEG V] INFL]]

(31) a. Paul verkauft das Grundstück *nicht*
(Paul is *not* selling the land.)

b. ... da*ß* Paul das Grundstück *nicht* verkauft.
(... that Paul has not sold the land.)

c. Paul hat das Grundstück *nicht* verkauft.
(Paul has not sold the land.)

d. ... da*ß* Paul das Grundtück *nicht* verkauft hat.
(... that Paul has not sold the land.)

In (31c) and (31d) the V-position within the VP is filled. NEG appears in these directly before the non-finite verbal element. This position is not filled in (31a) and (31b). In (31b) the verbal element remains in the underlying position and NEG therefore appears directly in front of the finite verb in the surface structure. In (31a) the finite verb is placed in the verb-front position; because of this NEG occurs in this case at the end.

The development of negation in *German child language* was investigated in Clahsen (1982, 1983). We saw that anaphoric negation and constituent negation are acquired without any problems. The children use the negation word *nein* (no) in early developmental phases for anaphoric and sometimes also for non-anaphoric negation. In constituent negation, we did not find any positional errors. NEG comes immediately before the negated element, whereby adverbials, NPs and adjectives (among others) are negated.

The results on sentence negation were more interesting, especially regarding the position of NEG in relation to the verb. In Clahsen (1983) a developmental sequence was suggested for this, which is also confirmed using the results of other acquisition studies. According to this sequence, NEG in phases II and III is in post- or preverbal position, but always immediately adjacent to the verb. Examples such as (31a), in which other elements occur between NEG and the verb do not occur here. In further development, the proportion of preverbal negation gradually decreases. In phase IV and V negation occurs in the correct position in most instances, and where it is required, NEG is separated from the verb.

The developmental sequence is directly related to the development of verb placement in German child language. As long as the verb-final pattern is used dominantly, there are word order errors in negated utterances, in particular preverbal negation in main clauses with simple verbs. The position of NEG in the syntactic constituent structure (cf. 30) is, however, already available in early phases; it is just the fronting of the finite verb which is not carried out systematically. Thus, preverbal negation, which seems incorrect at first glance is a secondary effect of the use of the verb-final pattern, which the children initially use in preference.

In phases IV and V verb placement is correct. Finite verbs are now categorised throughout as INFL-elements and placed into the CONFL-position in (30). On the other hand, as before, negation words fill the NEG-position within the VP. Thus, the children have now acquired NEG placement as in German (31), and now instances are found in which NEG appears separated from the verb. The analysis shows that no special rules for NEG placement need to be learned for this purpose. Instead, it results from the correct placement of the verb.

Given the assumption of parallelism, in dysphasia we expect similar correlations between verb placement and NEG placement. Additionally, we expect, given the assumption of an intact constituent structure in dysphasia, that the syntax offers the position which is required for NEG. I will test these claims in the available data. However, it should be mentioned that the amount of relevant data for this area is rather small. As we are dealing with spontaneous speech data, the frequency of use of negated utterances is left to chance. Some of the samples even had to be taken out of the analysis because of the lack of relevant instances. However, I still think that we can gain insights from this data into the structure of negated utterances in dysphasia. The conclusions must be checked against more extensive material which can be obtained using elicitation techniques, for cxamplc.

The profile charts in the appendix show that all of the children use *nein* (no) as a negation word, mostly for anaphoric negation (cf. phase I and example (32)). Additionally, we see from the entries for phase III in the profiles that all of the children have constituent negation, for example with objects and adverbials, where NEG – as in German – comes before the negated constituent (cf. 33). Similar to the early phases of normal language acquisition, we cannot see any specific problems for these forms of negation in dysphasia.

(32) Therapist: kann ich meine tiere in deinen stall tun?
(Can I put my animals into your barn?)
nein ('no') (Pat:117a)

(33) Th.: he bauer. wann kommst du endlich melken?
(Hey farmer. when are you coming to milk me?)
keinen bauer hier (Pat:140)
('no farmer here')

The classification in the charts is not enough to analyse the position of NEG in relation to the verb. For this, I use the description in Clahsen (1983); three possibilities will be distinguished:

(34) a. *preverbal negation* (... NEG V ...)
sie auch *nit* feis? (Jon2:176)
('you also not know?')
(Don't you know that either?)

b. *simple postverbal negation* (... V (X) NEG)
i. butter hab *net* (And1:105)
('butter have not')
(I don't have any butter.)
ii. deht immer *net* (And1:71)
('goes always not')
(A. says that the house always breaks.)

Table 16: *Negation*

	preverbal negation	simple postverbal negation	complex postverbal negation	separation
Anja 1	1	1	0	0
Anja 2	6	6	1	2
Andreas 1	1	4	0	1
Andreas 2	5	5	0	0
Klaus 1	0	0	0	0
Klaus 2	0	2	0	0
Julia 1	3	0	0	0
Julia 2	2	1	2	0
Patrick	1	15	0	8
Sven	0	8	3	2
Stefan	0	2	0	0
Jonas 1	2	13	1	2
Jonas 2	1	2	2	0
Petra 1	1	0	0	0
Petra 2	6	3	2	1
Petra 3	3	3	1	0
Wolfgang	1	10	0	1

As other descriptive categories are chosen for table 16, the values differ partly from those in the profile charts. Thus, for example, two-word utterances in the form of NEG+V are included in the first column of table 16, whereas in the profiles they are registered under NEG X in phase II. The same applies to two-word utterances with postverbal negation. The frequencies in the third column of table 16 only refer to auxiliaries and modal verb constructions; they are therefore not identical to the entries under ... NEG V_i in the profiles.

c. *complex postverbal negation* (... $\{{}^{\text{Mod}}_{\text{Aux}}\}$ (X) NEG V)
jetz kanne sech aber *nit* autstege. (Jon2:151)
de kamera
('now cannot itself but not turn off. the camera')
(Now the camera cannot turn itself off.)

In addition, we have to look at all of the instances with postverbal negation to see whether NEG appears separated from the verb as in (34bii).

Stefan and Klaus cannot be included in the present analysis, because for each of them there were only two negated utterances with verbal elements. Most of the other children use post- and preverbal negation. We also find examples such as (34a), in which NEG appears in main clauses before simple verbs. Preverbal negation in subordinate clauses only occurs twice in Petra (Pet3:78, 117). Additionally, we see from the last column in table 16 that NEG is only separated from the verb in very few instances. Closer analysis of the instances classified in table 16 shows that the order patterns for NEG do not vary freely, but are basically dependent upon the position of the verb. With regard to this, the following facts can be observed from the data:

(35) a. In constructions with modals and auxiliary verbs, NEG comes immediately before the non-finite verbal element, such as in (34c).

b. In preverbal negation, the verb and NEG come at the end of the sentence; there are only three exceptions to this (Anj2:142, And2:85, Pet2:115).

c. In simple postverbal negation,we mostly find modals or other inflected verbs, which occur in the V-front position:

i. der geht *nich* auf (Sve:72)
('it goes not open')
(It won't open)

ii. mach hoch deh*t nich* (Wol:54)
('make high goes not')
(It won't go up.)

iii. *muß nit* (And1:45b)
('must not')
(The hole should not be there.)

iv. momojan *is nich* (Anj2:32)
('momojan is not')
(M. wasn't there.)

d. In the instances where NEG is separated from the verb there are also modals and other inflected verbs, mostly with the inflection *t*, which occur in the V-front position:
   i. *kann* ich *nich* (Anj2:263)
      ('can I not')
      (I can't.)
   ii. geh*t* so eine *nich* (Pat:9)
      ('goes such a one not')
      (One like this doesn't work.)
   iii. *kann* das haus *nich* (Pat:167c)
      ('can the house not')
      (I can't build the house.)

These observations show correlations between the position of verbs and the position of NEG in the sentence. We conclude from (35a) and (35b) that NEG takes the position immediately before V in the syntactic constituent structure (cf. 30). Observations (35c) and (35d) show that other positions arise for NEG when the V-position in VP is empty and the verb appears in the syntactic INFL-position at the beginning of the sentence. In this respect there is no difference between the various instances in (35), except that in (35a) the position for the non-finite verbal element is lexically filled, while it remains unfilled in the other instances. Modal and auxiliary verbs are categorised in the children's lexicon as INFL-elements; they can therefore be placed into the V-front position in the syntactic constituent structure. The same applies to strongly inflected verbs, especially to those with the suffix *t*. NEG remains in its underlying position. In this way, postverbal negation (35c) occurs and sometimes also NEG-separation (35d). Instances with preverbal negation are found mostly for uninflected verbs. In these cases, the verb is placed into the corresponding position of the VP.

The proposed analysis shows that the position which is required for negation in the syntactic constituent structure is also offered in dysphasia. In accordance with our hypotheses, no deviant syntactic rules need to be assumed for NEG placement. The different surface structure positions for NEG depend upon the position of the verbal elements. Errors in placement which occur in the negated utterances are not due to deficits in the syntactic constituent structure, but to the fact that the verbs are mostly uninflected and the INFL-position remains empty. The children's problems in the area of morphology are the ultimate cause for this. On the basis of the proposed analysis, we expect that dysphasic children do not have to learn additional syntactic rules for the position of NEG and that the instances with preverbal negation disappear as soon as the placement of verbs is correct. As the verb-second placement of the finite verb is not used systematically by any of the children, this claim cannot be tested using the data here; we need additional studies, in which the children are observed over a longer period of time. However, the results on negation provide a further indication that the mechanisms for constructing syntactic constituent structure are also available in dysphasia.

8. Learnability theory and the acquisition of grammar

The major aim of this study was to gain insights into the internal structure and the development of the language acquisition device. We carried out comparative investigations on the acquisition of morphology and syntax by children without linguistic problems and by children with dysphasia. In Part I, a theory of the language acquisition device was developed which was mainly guided by learnability theory. Normal child grammar acquisition was interpreted in terms of this theory. In Part II this theoretical framework was used to analyse grammatical disorders in child language development.

In the following, I will firstly summarise some of the basic elements of the theoretical approach which I suggest for first language acquisition. Then I will suggest a grammatical characterisation of developmental dysphasia.

8.1 Child language development

The theory starts with the assumption that the child has access to an autonomous module with which it is possible to acquire the grammar of the target language on the basis of limited linguistic input. Note that the *autonomy hypothesis* is restricted to the acquisition of grammar. If we showed that, for example, children's pragmatic and semantic knowledge can be learned using general learning strategies and that in these areas specialised learning mechanisms are not needed, then this would not contradict the autonomy hypothesis. In learnability theory, it is assumed that the child requires task-specific mechanisms for the acquisition of linguistic *structure*. My investigations therefore concentrate on the development of syntax and morphology.

The *assumption of modularity* is a further central element of the theoretical approach which I suggest here. According to this, the learning mechanism consists of a set of autonomous components which each have their own structure and which interact with each other in a predetermined way, thus enabling normal syntactic and morphological development. This hypothesis is also limited to the acquisition of linguistic structure.

In analysing child grammar acquisition I have referred to the assumption of modularity at various points. Thus, for example, the development of word order is interpreted as the result of different components of the language acquisition device; for this purpose, I needed elements of X-bar theory, principles of government and a theory of possible movement rules (see Ch. 2.4.2). Also in the analysis of disordered child language, we made use of the idea of modular interaction, for example in analysing the position and inflection of verbs (see Ch. 6.2 and 7). We saw that the solutions developed in dysphasia, although not always correct in the sense of the norm for the target language do fall under UG.

A further element of the theory is the *parameter model* of grammar acquisition. Under this model, the language acquisition device is conceived of as a number of abstract, partly parameterised principles and mechanisms. An example of this is X-bar theory, including the learning mechanisms which are derived from it for the construction of syntactic structures (see Ch. 2.3). This example shows that the phrase structures with which child language is described are not the actual object for acquisition, but more the result of more abstract principles and learning mechanisms. We have to differentiate between various types of parameters (cf. Muysken 1985). In the simplest instance, a parameter is a chain of open binary choices. The child's task is to set the parameter at the value of the target language. Consider the following examples:

(1) a. Government is to the left/right.
b. The language is configurational/non-configurational.

Other parameterised principles take the form in (2a). An example of this is parameter (2b) stating which lexical categories come into consideration as heads of maximal projections:

(2) a. A has the feature xE, where $x = \{c_1, c_2, (c_3) \ldots (c_n)\}$
b. X^0 is the head of XP,
where $X^0 = \{N, A, V, (P), (INFL), (COMP)\}$

The set X in (2a) consists of constants (c), some of which are universal and others – in parentheses – only occur in certain languages. Similar to the principles in (1), here it is also the child's task to fix the parameterised elements in X at the value required by the target language. I referred to parameters of this type, at different points in the analysis, for example in investigating the position of the verb, constituent-internal word order and the construction of syntactic units. We saw that the parameter model can explain correlations in development between different grammatical phenomena.

A further element of the suggested theory is the assumption that the acquisition of language structure is lexically driven. This idea is known as the *lexical learning hypothesis*. We assume that all open parameters in the language acquisition device can be set at the values which are required using simple positive data from the linguistic input. Ideally, lexical categories suffice for this. Some of the parameters which I use here refer explicitly to lexical and morphological features. Consider as an example Kratzer's (1984) INFL/V parameter with which we explained correlations between the position and inflection of verbs:

(3) Verb inflections are
- [+strong], then $_{\text{INFL}}$ [V INFL]
- [-strong], then $_{\text{V}}$ [V INFL]

Parameters of this type correspond with the idea of a lexically driven syntax, which has in the meantime become part of modern grammatical theory. This idea has considerable effects on the acquisition of grammar. The child no longer has to learn all of the structural features of the target language separately, but instead his/her main task becomes to recognise the lexical and morphological units, or rather their features, in the input and then categorise them correspondingly. Syntactic properties, e.g. regularities in word order, then result from the availability of UG principles, without the need for any additional learning; cf. also Borer (1984).

In the grammatical analysis of German child language I made use of principles of this type at different points. The INFL/V parameter is, for example, used to explain correlations in development between the position of the verb and subject-verb-agreement acquisition (see Ch. 3). I used it again to define the difficulties which dysphasic children have in using V2 placement in German (see Ch. 7.1). We saw there that the deficits in dysphasia mainly affect the morphological components of the lexicon, and not the mechanisms for constructing syntactic configurations. These results tally with the theory of lexical learning.

In close connection with this is the *continuity assumption* which claims that the child's learning mechanisms do not change during development. Instead, we trace back the advances which are observed to extensions in the child's lexicon. The continuity hypothesis is a learnability condition motivated by heuristic considerations. An analysis made under continuity is preferable to an alternative analysis, because in the latter we also have to assume a maturational schedule. Here, I have suggested analyses for different areas of syntactic and morphological development which correspond with the continuity hypothesis. The idea of continuity also applies to dysphasia. We saw that no deviant learning mechanisms have to be formulated for the rule systems which are developed by these children.

The continuity assumption does not apply to all areas of linguistic development. It has to be limited to the acquisition of linguistic *structure*. With regard to the children's language processing capacities, the idea of continuity does not apply. At the start of language development, for example, there are no sentences of more than a certain length, although the grammar allows these structures. The condition for their use is that the child first, step by step, develops the required production strategies. Similar applies to perception. The corresponding strategies are available only gradually during child development. Consequently, the child cannot identify all of the words and morphemes which occur in the linguistic input at the start of his/her development. At first the child only has access to a small part of the target language's lexicon, so that certain – latently present – learning mechanisms for acquiring linguistic structure cannot become effective. The development of child linguistic processing must be investigated more closely in suitable psycholinguistic experiments. In any case, the results depicted provide evidence for the idea of continuity in the acquisition of grammatical competence.

8.2 Developmental dysphasia

The data analyses in Part II of the present study should contribute to answering the following questions:

(4) a. What do the grammatical rule systems of dysphasic children look like?
b. According to which principles do the children's grammars change?
c. Which mechanisms do the children use to acquire their grammars?
d. What do the different types of dysphasia look like?

Based on theoretical considerations, we developed hypotheses from these questions. In the following, some of the results will be summarised and related to the questions in (4).

Concerning (4a), I started with the hypothesis that dysphasic children do not construct bizzare linguistic systems, but grammars which fall under UG. This claim derived from the assumption of parallelism, according to which we can expect that the constraints established in learnability theory for the construction of child grammars also apply to the rule systems of dysphasic children. These claims are confirmed in the data analysis. To illustrate this, I will point out some of the results from the previous analyses.

First, the data analysis shows that dysphasic children also construct a linguistic system which can be described in terms of *grammatical* rules and principles. The conclusion which has often been mentioned by the children's therapists that they produce "loose strings of words without any recognisable grammatical structure" obviously does not not apply. Instead, grammatical principles come into effect in these children's utterances.

More importantly, we found that the children choose options in their rule systems which are possible under UG. This can be seen from numerous results. We saw, for example, that the principles of X-bar theory apply to the composition and placement of syntactic units in dysphasia. The availability of these principles ensures that errors in constituent-internal word order do not occur and that the required PS-rules are constructed. The PS-rules contain major lexical categories as heads, and specifying elements, such as determiners, and complements as sisters of the heads. These rules provide the positions needed in the syntax, into which elements from the lexicon are inserted. As an example of this, consider the PS-rules for the construction of NPs and PPs (Ch. 5.1, 5.2).

In some of the other investigations, dysphasics have been seen to use structural patterns which are not part of the adult language but which occur during the acquisition of grammar by linguistically normal children. Examples of this are the usage of the inflection *t* as a marker for intransitivity (see Ch. 6.2.2) and the preference of locative prepositions (Ch. 5.2). Phenomena of this type have been traced back to semantic bootstrapping, which is also accessible in dysphasia.

Lastly, we see that the principles of linguistic typology apply to the systems constructed in dysphasia. A central principle which is stressed in the studies by, for example, Greenberg (1963), Dixon (1979) and Comrie (1981), concerns the encoding of grammatical relations. It requires that each natural language has a system for distinguishing between the arguments of the verb. Morphological markers (e.g. case morphology, subject-verb agreement) and word order (among others) are possible here. Typological investigations demonstrate that in morphologically rich languages the position of arguments does not have to be fixed. However, in languages where morphological means are insufficient for the identification of subject and object, word order is restricted. Hence, for example, grammatical relations are marked in English by means of their position. The results on dysphasia fit into this picture. The analysis in Ch. 7.2 showed that the children distinguish between grammatical relations using word order and that morphological devices do not play a role (except in Petra 3). This means that, although they do not have access to the coding system of the adult language, they choose an option which is possible in natural languages. The system of dysphasia corresponds to the early phases II and III of normal German child language.

The second question (cf. 4b) concerns the development of grammar in dysphasic children. The results available from earlier empirical investigations about this are contradictory. Some authors (Morehead/Ingram 1973, Dannenbauer 1983) found that the developmental sequences in dysphasia do not differ from those of normal grammar acquisition. In their theories, dysphasia is understood as a general, developmental delay (retardation hypothesis). Others, such as Schöler (1985) and Kaltenbacher/Kany (1985) however, stress that dysphasics go through qualitatively different developmental stages than linguistically normal children. Given the fact that dysphasic children do not form a homogenous group, it could be that different forms of dysphasia are reflected in the results. The temporal delay of language development would then simply be one of the possible types of dysphasia.

The data analysed in the previous chapters provide insights into the development of grammar in dysphasia. Firstly, we found that the acquisition of grammar is definitely retarded in all of the children. Even if we compare the most advanced areas of the children's grammars, we see that the development is retarded compared to other children of their age. In most parts of grammar, the dysphasics in the age group investigated (about 4 to 10 years) belong to phase II, which is reached by linguistically normal children when they are about 2 to 2½ years old. These observations show that the elements of early child grammar (see Ch. 2) are also available in dysphasia.

On the other hand, the rule systems of phase II and those constructed by dysphasic children do not correspond with one another completely. The dysphasic children are, for example, not restricted to the two-constituent utterances characteristic of phase II; instead, they use extended sentence structures with several constituents. Moreover, the children's grammars also have some of the elements from the more advanced developmental phases, e.g. modal verbs and co-ordinating conjunctions. Elements of this type are acquired in dysphasia, too, and the available longitudinal data also show some advance in development in this area.

By contrast, no developmental progress was seen in grammatical function words nor in morphological elements, not even in those which are acquired comparatively early in normal grammar acquisition. The children's problems in this area are, instead, a stable feature of dysphasia which does not simply disappear during development. From this it follows that developmental sequences can arise in dysphasia which are different from those of normal grammar acquisition. The clearest instance of this is provided by the data for Petra. The investigations in Part I showed that there are close links between the position and inflection of verbs in the utterances of linguistically normal children. As soon as the agreement system has been learned, the position of the verb changes drastically. Within a very short period of time the previously used verb-final patterns disappear and in their place in main clauses we find the verb-second pattern (V2) required for finite verbs. Correlations in development of this kind do not apply to Petra. However, additional data are needed in order to check on the further development of verb placement and verbal inflection. In addition, whether Petra's sequence of development can also be found in other children has to be tested. This case shows that in dysphasia we can also find developmental sequences that qualitatively differ from those of linguistically normal children.

The linguistic problems of the observed dysphasic children cannot be accounted for in terms of a general delay in the development of grammar. If this were the case, the child's linguistic system would have to be identical to one of the phases of normal development in all of the relevant areas. The data analysis shows that this condition is not fulfilled. The retardation hypothesis must therefore – at least in its undifferentiated form – be rejected. Instead, in dysphasia we typically find *selective* developmental retardations, usually in the area of morphology. Consequently the children's grammars do not correspond to any one phase of normal development completely. These results tally with the idea that there are no global linguistic deficits in dysphasia, but that, instead, there are selective impairments which largely affect morphology.

The third aim of the investigation was to define the impairments which occur in dysphasia. For this, I took a psycholinguistic perspective; observed retardations and disorders in the normal development of grammar were traced back to underlying learning and processing mechanisms. On the basis of the data analysis we have been able to reconstruct the learning mechanisms which guide dysphasic children (see 4c). The non-linguistic factors which play a role in etiological typologies have not been investigated here. For this, in addition to the linguistic analyses carried out, we would have needed medical and neurological studies which can only be realised in the framework of a larger inter-disciplinary project.

I started my investigation with the idea that, in principle, dysphasic children have access to the same learning and processing mechanisms as linguistically normal children. This assumption of parallelism is motivated by heuristic considerations. In particular, it introduces a constraint on possible explanatory accounts, and it prevents us from assuming global deficits in cases where it is enough to assume specific impairments of single learning mechanisms. The assumption of parallelism also requires that dysphasia be explained in terms of theories of normal grammatical development. In the present study, I was mainly guided by elements of learnability theory.

Learnability theory assumes that the language acquisition device is a system with a modular structure which consists of autonomous components for the acquisition of morphological and syntactic features, among other things. Given this theoretical model and the assumption of parallelism, we expect that the different components of the language acquisition device can be impaired selectively. Also, it should be expected that there are different kinds of dysphasia, according to the type of impairment (cf. 4d). For example, the application of morphological paradigms could be impaired while at the same time the mechanisms for the construction of syntactic representations remain intact. The case would be different if the learning mechanisms for phrase structure rules were damaged, as this means that the positions required in syntax would not be offered. One can imagine further possibilities. Those types of dysphasia which occur in reality can only be determined by means of appropriate empirical investigations.

The available data provide insights into the linguistic system typical of dysphasia. Regarding question (4d), however, the results are less conclusive. In order to work out empirically a typology of the possible types of dysphasia, a larger number of dysphasic children would have to be investigated; this, however, can only be done in an extensive research project.

As mentioned, the data analysis showed that dysphasic children mainly have problems in the area of morphology, while we cannot see any deficits in the construction of the syntactic constituent structure. Inflectional morphology is affected the most , i.e. grammatical function words and bound morphemes with which case, gender, number, grammatical person, etc. are marked. These elements are often omitted or used incorrectly in dysphasia. In the children's utterances, we find only a small number of the forms present in adult German. Also, we do not observe systematic developmental progress in this area. It appears that, as far as inflection is concerned, the children are on a developmental plateau from which acquisition cannot simply advance without difficulties. Conversely, the mechanisms for the acquisition of PS-rules are intact and the syntax offers the positions required. There are numerous examples for this in the data analysis. Consider, for example, the results on verb placement and on the position of negation words (Ch. 7) as well as on the composition of syntactic constituents (Ch. 5).

The above statements apply to all of the children studied. Only Petra does not fit into the overall picture, at least in some respects. For example, she is the only child to have aquired the correct subject-verb agreement paradigm. Petra also develops verb placement differently from the other children. It is not possible to decide here whether Petra's system represents a separate type of dysphasia or only a phenomenon of peripheral importance.

Results from an unpublished case study from Gopnik (1985) show that the features described also apply to dysphasia in English. Let us look at the following examples from the child investigated by Gopnik:

(5) a. you got a tape recorders
b. the four bus go in Boucherville
c. when the cup break *he* get repair
d. *the* Marie-Louise look at the bird
e. the superman *is say* good-bye and *hiding*
f. the ambulance arrive
g. the restaurant *is* upstairs
h. *is* everything true?
i. *will* farmer cut in July?

In the examples we can see similar patterns and errors to those made in dysphasia in German. There are problems in number markings within the NP (5a, 5b), in choosing the correct article (5d), in auxiliary verbs (5e) and in subject-verb agreement (5c, 5f). On the other hand, we cannot see any clear deficits in syntactic constituent structure. The word order is correct and the child under investigation can construct questions using the inversion of the subject and the auxiliary verb, as required in English (see 5h, 5i). On the basis of these observations, we cannot yet provide a universal characterisation of dysphasia; however, the indications are that my analysis does not only have to apply to dysphasia in German. It appears to apply, at least, to languages which are typologically related. This assumption would have to be cross-checked in comparative linguistic studies on dysphasia.

The problems which dysphasics have with elements of inflection can be defined more precisely in the framework of learnability theory. Following Pinker (1984), we can assume that elements of inflection are represented in the lexicon as paradigms. The fundamental idea behind this is that grammatical information is used to help in the lexical organisation of elements of inflection. In Ch. 3, learning mechanisms were given for the construction of paradigms, and I tried to show how the acquisition of the features of inflection in German child language can be explained in the framework of this theory. At that point we saw that semantic bootstrapping alone is not enough to construct a paradigm for inflection. Instead, the child has to compare different forms from the input with regard to a number of grammatical dimensions and then categorise them correspondingly. Semantic bootstrapping is available in dysphasia, the deficits, however, affect the construction of paradigms for grammatical inflection. These conclusions can be drawn from numerous individual results. We saw, for example, that the children insert articles as markers for definiteness, but they do not have access to a system for gender. They also use locative prepositions and modal verbs, and we even find bound grammatical morphemes, in particular the verbal inflection *t* which can be categorised as a transitivity marker using semantic bootstrapping. By contrast, grammatical function words, such as auxiliaries, and inflections which are used to mark grammatical information, such as the *st* for the 2nd pers. sing., are missing.

On the basis of the data analysis the impairments in dysphasia can be defined more closely. The results indicate that the children's problems have something to do mainly with the way they use *grammatical agreement*. Dysphasia does not require the assumption of a general deficit in constructing paradigms. Instead, the data analysis shows that only elements of grammatical agreement cannot be used as dimensions for constructing morphological paradigms.

In German, auxiliaries, case and gender markers and the inflection of person and number on the finite verb, among other things, belong to the phenomenon of grammatical agreement. The basic property of grammatical agreement is that the form of an element is determined by another element in the appropriate structure. Hence, there is an asymmetrical, structural relation between two categories, whereby one is the functor, and the other is the argument, and the argument category controls the functor. The classic case of this is subject-verb agreement. The morphological form of the finite verb in German depends upon the element occuring in the subject position. Case markers also belong to the phenomenon of agreement. The case is only visible on the NP, but it is a particular feature (of verbs or of prepositions) which marks the role of the NP in the sentence. A similar principle applies to gender markers, but on a lower projection level. Articles themselves do not have gender. Instead, this feature is given to them in a local NP-structure, whereby the article can be the functor and the noun the argument. Auxiliaries are, after all, not predicates which subcategorise arguments. They are, instead, lexical means of encoding the person and number features and to that extent belong to the area of grammatical agreement, too. The children's problems with acquisition are mostly restricted to phenomena of this type.

As mentioned, the children's difficulties with grammatical agreement do *not* stem from deficits in the construction of syntactic configurations. The availability of the X-bar scheme ensures that the sub-structures, which are needed in the syntax for the placement of agreement features, are also present in dysphasia. The children's deficit is limited to the projections of grammatical features. It affects the stream of information within syntactic structures, especially the control and percolation of grammatical features. Agreement phenomena result when features of one element are projected onto another element in the configuration, whereby one element asymmetrically controls the other. In Generalised Phrase Structure Grammar (GPSG), this is an instance of the Control-Agreement Principle (cf. Gazdar et al. 1985:89). The children's difficulties are concentrated in this component of the grammar. Grammatical features which are not primary features of the category concerned, but come from another position cannot be used in dysphasia as dimensions for constructing a morphological paradigm. Consequently, the children categorise certain function words and elements of inflection incorrectly, or they are not even able to identify them. Thus, the observed characteristics arise in dysphasia. Further damage to the mechanisms for the acquisition of grammar does not have to be assumed for the children under investigation.

The next task of dysphasia research is to carry out cross-linguistic studies. The aim of these would be to characterise child language disorders as universally as possible. This step has already been taken in the research into aphasia. Theoretical discussions, especially on Broca's aphasia, has gained new impetus from the results of cross-linguistic studies (cf. Kean 1985). We expect something similar for the research into dysphasia.

9. Appendix

The first part of the appendix contains the profile charts, the second has extracts of the transcripts from the dysphasic children. Information on the interpretation of the profiles can be found in Clahsen (1986) and in Part II of this book. The second part of the appendix contains the first three pages of each transcript. Information on the transcription can be found in Chap. 4.4.

9.1 Profile charts

Name:andreas 1 Age: 7.0 Date: May-84

A. Unanalysed utterances

Unintelligible:	8	Incomplete:	4
Ambiguous:	0	Imitations:	9
Simple replies:	19	Stereotypes:	12
Formulaic:	19	Other:	0

B. Analysed utterances

	One constituent	Two constituents	More constituents
Elliptical:	69	5	0
Other:	26	39	13
Repetitions:	10	3	0

	Word and phrase structure	Sentence structure
I	N: 45 da: 7 Pr: 0 Other: 6	Sequences: 2 Reduplications: 0 0+X: 0 Other: 0 Negation:nein (no): 16 Question:'Q': 15
II	Pro^P: 12 Pro^A: 21 DN: 7 AdjN: 5 NNP: 0 Adv: 41 PNP: 0 V: 42 Adj: 11 PrV: 12 Ø: 18 n: 2 t: 9	SV: 1 SAdj: 4 SO: 1 SA: 3 OS: 0 AS: 2 VO: 5 OV: 5 VA: 4 AV: 11 OA: 1 AdjA: 0 AO: 0 AA: 0 AAdj: 0 Other: 2 Negation: Neg X: 5 X Neg: 2 Question: QXY: 0 No: 0 Ac: 8 Ol: 5 Al: 1 At: 5 Po: 3 Imp: 5 Other: 12 Missing elements: Cop: 9 Aux: 0 V: 19 P: 3 Art: 24 S: 42
III.	Aux: 0 Mod: 2 Cop: 0 Gen.suff.: 0 e: 26	VXA: 7 VXAA: 1 Other: 0 SXV: 4 XS(Y)V: 1 XYV: 0 SXY: 3 SXAdj: 0 XS(Y)Adj: 0 XYAdj: 0 X(Y)S(Z)*: 1 SXPr(V): 0 XS(Y)Pr(V): 0 XYPr(V): 1 XYZ: 0 SXPt: 0 XS(Y)Pt: 0 XYPt: 0 Other: 1 SVX: 1 XSVY: 0 (X)VY(Z)* : 1 Negation:(X)NEGO(Y)*: 1 (X)NEGA(Y)*: 2 Other: 1 (X)NEGV_i(Y)*: 0 (X)NEGV(Y)*: 0 Question:QXYZ: 4
IV	Nominative Acc.con.: 0 Dat.con.: 0 st: 0 Other: 0	(X) Aux Y Pt: 0 (X) V_f Y Pr: 0 X V_f S (Y): 0 (X) Mod Y Inf: 1 (X) V_f A O: 0 Other: 0 (X) Kop Y Adj: 0 Negation: (X) V NEG (Y)*: 1 Question: +w V_f S (X): 0 Q V_f S (X): 0
V	Accusative Acc.con.: 1 Dat.con.: 0 Dative: 0 Other: 0 K_s: 0 K_c: 1	V O_i O_d: 0 V O_i O_d A: 0 Other: 0 (K_s)SXV_f: 0 (K_s)SV: 0 (K_s)X: 0 (K_s)XV_f: 0 (K_s)SX: 0 Other: 0 Negation:(K_s) X Neg V_f: 0 (X) V_f Y NEG Z: 0 Question:(ob) (whether) X: 0 (+w) X:1 Addition: 0 Temporal: 0 Causal: 0 Adversative: 1 Other: 1

MLU: 1.71 OWU: 74 TWU: 56 MWU: 23

Name: andreas 2 Age: 7.1 Date: June-84

A. Unanalysed utternaces

Unintelligible:	15	Incomplete:	6
Ambiguous:	0	Imitations:	2
Simple replies:	32	Stereotypes	13
Formulaic:	26	Other:	0

B. Analysed utternaces

	One constituent	Two constituents	More constituents
Elliptical:	47	0	0
Other:	27	66	12
Repetitions:	8	2	0

	Word and phrase structur	Sentence structure
I	N: 52 da: 6 Pr: 0 Other: 1	Sequences: 1 Reduplications: 0 0+X: 0 Other: 0 Negation: nein (no): 7 Question: 'Q': 8
II	Pro^P: 13 Pro^A: 21 DN: 1 AdjN: 3 NNP: 0 Adv: 31 PNP: 0 V: 71 Adj: 10 PrV: 23 Ø: 19 n: 5 t: 1	SV: 4 SAdj: 2 SO: 0 SA: 6 OS: 1 AS: 0 VO: 10 OV: 16 VA: 6 AV: 17 OA: 0 AdjA: 0 AO: 0 AA: 0 AAdj: 1 Other: 3 Negation: Neg X: 2 X Neg: 5 Question: QXY: 0 No: 5 Ak: 28 Ol: 3 A1: 4 At: 3 Po: 0 Imp: 9 Other: 14 Missing elements: Cop: 6 Aux: 0 V: 12 P: 8 Art: 24 S: 62
III.	Aux: 0 Mod: 0 Cop: 0 Gen.suff.: 0 e: 69	VXA: 6 VXAA: 0 Other: 0 SXV: 2 XS(Y)V: 0 XYV: 3 SXY: 0 SXAdj: 0 XS(Y)Adj: 0 XYAdj: 0 X(Y)S(Z)*: 0 SXPr(V): 0 XS(Y)Pr(V): 0 XYPr(V): 0 XYZ: 0 SXPt: 0 XS(Y)Pt: 0 XYPt: 0 Other: 3 SVX: 0 XSVY: 0 (X)VY(Z)*: 3 Negation: (X)NEGO(Y)*: 0 (X)NEGA(Y)*: 7 Other: 0 (X)NEGV_i(Y)*: 0 (X)NEGV(Y)*: 3 Question: QXYZ: 0
IV	Nominative Acc.con.: 0 Dat.con.: 0 st: 0 Other: 0	(X) Aux Y Pt: 0 (X) V_f Y Pr: 0 X V_f S (Y): 0 (X) Mod Y Inf: 0 (X) V_f A O: 0 Other: 0 (X) Cop Y Adj: 0 Negation: (X) V NEG (Y)*: 0 Question: +w V_f S (X): 1 Q V_f S (X): 0
V	Accusative Acc.con.: 0 Dat.con.: 0 Dative: 0 Other: 3 K_s: 0 K_c: 1	V O_i O_d: 1 V O_i O_d A: 0 Other: 0 (K_s)SXV_f: 0 (K_s)SV: 0 (K_s)X: 0 (K_s)XV_f: 0 (K_s)SX: 0 Other: 0 Negation: (K_s) X Neg V_f: 0 (X) V_f Y NEG Z: 0 Question: (ob) (whether) X: 0 (+w) X: 0 Addition: 0 Temporal: 0 Causal: 0 Adversative: 1 Other: 0

MLU: 1.76 OWU: 63 TWU: 62 MWU: 27

Name:anja 1 Age: 9.6 Date: Sept-83

A. Unanalysed utterances

Unintelligible:	33	Incomplete:	0
Ambiguous:	1	Imitations:	18
Simple replies:	37	Stereotypes:	0
Formulaic:	7	Other:	1

B. Analysed utterances

	One constituent	Two constituents	More constituents
Elliptical:	50	3	0
Other:	59	24	7
Repetitions:	7	3	0

	Word and phrase structure	Sentence structure
I	N: 68 da: 0 Pr: 5 Other: 6	Sequences: 25 Reduplications: 0 0+X: 0 Other: 0 Negation:nein (no): 8 Question:'Q': 9
II	Pro^P: 5 Pro^A: 1 DN: 8 AdjN: 2 NNP: 0 Adv: 32 PNP: 1 V: 19 Adj: 6 PrV: 19 Ø: 11 n: 19 t: 1	SV: 1 SAdj: 0 SO: 0 SA: 5 OS: 0 AS: 1 VO: 0 OV: 12 VA: 1 AV: 5 OA: 1 AdjA: 0 AO: 0 AA: 1 AAdj: 0 Other: 0 Negation: Neg X: 0 X Neg: 0 Question: QXY: 0 No: 0 Ac: 13 Ol: 3 Al: 1 At: 0 Po: 0 Imp: 1 Other: 8 Missing elements: Cop: 0 Aux: 0 V: 10 P: 5 Art: 22 S: 31
III.	Aux: 0 Mod: 1 Cop: 0 Gen.suff.: 0 e: 7	VXA: 3 VXAA: 0 Other: 0 SXV: 0 XS(Y)V: 1 XYV: 1 SXY: 0 SXAdj: 0 XS(Y)Adj: 0 XYAdj: 0 X(Y)S(Z)*: 0 SXPr(V): 1 XS(Y)Pr(V): 0 XYPr(V): 1 XYZ: 0 SXPt: 0 XS(Y)Pt: 0 XYPt: 0 Other: 0 SVX: 1 XSVY: 0 (X)VY(Z)* : 1 Negation:(X)NEGO(Y)*: 0 (X)NEGA(Y)*: 0 Other: 0 (X)NEGV_i(Y)*: 1 (X)NEGV(Y)*: 1 Question:QXYZ: 2
IV	Nominative Acc.con.: 5 Dat.con.: 1 st: 0 Other: 0	(X) Aux Y Pt: 0 (X) V_f Y Pr: 0 X V_f S (Y): 1 (X) Mod Y Inf: 1 (X) V_f A O: 0 Other: 0 (X) Cop Y Adj: 0 Negation: (X) V NEG (Y)*: 0 Question: +w V_f S (X): 0 Q V_f S (X): 0
V	Accusative Acc.con.: 0 Dat.con.: 0 Dative: 0 Other: 0 K_s: 0 K_c: 0	V O_i O_d: 0 V O_i O_d A: 0 Other: 0 (K_s)SXV_f: 0 (K_s)SV: 0 (K_s)X: 0 (K_s)XV_f: 0 (K_s)SX: 0 Other: 0 Negation:(K_s) X Neg V_f: 0 (X) V_f Y NEG Z: 0 Question:(ob) (whether) X: 0 (+w) X:0 Addition: 0 Temporal: 0 Causal: 0 Adversative: 0 Other: 0

MLU: 1.46 OWU: 93 TWU: 38 MWU: 12

Name: anja 2 | Age: 10.8 | Date: Nov-84

A. Unanalysed utterances

Unintelligible:	5	Incomplete:	1
Ambiguous:	0	Imitations:	0
Simple replies:	26	Stereotypes:	1
Formulaic:	0	Other:	0

B. Analysed utterances

	One constituent	Two constituents	More constituents
Elliptical:	115	12	2
Others:	36	80	42
Repetitions:	27	2	0

	Word and phrase structure	Sentence structure
I	N: 122 da: 5 Pr: 10 Other: 8	Sequences: 8 Reduplications: 3 0+X: 0 Other: 0 Negation: nein (no): 30 Question: 'Q': 26
II	Pro^{P}: 20 Pro^{A}: 17 DN: 23 AdjN: 11 NNP: 3 Adv: 97 PNP: 11 V: 68 Adj: 2 PrV: 31 Ø: 33 n: 55 t: 2	SV: 9 SAdj: 0 SO: 3 SA: 4 OS: 0 AS: 8 VO: 4 OV: 11 VA: 2 AV: 21 OA: 1 AdjA: 0 AO: 4 AA: 4 AAdj: 0 Other: 1 Negation: Neg X: 8 X Neg: 5 Question: QXY: 0 No: 4 Ac: 27 Ol: 7 Al: 3 At: 3 Po: 2 Imp: 1 Other: 28 Missing elements: Cop: 2 Aux: 9 V: 51 P: 26 Art: 32 S: 79
III.	Aux: 0 Mod: 1 Cop: 0 Gen.suff.: 0 e: 8	VXA: 32 VXAA: 2 Other: 0 SXV: 9 XS(Y)V: 0 XYV: 6 SXY: 0 SXAdj: 0 XS(Y)Adj: 0 XYAdj: 1 X(Y)S(Z)*: 0 SXPr(V): 1 XS(Y)Pr(V): 1 XYPr(V): 8 XYZ: 1 SXPt: 1 XS(Y)Pt: 1 XYPt: 3 Other: 4 SVX: 0 XSVY: 1 (X)VY(Z)*: 2 Negation: (X)NEGO(Y)*: 2 (X)NEGA(Y)*: 2 Other: 1 (X)NEGV$_i$(Y)*: 2 (X)NEGV(Y)*: 2 Question: QXYZ: 3
IV	Nominative Acc.con.: 6 Dat.con.: 1 st: 0 Other: 1	(X) Aux Y Pt: 0 (X) V$_f$ Y Pr: 0 X V$_f$ S (Y): 1 (X) Mod Y Inf: 0 (X) V$_f$ A O: 0 Other: 0 (X) Cop Y Adj: 0 Negation: (X) V NEG (Y)*: 2 Question: +w V$_f$ S (X): 3 Q V$_f$ S (X): 0
V	Accusative Acc.con.: 1 Dat.con.: 0 Dative: 5 Other: 2 K$_s$: 0 K$_c$: 2	V O$_i$ O$_d$: 0 V O$_i$ O$_d$ A: 0 Other: 0 (K$_s$)SXV$_f$: 0 (K$_s$)SV: 0 (K$_s$)X: 0 (K$_s$)XV$_f$: 0 (K$_s$)SX: 0 Other: 0 Negation: (K$_s$) X Neg V$_f$: 0 (X) V$_f$ Y NEG Z: 2 Question: (ob) (whether) X: 0 (+w) X: 0 Addition: 2 Temporal: 0 Causal: 0 Adversative: 0 Other: 0

MLU: 1.98 OWU: 114 TWU: 97 MWU: 76

Name:jonas 1 Age: 6.6 Date: May-83

A. Unanalysed utterances

Unintelligible:	15	Incomplete:	2
Ambiguous:	0	Imitations:	3
Simple replies:	7	Stereotypes:	32
Formulaic:	12	Other:	1

B. Analysed utterances

	One constituent	Two constituents	More constituents
Elliptical:	41	7	2
Other:	8	66	58
Repetitions:	14	1	0

	Word and phrase structure	Sentence structure	
I	N: 89 da: 6 Pr: 0 Other: 13	Sequences: 2 Reduplications: 0 0+X: 0 Other: 0 Negation:nein (no): 1 Question:'Q':11	
II	Pro^P: 16 Pro^A: 22 DN: 31 AdjN: 10 NNP: 0 Adv: 72 PNP: 0 V: 56 Adj: 6 PrV: 37 Ø: 8 n: 1 t: 1	SV: 7 SAdj: 2 SO: 2 SA: 4 OS: 1 AS:12 VO: 1 OV: 16 VA: 4 AV: 5 OA: 1 AdjA: 0 AO: 4 AA: 2 AAdj: 0 Other: 7 Negation: Neg X: 3 X Neg: 0 Question: QXY: 0	No: 4 Ac: 27 Ol: 16 Al: 0 At: 5 Po: 1 Imp: 4 Other:14 Missing elements: Cop:11 Aux: 2 V: 31 P: 7 Art: 50 S: 61
III.	Aux: 0 Mod: 5 Cop: 0 Gen.suff.: 0 e: 84	VXA:34 VXAA: 3 Other: 0 SXV: 5 XS(Y)V: 2 XYV: 6 SXY: 2 SXAdj: 0 XS(Y)Adj: 0 XYAdj: 0 X(Y)S(Z)*: 6 SXPr(V): 2 XS(Y)Pr(V): 1 XYPr(V): 6 XYZ: 1 SXPt: 1 XS(Y)Pt: 0 XYPt: 0 Other: 8 SVX: 6 XSVY: 0 (X)VY(Z)* : 2 Negation:(X)NEGO(Y)*: 1 (X)NEGA(Y)*: 1 Other: 0 (X)NEGV_i(Y)*: 1 (X)NEGV(Y)*: 2 Question:QXYZ: 6	
IV	Nominative Acc.con.: 7 Dat.con.: 0 st: 0 Other: 2	(X) Aux Y Pt: 0 (X) V_f Y Pr: 0 X V_f S (Y): 1 (X) Mod Y Inf: 0 (X) V_f A O: 0 Other: 0 (X) Kop Y Adj: 0 Negation: (X) V NEG (Y)*: 8 Question: +w V_f S (X): 2 Q V_f S (X): 0	
V	Accusative Acc.con.: 0 Dat.con.: 0 Dative: 0 Other: 1 K_s: 0 K_c: 36	V O_i O_d: 0 V O_i O_d A: 0 Other: 0 (K_s)SXV_f: 0 (K_s)SV: 1 (K_s)X: 0 (K_s)XV_f: 1 (K_s)SX: 0 Other: 0 Negation:(K_s) X Neg V_f: 0 (X) V_f Y NEG Z: 2 Question:(ob) (whether)X: 0 (+w) X:1	Addition: 36 Temporal: 0 Causal: 0 Adversative: 0 Other: 1

MLU: 2.76 OWU: 25 TWU: 54 MWU: 103

Name:jonas 2 Age: 7.7 Date: June-84

A. Unanalysed utterances

Unintelligible:	16	Incomplete:	4
Ambiguous:	0	Imitations:	5
Simple replies:	18	Stereotypes:	10
Formulaic:	3	Other:	3

B. Analysed utterances

	One constituent	Two constituents	More constituents
Elliptical:	59	5	0
Other:	2	29	53
Repetitions:	10	0	1

	Word and phrase structure	Sentence structure
I	N: 24 da: 8 Pr: 0 Other: 4	Sequences: 0 Reduplications: 0 0+X: 0 Other: 0 Negation:nein (no): 6 Question:'Q':37
II	Pro^P: 33 Pro^A: 30 DN: 50 AdjN: 0 NNP: 0 Adv: 53 PNP: 5 V: 53 Adj: 2 PrV: 20 Ø: 10 n: 2 t: 2	SV: 8 SAdj: 1 SO: 2 SA: 2 OS: 0 AS: 3 VO: 1 OV: 3 VA: 4 AV: 2 OA: 1 AdjA: 0 AO: 0 AA: 0 AAdj: 0 Other: 0 Negation: Neg X: 0 X Neg: 2 Question: QXY: 0 No: 2 Ak: 9 Ol: 4 Al: 2 At: 1 Po: 1 Imp: 4 Other: 2 Missing elements: Cop: 2 Aux: 3 V: 14 P: 1 Art: 8 S: 22
III.	Aux: 3 Mod: 12 Cop: 1 Gen.suff.: 0 e: 55	VXA:24 VXAA: 1 Other: 1 SXV: 9 XS(Y)V: 2 XYV: 2 SXY: 2 SXAdj: 0 XS(Y)Adj: 0 XYAdj: 0 X(Y)S(Z)*: 1 SXPr(V): 1 XS(Y)Pr(V): 0 XYPr(V): 2 XYZ: 0 SXPt: 0 XS(Y)Pt: 0 XYPt: 0 Other: 15 SVX: 7 XSVY: 1 (X)VY(Z)* : 4 Negation:(X)NEGO(Y)*: 1 (X)NEGA(Y)*: 0 Other: 0 (X)NEGV_i(Y)*: 2 (X)NEGV(Y)*: 1 Question:QXYZ: 2
IV	Nominative Acc.con.: 7 Dat.con.: 2 st: 0 Other: 6	(X) Aux Y Pt: 3 (X) V_f Y Pr: 0 X V_f S (Y): 1 (X) Mod Y Inf: 4 (X) V_f A O: 0 Other: 0 (X) Cop Y Adj: 0 Negation: (X) V NEG (Y)*: 0 Question: +w V_f S (X): 3 Q V_f S (X): 3
V	Accusative Acc.con.: 0 Dat.con.: 0 Dative: 3 Other: 0 K_s: 0 K_c: 20	V O_i O_d: 0 V O_i O_d A: 0 Other: 0 (K_s)SXV_f: 0 (K_s)SV: 0 (K_s)X: 0 (K_s)XV_f: 0 (K_s)SX: 0 Other: 0 Negation:(K_s) X Neg V_f: 0 (X) V_f Y NEG Z: 0 Question:(ob) (whether) X: 0 (+w) X:0 Addition: 9 Temporal: 2 Causal: 0 Adversative: 1 Other: 7

MLU: 2.79 OWU: 43 TWU: 32 MWU: 73

Name: julia 1 Age: 3.2 Date: June-85

A. Unanalysed utterances

Unintelligible:	9	Incomplete:	8
Ambiguous:	0	Imitations:	0
Simple replies:	27	Stereotypes:	9
Formulaic:	3	Other:	0

B. Analysed utterances

	One constituent	Two constituents	More constituents
Elliptical:	90	2	0
Other:	4	45	15
Repetitions:	13	1	0

	Word and phrase structure	Sentence structure
I	N: 103 da: 37 Pr: 0 Other: 0	Sequences: 0 Reduplications: 0 0+X: 0 Other: 0 Negation: nein (no): 25 Question: 'Q': 7
II	Pro^P: 1 Pro^A: 8 DN: 8 AdjN: 7 NNP: 3 Adv: 9 PNP: 4 V: 22 Adj: 6 PrV: 8 Ø: 5 n: 20 t: 8	SV: 3 SAdj: 3 SO: 5 SA: 2 OS: 0 AS: 21 VO: 0 OV: 5 VA: 0 AV: 3 OA: 0 AdjA: 0 AO: 0 AA: 0 AAdj: 0 Other: 1 Negation: Neg X: 2 X Neg: 0 Question: QXY: 0 No: 2 Ac: 9 Ol: 4 Al: 3 At: 3 Po: 1 Imp: 1 Other: 4 Missing elements: Cop: 1 Aux: 2 V: 30 P: 3 Art: 52 S: 15
III.	Aux: 2 Mod: 1 Cop: 4 Gen.suff.: 4 e: 1	VXA: 5 VXAA: 0 Other: 0 SXV: 5 XS(Y)V: 2 XYV: 2 SXY: 0 SXAdj: 0 XS(Y)Adj: 1 XYAdj: 0 X(Y)S(Z)*: 2 SXPr(V): 0 XS(Y)Pr(V): 0 XYPr(V): 0 XYZ: 0 SXPt: 0 XS(Y)Pt: 0 XYPt: 0 Other: 2 SVX: 1 XSVY: 0 (X)VY(Z)* : 0 Negation: (X)NEGO(Y)*: 1 (X)NEGA(Y)*: 0 Other: 1 (X)$NEGV_i$(Y)*: 1 (X)NEGV(Y)*: 2 Question: QXYZ: 1
IV	Nominative Acc.con.: 1 Dat.con.: 0 st: 0 Other: 0	(X) Aux Y Pt: 0 (X) V_f Y Pr: 0 X V_f S (Y): 0 (X) Mod Y Inf: 0 (X) V_f A O: 0 Other: 0 (X) Cop Y Adj: 0 Negation: (X) V NEG (Y)*: 0 Question: +w V_f S (X): 0 Q V_f S (X): 0
V	Accusative Acc.con.: 0 Dat.con.: 1 Dative: 0 Other: 1 K_s: 0 K_c: 4	V O_i O_d: 1 V O_i O_d A: 0 Other: 0 (K_s)SXV_f: 0 (K_s)SV: 0 (K_s)X: 0 (K_s)XV_f: 0 (K_s)SX: 0 Other: 0 Negation: (K_s) X Neg V_f: 0 (X) V_f Y NEG Z: 0 Question: (ob) (whether) X: 0 (+w) X: 0 Addition: 4 Temporal: 0 Causal: 1 Adversative: 0 Other: 1

MLU: 1.76 OWU: 75 TWU: 49 MWU: 32

Name: julia 2 Age: 3.3 Date: June-85

A. Unanalysed utterances

Unintelligible:	15	Incomplete:	10
Ambiguous:	2	Imitations:	7
Simple replies:	82	Stereotypes:	9
Formulaic:	6	Other:	0

B. Analysed utterances

	One constituent	Two constituents	More constituents
Elliptical:	81	5	0
Other:	2	35	49
Repetitions:	12	2	0

	Word and phrase structure	Sentence structure
I	N: 150 da: 13 Pr: 0 Other: 5	Sequences: 0 Reduplications: 0 0+X: 0 Other: 0 Negation: nein (no) :14 Question: 'Q': 0
II	Pro^P: 1 Pro^A: 10 DN: 11 AdjN: 3 NNP: 9 Adv: 29 PNP: 17 V: 53 Adj: 6 PrV: 7 Ø: 14 n: 45 t: 3	SV: 6 SAdj: 2 SO: 4 SA: 6 OS: 1 AS: 6 VO: 0 OV: 1 VA: 0 AV: 3 OA: 0 AdjA: 0 AO: 0 AA: 0 AAdj: 0 Other: 2 Negation: Neg X: 1 X Neg: 0 Question: QXY: 0 No: 5 Ac: 7 Ol: 4 Al: 2 At: 4 Po: 2 Imp: 0 Other: 9 Missing elements: Cop: 3 Aux: 0 V: 22 P: 24 Art: 33 S: 15
III.	Aux: 1 Mod: 3 Cop: 3 Gen.suff.: 1 e: 0	VXA: 18 VXAA: 1 Other: 0 SXV: 17 XS(Y)V: 10 XYV: 4 SXY: 4 SXAdj: 0 XS(Y)Adj: 0 XYAdj: 0 X(Y)S(Z)*: 0 SXPr(V): 1 XS(Y)Pr(V): 0 XYPr(V): 1 XYZ: 0 SXPt: 0 XS(Y)Pt: 0 XYPt: 0 Other: 2 SVX: 5 XSVY: 1 (X)VY(Z)* : 3 Negation: (X)NEGO(Y)*: 1 (X)NEGA(Y)*: 3 Other: 2 (X)NEGV_i(Y)*: 2 (X)NEGV(Y)*: 1 Question: QXYZ: 0
IV	Nominative Acc.con.: 1 Dat.con.: 5 st: 0 Other: 1	(X) Aux Y Pt: 0 (X) V_f Y Pr: 0 X V_f S (Y): 0 (X) Mod Y Inf: 0 (X) V_f A O: 0 Other: 1 (X) Cop Y Adj: 0 Negation: (X) V NEG (Y)*: 1 Question: +w V_f S (X): 0 Q V_f S (X): 0
V	Accusative Acc.con.: 0 Dat.con.: 1 Dative: 0 Other: 0 K_s: 0 K_c: 15	V O_i O_d: 2 V O_i O_d A: 0 Other: 0 (K_s)SXV_f: 0 (K_s)SV: 1 (K_s)X: 0 (K_s)XV_f: 1 (K_s)SX: 1 Other: 1 Negation: (K_s) X Neg V_f: 0 (X) V_f Y NEG Z: 0 Question: (ob) X: 0 (+w) X:0 Addition: 14 Temporal: 0 Causal: 2 Adversative: 0 Other: 2

MLU: 2.29 OWU: 53 TWU: 53 MWU: 66

Name:klaus 1 Age: 4.6 Date: Nov-84

A. Unanalysed utterances

Unintelligible:	7	Incomplete:	0
Ambiguous:	3	Imitations:	1
Simple replies:	8	Stereotypes:	1
Formulaic:	3	Other:	0

B. Analysed utterances

	One constituent	Two constituents	More constituents
Elliptical:	45	3	1
Other:	18	15	16
Repetitions:	11	0	0

	Word and phrase structure	Sentence structure	
I	N: 31 da: 9 Pr: 0 Other: 3	Sequences: 1 Reduplications: 0 0+X: 0 Other: 0 Negation:nein (no): 8 Question:'Q': 21	
II	Pro^P: 0 Pro^A: 25 DN: 15 AdjN: 3 NNP: 0 Adv: 18 PNP: 2 V: 17 Adj: 6 PrV: 10 Ø: 6 n: 16 t: 3	SV: 1 SAdj: 0 SO: 0 SA: 1 OS: 0 AS: 5 VO: 2 OV: 1 VA: 1 AV: 3 OA: 0 AdjA: 0 AO: 0 AA: 0 AAdj: 0 Other: 0 Negation: Neg X: 1 X Neg: 1 Question: QXY: 0	No: 5 Ac: 4 Ol: 2 Al: 1 At: 1 Po: 0 Imp: 0 Other: 5 Missing elements: Cop: 3 Aux: 3 V: 11 P: 2 Art:14 S: 25
III.	Aux: 0 Mod: 0 Kop: 3 Gen.suff.: 0 e: 4	VXA:10 VXAA: 0 Other: 1 SXV: 1 XS(Y)V: 0 XYV: 4 SXY: 1 SXAdj: 2 XS(Y)Adj: 0 XYAdj: 0 X(Y)S(Z)*: 2 SXPr(V): 0 XS(Y)Pr(V): 0 XYPr(V): 0 XYZ: 0 SXPt: 0 XS(Y)Pt: 0 XYPt: 0 Other: 0 SVX: 2 XSVY: 0 (X)VY(Z)* : 2 Negation:(X)NEGO(Y)*: 1 (X)NEGA(Y)*: 0 Other: 0 (X)NEGV_i(Y)*: 0 (X)NEGV(Y)*: 0 Question:QXYZ: 6	
IV	Nominative Acc.con.: 5 Dat.con.: 1 st: 0 Other: 0	(X) Aux Y Pt: 0 (X) V_f Y Pr: 0 X V_f S (Y): 0 (X) Mod Y Inf: 0 (X) V_f A O: 0 Other: 0 (X) Cop Y Adj: 1 Negation: (X) V NEG (Y)*: 0 Question: +w V_f S (X): 1 Q V_f S (X): 0	
V	Accusative Acc.con.: 2 Dat.con.: 1 Dative: 0 Other: 4 K_s: 0 K_c: 18	V O_i O_d: 0 V O_i O_d A: 0 Other: 0 (K_s)SXV_f: 0 (K_s)SV: 0 (K_s)X: 0 (K_s)XV_f: 0 (K_s)SX: 0 Other: 0 Negation:(K_s) X Neg V_f: 0 (X) V_f Y NEG Z: 0 Question:(ob) (whether) X: 0 (+w) X:0	Addition: 17 Temporal: 1 Causal: 0 Adversative: 0 Other: 0

MLU: 2.00 OWU: 42 TWU: 32 MWU: 24

Name:klaus 2 Age: 4.7 Date: Dec-84

A. Unanalysed utterances

Unintelligible:	4	Incomplete:	2
Ambiguous:	0	Imitations:	4
Simple replies:	9	Stereotypes:	2
Formulaic:	2	Other:	0

B. Analysed utterances

	One constituent	Two constituents	More constituents
Elliptical:	57	4	0
Other:	21	44	20
Repetitions:	11	1	0

Stage	Word and phrase structure	Sentence structure
I	N: 31 da: 15 Pr: 0 Other: 7	Sequences: 0 Reduplications: 0 0+X: 0 Other: 0 Negation:nein (no): 11 Question:'Q': 29
II	Pro^P: 0 Pro^A: 44 DN: 31 AdjN: 7 NNP: 0 Adv: 32 PNP: 4 V: 41 Adj: 2 PrV: 14 Ø: 10 n: 22 t: 19	SV: 6 SAdj: 0 SO: 1 SA: 4 OS: 0 AS: 2 VO: 3 OV: 8 VA: 2 AV: 5 OA: 1 AdjA: 0 AO: 3 AA: 4 AAdj: 1 Other: 2 Negation: Neg X: 0 X Neg: 3 Question: QXY: 0 No: 2 Ac: 13 Ol: 11 Al: 1 At: 4 Po: 0 Imp: 2 Other: 8 Missing elements: Cop: 2 Aux: 3 V: 30 P: 5 Art:18 S: 49
III.	Aux: 0 Mod: 0 Cop: 1 Gen.suff.: 0 e: 2	VXA:11 VXAA: 1 Other: 0 SXV: 2 XS(Y)V: 0 XYV: 3 SXY: 0 SXAdj: 0 XS(Y)Adj: 0 XYAdj: 0 X(Y)S(Z)*: 0 SXPr(V): 0 XS(Y)Pr(V): 0 XYPr(V): 1 XYZ: 0 SXPt: 0 XS(Y)Pt: 0 XYPt: 1 Other: 1 SVX: 2 XSVY: 0 (X)VY(Z)* : 2 Negation:(X)NEGO(Y)*: 0 (X)NEGA(Y)*: 0 Other: 1 (X)NEGV_i(Y)*: 0 (X)NEGV(Y)*: 0 Question:QXYZ: 1
IV	Nominative Acc.con.: 1 Dat.con.: 1 st: 0 Other: 1	(X) Aux Y Pt: 0 (X) V_f Y Pr: 1 X V_f S (Y): 0 (X) Mod Y Inf: 0 (X) V_f A O: 0 Other: 0 (X) Cop Y Adj: 0 Negation: (X) V NEG (Y)*: 0 Question: +w V_f S (X): 7 Q V_f S (X): 0
V	Accusative Acc.con.: 5 Dat.con.: 1 Dative: 0 Other: 3 K_s: 2 K_c: 31	V O_i O_d: 0 V O_i O_d A: 0 Other: 0 (K_s)SXV_f: 0 (K_s)SV: 1 (K_s)X: 1 (K_s)XV_f: 0 (K_s)SX: 0 Other: 0 Negation:(K_s) X Neg V_f: 0 (X) V_f Y NEG Z: 0 Question:(ob) (whether) X: 0 (+w) X:0 Addition: 26 Temporal: 2 Causal: 0 Adversative: 1 Other: 3

MLU: 2.30 OWU: 41 TWU: 60 MWU: 45

Name:patrick Age: 4.5 Date: Nov-85

A. Unanalysed utterances

Unintelligible:	12	Incomplete:	1
Ambiguous:	5	Imitations:	2
Simple replies:	42	Stereotypes:	25
Formulaic:	12	Other:	0

B. Analysed utterances

	One constituent	Two constituents	More constituents
Elliptical:	55	10	0
Other:	8	44	34
Repetitions:	8	2	0

	Word and phrase structure	Sentence structure
I	N: 37 da: 0 Pr: 3 Other: 13	Sequences: 0 Reduplications: 0 0+X: 0 Other: 0 Negation:nein (no): 28 Question:'Q': 7
II	Pro[P]: 19 Pro[A]: 49 DN: 18 AdjN: 2 NNP: 0 Adv: 44 PNP: 1 V: 51 Adj: 3 PrV: 12 Ø: 25 n: 23 t: 9	SV: 7 SAdj: 2 SO: 2 SA: 3 OS: 0 AS: 2 VO: 5 OV: 10 VA: 3 AV: 3 OA: 0 AdjA: 0 AO: 1 AA: 0 AAdj: 0 Other: 5 Negation: Neg X: 0 X Neg: 6 Question: OXY: 0 No: 2 Ac: 8 Ol: 7* Al: 1 At: 2 Po: 3 Imp: 2 Other:17 Missing elements: Cop: 4 Aux: 0 V: 18 P: 5 Art:27 S: 36
III.	Aux: 0 Mod: 2 Cop: 4 Gen.suff.: 0 e: 11	VXA:18 VXAA: 0 Other: 0 SXV: 2 XS(Y)V: 1 XYV: 2 SXY: 3 SXAdj: 0 XS(Y)Adj: 0 XYAdj: 0 X(Y)S(Z)*: 2 SXPr(V): 1 SX(Y)Pr(V): 0 XYPr(V): 1 XYZ: 0 SXPt: 0 XS(Y)Pt: 0 XYPt: 0 Other: 3 SVX: 8 XSVY: 0 (X)VY(Z) *: 3 Negation:(X)NEGO(Y)*: 6 (X)NEGA(Y)*: 0 Other: 1 (X)NEGV$_i$(Y)*: 2 (X)NEGV(Y)*: 0 Question:QXYZ: 2
IV	Nominative Acc.con.: 3 Dat.con.: 1 st: 0 Other: 0	(X) Aux Y Pt: 0 (X) V_f Y Pr: 0 X V_f S (Y): 9 (X) Mod Y Inf: 0 (X) V_f A O: 0 Other: 0 (X) Cop Y Adj: 0 Negation: (X) V NEG (Y)*: 4 Question: +w V_f S (X): 0 Q V_f S (X): 0
V	Accusative Acc.con.: 15 Dat.con.: 0 Dative: 0 Other: 3 K_s: 0 K_c: 0	V O_i O_d: 0 V O_i O_d A: 0 Other: 0 (K_s)SXV_f: 0 (K_s)SV: 0 (K_s)X: 0 (K_s)XV_f: 0 (K_s)SX: 0 Other: 0 Negation: (K_s) X Neg V_f: 0 (X) V_f Y NEG Z: 18 Question: (ob) X: 0 (+w) X:0 Addition: 1 Temporal: 0 Kausal: 0 Adversative: 0 Other: 0

MLU: 2.25 OWU: 48 TWU: 38 MWU: 65

Name:petra 1 Age: 3.8 Date: Mar-83

A. Unanalysed utterances

Unintelligible:	6	Incomplete:	2
Ambiguous:	1	Imitations:	1
Simple replies:	22	Stereotypes:	1
Formulaic:	9	Other:	0

B. Analysed utterances

	One constituent	Two constituents	More constituents
Elliptical:	26	1	0
Other:	16	11	9
Repetitions:	9	5	0

	Word and phrase structure	Sentence structure
I	N: 19 da: 2 Pr: 0 Other: 3	Sequences: 2 Reduplications: 0 0+X: 0 Other: 0 Negation:nein (no): 6 Question:'Q': 1
II	Pro^{P}: 7 Pro^{A}: 5 DN: 23 AdjN: 0 NNP: 0 Adv: 14 PNP: 1 V: 11 Adj: 2 PrV: 2 Ø: 5 n: 7 t: 2	SV: 0 SAdj: 0 SO: 4 SA: 0 OS: 0 AS: 0 VO: 0 OV: 2 VA: 0 AV: 2 OA: 0 AdjA: 0 AO: 1 AA: 1 AAdj: 0 Other: 0 Negation: NegX: 1 X Neg: 1 Question: QXY: 0 No: 1 Ac: 5 Ol: 1 Al: 0 At: 0 Po: 0 Imp: 1 Other: 2 Missing elements: Cop: 0 Aux: 0 V: 8 P: 2 Art: 9 S: 11
III.	Aux: 0 Mod: 0 Cop: 1 Gen.suff.: 0 e: 0	VXA: 5 VXAA: 1 Other: 0 SXV: 1 XS(Y)V: 1 XYV: 3 SXY: 1 SXAdj: 0 XS(Y)Adj: 0 XYAdj: 0 X(Y)S(Z)*: 1 SXPr(V): 0 XS(Y)Pr(V): 0 XYPr(V): 0 XYZ: 0 SXPt: 0 XS(Y)Pt: 0 XYPt: 0 Other: 1 SVX: 1 XSVY: 0 (X)VY(Z)* : 0 Negation:(X)NEGO(Y)*: 1 (X)NEGA(Y)*: 0 Other: 0 (X)NEGV$_i$(Y)*: 0 (X)NEGV(Y)*: 0 Question:QXYZ: 1
IV	Nominative Acc.con.: 4 Dat.con.: 0 st: 0 Other: 0	(X) Aux Y Pt: 0 (X) V$_f$ Y Pr: 0 X V$_f$ S (Y): 0 (X) Mod Y Inf: 0 (X) V$_f$ A O: 0 Other: 0 (X) Cop Y Adj: 0 Negation: (X) V NEG (Y)*: 0 Question: +w V$_f$ S (X): 0 Q V$_f$ S (X): 0
V	Accusative Acc.con.: 0 Dat.con.: 0 Dative: 1 Other: 1 K$_s$: 0 K$_c$: 6	V O$_i$ O$_d$: 0 V O$_i$ O$_d$ A: 0 Other: 0 (K$_s$)SXV$_f$: 0 (K$_s$)SV: 0 (K$_s$)X: 0 (K$_s$)XV$_f$: 0 (K$_s$)SX: 0 Other: 0 Negation:(K$_s$) X Neg V$_f$: 0 (X) V$_f$ Y NEG Z: 0 Question:(ob) (whether) X: 0 (+w) X:0 Addition: 6 Temporal: 0 Causal: 0 Adversative: 0 Other: 0

MLU: 2.11 OWU: 25 TWU: 17 MWU: 21

Name:petra 2 Age: 3.11 Date: Jun-83

A. Unanalysed utterances

Unintelligible:	8	Incomplete:	3
Ambiguous:	3	Imitations:	1
Simple replies:	26	Stereotypes:	8
Formulaic:	16	Other:	8

B. Analysed utterances

	One constituent	Two constituents	More constituents
Elliptical:	45	5	1
Other:	11	70	51
Repetitions:	27	4	0

	Word and phrase structure	Sentence structure
I	N: 15 da: 2 Pr: 1 Other: 15	Sequences: 0 Reduplications: 0 0+X: 0 Other: 0 Negation:nein (no): 20 Question:'Q': 7
II	Pro^P: 101 Pro^A: 13 DN: 20 AdjN: 5 NNP: 0 Adv: 69 PNP: 8 V: 67 Adj: 27 PrV: 7 Ø: 33 n: 35 t: 5	SV: 21 SAdj: 19 SO: 6 SA: 7 OS: 0 AS: 3 VO: 2 OV: 2 VA: 1 AV: 9 OA: 0 AdjA: 0 AO: 0 AA: 3 AAdj: 1 Other: 2 Negation: Neg X: 3 X Neg: 0 Question: QXY: 0 No: 2 Ac: 9 Ol: 4 Al: 5 At: 25 Po: 2 Imp:10 Other:18 Missing elements: Cop:29 Aux: 1 V: 19 P: 4 Art:16 S: 22
III.	Aux: 0 Mod: 8 Cop: 2 Gen.suff.: 0 e: 0	VXA:24 VXAA: 0 Other: 0 SXV: 18 XS(Y)V: 2 XYV: 3 SXY: 2 SXAdj: 1 XS(Y)Adj: 1 XYAdj: 0 X(Y)S(Z)*: 1 SXPr(V): 5 XS(Y)Pr(V): 1 XYPr(V): 0 XYZ: 0 SXPt: 0 XS(Y)Pt: 0 XYPt: 0 Other: 3 SVX: 5 XSVY: 0 (X)VY(Z)* : 0 Negation:(X)NEGO(Y)*: 0 (X)NEGA(Y)*: 0 Other: 2 (X)NEGV_i(Y)*: 2 (X)NEGV(Y)*: 6 Question:QXYZ: 3
IV	Nominative Acc.con.: 2 Dat.con.: 7 st: 3 Other: 1	(X) Aux Y Pt: 0 (X) V_f Y Pr: 0 X V_f S (Y): 1 (X) Mod Y Inf: 0 (X) V_f A O: 0 Other: 0 (X) Cop Y Adj: 0 Negation: (X) V NEG (Y)*: 3 Question: +w V_f S (X): 0 Q V_f S (X): 0
V	Accusative Acc.con.: 0 Dat.con.: 0 Dative: 2 Other: 5 K_s: 5 K_c: 22	V O_i O_d: 0 V O_i O_d A: 1 Other: 0 (K_s)SXV_f: 0 (K_s)SV: 1 (K_s)X: 0 (K_s)XV_f: 0 (K_s)SX: 3 Other: 2 Negation:(K_s) X Neg V_f: 0 (X) V_f Y NEG Z: 0 Question:(ob) (whether) X: 0 (+w) X:0 Addition: 7 Temporal: 0 Kausal: 5 Adversative: 12 Other: 3

MLU: 2.75 OWU: 37 TWU: 43 MWU: 103

Name: petra 3 Age: 4.7 Date: Feb-84

A. Unanalysed utterances

Unintelligible:	15	Incomplete:	13
Ambiguous:	1	Imitations:	0
Simple replies:	24	Stereotypes:	1
Formulaic:	16	Other:	0

B. Analysed utterances

	One constituent	Two constituents	More constituents
Elliptical:	34	12	7
Other:	11	31	92
Repetitions:	25	4	1

	Word and phrase structure	Sentence structure
I	N: 49 da: 12 Pr: 1 Other: 1	Sequences: 0 Reduplications: 0 0+X: 0 Other: 0 Negation: nein (no): 7 Question: 'Q': 0
II	Pro^P: 96 Pro^A: 50 DN: 36 AdjN: 5 NNP: 0 Adv: 91 PNP: 11 V: 83 Adj: 8 PrV: 4 Ø: 33 n: 25 t: 24	SV: 7 SAdj: 2 SO: 10 SA: 1 OS: 1 AS: 5 VO: 1 OV: 1 VA: 0 AV: 5 OA: 0 AdjA: 0 AO: 0 AA: 0 AAdj: 1 Other: 0 Negation: Neg X: 2 X Neg: 2 Question: QXY: 0 No: 4 Ac: 7 Ol: 4 Al: 1 At: 12 Po: 1 Imp: 1 Other: 4 Missing elements: Cop: 18 Aux: 12 V: 27 P: 0 Art: 16 S: 17
III.	Aux: 0 Mod: 12 Cop: 4 Gen.suff.: 0 e: 13	VXA: 51 VXAA: 11 Other: 0 SXV: 11 XS(Y)V: 13 XYV: 5 SXY: 10 SXAdj: 1 XS(Y)Adj: 2 XYAdj: 1 X(Y)S(Z)*: 10 SXPr(V): 0 XS(Y)Pr(V): 0 XYPr(V): 0 XYZ: 2 SXPt: 2 XS(Y)Pt: 5 XYPt: 0 Other: 7 SVX: 6 XSVY: 5 (X)VY(Z)* : 1 Negation: (X)NEGO(Y)*: 2 (X)NEGA(Y)*: 1 Other: 1 $(X)NEGV_i(Y)$*: 2 (X)NEGV(Y)*: 0 Question: QXYZ: 7
IV	Nominative Acc.con.: 9 Dat.con.: 0 st: 8 Other: 0	(X) Aux Y Pt: 0 $(X)\ V_f$ Y Pr: 0 $X\ V_f$ S (Y): 4 (X) Mod Y Inf: 8 $(X)\ V_f$ A O: 0 Other: 0 (X) Kop Y Adj: 0 Negation: (X) V NEG (Y)*: 3 Question: +w V_f S (X): 0 Q V_f S (X): 0
V	Accusative Acc.con.: 1 Dat.con.: 0 Dative: 7 Other: 0 K_s: 8 K_c: 29	V O_i O_d: 1 V O_i O_d A: 2 Other: 0 $(K_s)SXV_f$: 3 (K_s)SV: 2 (K_s)X: 0 $(K_s)XV_f$: 0 (K_s)SX: 0 Other: 3 Negation: (K_s) X Neg V_f: 2 (X) V_f Y NEG Z: 0 Question: (ob) (whether) X: 0 (+w) X: 0 Addition: 14 Temporal: 3 Causal: 4 Adversative: 10 Other: 5

MLU: 3.25 OWU: 24 TWU: 39 MWU: 124

Name:stefan   Age: 4.8   Date: May-85

A. Unanalysed utterances

Unintelligible:	29	Incomplete:	4
Ambiguous:	6	Imitations:	0
Simple replies:	84	Stereotypes:	7
Formulaic:	71	Other:	17

B. Analysed utterances

	One constituent	Two constituents	More constituents
Elliptical:	98	19	5
Other:	6	41	48
Repetitions:	11	1	0

	Word and phrase structure	Sentence structure
I	N: 44 da: 9 Pr: 0 Other: 9	Sequences: 0 Reduplications: 0 0+X: 0 Other: 0 Negation:nein (no): 25 Question:'Q': 2
II	Pro^P: 60 Pro^A: 35 DN: 38 AdjN: 4 NNP: 0 Adv: 74 PNP: 3 V: 64 Adj: 0 PrV: 22 Ø: 47 n: 34 t: 4	SV: 2 SAdj: 0 SO: 15 SA: 0 OS: 1 AS: 4 VO: 4 OV: 0 VA: 6 AV: 5 OA: 0 AdjA: 0 AO: 2 AA: 1 AAdj: 0 Other: 2 Negation: Neg X: 1 X Neg: 2 Question: QXY: 0

No: 9	Ac: 5	Ol: 6	Al: 3	At: 0	Po: 4
Imp:10	Other: 9				

Missing elements: Cop:14 Aux: 2 V: 16 P: 16 Art: 11 S: 18

III.								
	VXA:26	VXAA: 2	Other: 0					
Aux: 1	SXV: 7	XS(Y)V: 2	XYV: 2	SXY: 6				
Mod: 2	SXAdj: 0	XS(Y)Adj: 0	XYAdj: 0	X(Y)S(Z)*: 0				
Cop: 7	SXPr(V): 4	XS(Y)Pr(V): 1	XYPr(V): 3	XYZ: 0				
Gen.suff.: 0	SXPt: 1	XS(Y)Pt: 0	XYPt: 1	Other: 0				
e: 1	SVX: 3	XSVY: 0	(X)VY(Z)* : 5					

Negation:(X)NEGO(Y)*: 3 (X)NEGA(Y)*: 0 Other: 4
$(X)NEGV_i(Y)$*: 0 (X)NEGV(Y)*: 0
Question:QXYZ: 0

IV

Nominative	(X) Aux Y Pt: 1	(X) V_f Y Pr: 4	X V_f S (Y): 6	
Acc.con.: 2	(X) Mod Y Inf: 2	(X) V_f A O: 1	Other: 2	
Dat.con.: 3	(X) Cop Y Adj: 0			
	Negation: (X) V NEG (Y)*: 0			
	Question: +w V_f S (X): 2			
st: 0 Other: 9	Q V_f S (X): 1			

V

Accusative	V O_i O_d: 3	V O_i O_d A: 1	Other: 0	
Acc.con.: 0	$(K_s)SXV_f$: 1	$(K_s)SV$: 0	$(K_s)X$: 0	Addition: 8
Dat.con.: 0	$(K_s)XV_f$: 0	$(K_s)SX$: 0	Other: 0	Temporal: 3
Dative: 6	Negation:(K_s) X Neg V_f: 0			Causal: 0
Other: 4	(X) V_f Y NEG Z: 0			Adversative: 0
K_s: 0 K_c: 11	Question:(ob) (whether) X: 0	(+w) X:0		Other: 0

MLU: 2.31 OWU: 75 TWU: 54 MWU: 88

Name:sven Age: 7.4 Date: Jun-84

A. Unanalysed utterances

Unintelligible:	14	Incomplete:	3
Ambiguous:	4	Imitations:	2
Simple replies:	56	Stereotypes:	15
Formulaic:	38	Other:	15

B. Analysed utterances

	One constituent	Two constituents	More constituents
Elliptical:	91	4	0
Other:	10	59	64
Repetitions:	14	1	0

	Word and phrase structure	Sentence structure
I	N: 79 da: 20 Pr: 1 Other: 0	Sequences: 0 Reduplications: 0 0+X: 0 Other: 0 Negation:nein (no): 14 Question:'Q': 5
II	Pro^P: 55 Pro^A: 55 DN: 25 AdjN: 0 NNP: 0 Adv: 52 PNP: 3 V: 90 Adj: 4 PrV: 19 Ø: 43 n: 32 t: 25	SV: 18 SAdj: 2 SO: 8 SA: 5 OS: 0 AS: 7 VO: 0 OV: 4 VA: 2 AV: 6 OA: 0 AdjA: 0 AO: 2 AA: 0 AAdj: 0 Other: 5 Negation: Neg X: 0 X Neg: 4 Question: QXY: 0 No: 8 Ac: 14 Ol:12 Al: 2 At: 4 Po: 2 Imp: 4 Other: 10 Missing elements: Cop: 7 Aux: 1 V: 22 P: 8 Art: 42 S: 25
III.	Aux: 0 Mod: 5 Cop: 4 Gen.suff.: 0 e: 6	VXA:11 VXAA: 1 Other: 0 SXV: 14 XS(Y)V: 1 XYV: 4 SXY: 1 SXAdj: 0 XS(Y)Adj: 0 XYAdj: 0 X(Y)S(Z)*: 0 SXPr(V): 0 XS(Y)Pr(V): 1 XYPr(V): 0 XYZ: 0 SXPt: 2 XS(Y)Pt: 0 XYPt: 0 Other: 1 SVX: 16 XSVY: 0 (X)VY(Z)* : 2 Negation:(X)NEGO(Y)*: 0 (X)NEGA(Y)*: 1 Other: 0 (X)NEGV_i(Y)*: 2 (X)NEGV(Y)*: 0 Question:QXYZ: 2
IV	Nominative Acc.con.: 2 Dat.con.: 3 st: 1 Other: 11	(X) Aux Y Pt: 0 (X) V_f Y Pr: 4 X V_f S (Y): 15 (X) Mod Y Inf: 1 (X) V_f A O: 0 Other: 0 (X) Cop Y Adj: 0 Negation: (X) V NEG (Y)*: 6 Question: +w V_f S (X): 1 Q V_f S (X): 1
V	Accusative Acc.con.: 3 Dat.con.: 0 Dative: 0 Other: 2 K_s: 0 K_c: 2	V O_i O_d: 0 V O_i O_d A: 0 Other: 0 (K_s)SXV_f: 0 (K_s)SV: 0 (K_s)X: 0 (K_s)XV_f: 0 (K_s)SX: 0 Other: 0 Negation:(K_s) X Neg V_f: 0 (X) V_f Y NEG Z: 2 Question:(ob) (whether) X: 0 (+w) X:0 Addition: 2 Temporal: 0 Kausal: 0 Adversative: 0 Other: 0

MLU: 2.17 OWU: 80 TWU: 57 MWU: 91

Name: wolfgang Age: 4.5 Date: Oct-82

A. Unanalysed utterances

Unintelligible:	9	Incomplete:	0
Ambiguous:	7	Imitations:	1
Simple replies:	10	Stereotypes:	1
Formulaic:	48	Other:	14

B. Analysed utterances

	One constituent	Two constituents	More constituents
Elliptical:	22	9	0
Other:	19	66	84
Repetitions:	5	7	4

	Word and phrase structure	Sentence structure
I	N: 51 da: 6 Pr: 3 Other: 5	Sequences: 0 Reduplications: 0 0+X: 0 Other: 0 Negation: nein (no): 3 Question: 'Q': 3
II	Pro^{P}: 52 Pro^{A}: 48 DN: 60 AdjN: 2 NNP: 0 Adv: 93 PNP: 1 V: 83 Adj: 9 PrV: 28 Ø: 85 n: 4 t: 6	SV: 17 SAdj: 3 SO: 8 SA: 4 OS: 0 AS: 5 VO: 1 OV: 5 VA: 1 AV: 11 OA: 3 AdjA: 0 AO: 0 AA: 3 AAdj: 0 Other: 3 Negation: Neg X: 0 X Neg: 7 Question: QXY: 0 No: 4 Ac: 14 Ol: 9 Al: 4 At: 5 Po: 7 Imp: 4 Other: 17 Missing elements: Cop: 12 Aux: 1 V: 29 P: 4 Art: 37 S: 41
III.	Aux: 0 Mod: 0 Cop: 3 Gen.suff.: 0 e: 6	VXA: 36 VXAA: 2 Other: 0 SXV: 22 XS(Y)V: 20 XYV: 7 SXY: 7 SXAdj: 1 XS(Y)Adj: 1 XYAdj: 0 X(Y)S(Z)*: 2 SXPr(V): 2 XS(Y)Pr(V): 3 XYPr(V): 0 XYZ: 0 SXPt: 1 XS(Y)Pt: 0 XYPt: 0 Other: 5 SVX: 4 XSVY: 1 (X)VY(Z)* : 4 Negation: (X)NEGO(Y)*: 0 (X)NEGA(Y)*: 2 Other: 4 (X)NEGV_i(Y)*: 0 (X)NEGV(Y)*: 1 Question: QXYZ: 7
IV	Nominative Acc.con.: 10 Dat.con.: 1 st: 0 Other: 13	(X) Aux Y Pt: 0 (X) V_f Y Pr: 2 X V_f S (Y): 1 (X) Mod Y Inf: 0 (X) V_f A O: 0 Other: 0 (X) Kop Y Adj: 0 Negation: (X) V NEG (Y)*: 7 Question: +w V_f S (X): 0 Q V_f S (X): 0
V	Accusative Acc.con.: 0 Dat.con.: 1 Dative: 0 Other: 0 K_s: 0 K_c: 0	V O_i O_d: 1 V O_i O_d A: 0 Other: 0 (K_s)SXV_f: 0 (K_s)SV: 0 (K_s)X: 0 (K_s)XV_f: 0 (K_s)SX: 0 Other: 0 Negation: (K_s) X Neg V_f: 0 (X) V_f Y NEG Z: 1 Question: (ob) (whether) X: 0 (+w) X: 0 Addition: 0 Temporal: 0 Causal: 0 Adversative: 0 Other: 0

MLU: 2.84 OWU: 26 TWU: 62 MWU: 112

9.2 Transcripts

Transcript: andreas 1

No.	Utterances and comments
001	haus ('house') (A. is building a Legohouse.)
002	ja.so haus ('yes.so house') (P: do you mean in the zoo? A. is showing two pieces of Lego.)
003	ja.des wohl aud.aud.aud haus ('yes. that really house') (P. also picks up two pieces of Lego.)
004a	ganz mache ('repair') (I want to repair the thing.) (P: and then you can make a garden.)
004b	viel ('many') (Follows on from 4a)
005	ja ('yes')
006	zei häuser ('two houses') (P: how many houses would you like to make?)
007	elefantene dinne ('elephants in') (E. are in the house.)
008	häuser ('houses') (imitative)
009	dinne elefant ('in elephant') (E. is in the house.)
010	so ('like this') (A. points at the elephant in the house.)
011	ledo (A. wants to make an elephant out of Lego.)
012	tolle idee ('great idea') (Stereotype)
013	itte mal daf? ('I may?') (May I?) (A. wants to have W's house.)
014	neilange? ('get in?') (A. wants to fetch out the steps.)
015	nit? ('not?') (W. shakes his head.)
016	hinschaue ('look in') (P. should look.)

017 du nimm sabe.diwan.dann
('you take ... then')
(P. should take something.)
018 baue elefant ('make elephant')
(P: what do we do then?)
019 ba.eisbär ('ma.polar bear')
(We make a p.)
020 wolfi.äh (interrupted)
021 elefantfoto ('elephant photo')
(I've got a photo of an E.)
022 ja.hanes foto.äh ('yes.hanes photo.')
(Hannes has the photo.)
023 anes o (= anderes, 'other'. Follows on from 022)
024 äh.zoo dinne ('zoo in')
(In the zoo.)
(P: where was the photo taken?)
025 oh.lat ('oh.ladder')
(A. is looking into his house.)
026 snell da lat dinne ('quick the ladder in')
(P. should put a ladder in.)
027 wo? ('where?') (Question)
028 was denn? ('what then?') (Question)
029 so it messe? ('so I measure')
(A. is measuring houses.)
030a messe aber wolfi ('measure but wolfi')
(W. should measure.)
030b wie goβ ('how big')
(Continuation of 30a, how big the houses are.)
031 messe! ('measure!')
(W. should measure.)
032 nein ('no')
033 o.unser aud doβ.doβ ('our house big big')
(Our house is big.)
034 aud viel groβ ('house much big')
(House is very big.)
035 seds (= sechs, 'six'. Reference to what is not clear)
036 wieder ('again')
(A. drops a stone into the house.)
037 ui.lot dinne ('hole in')
(A. finds a hole in the house.)
038 was? ('what?') (Question)
039 m.nicht ('not')
(P: when were you in the zoo?)

040 lot dinne ('hole in')
(There's a hole in it.)
(A. points to the hole.)
041 warum? ('why?') (Question)
042 nein ('no')
043 was? ('what?')
044 nein ('no')
045a sage (= Ich sage, 'I say'. Continuation cf. 45b)
045b muβ nit.muβ nit ('must not.must not')
(The hole should not be there.)
046 so zu aud ('so shut house')
(Thus the house is closed.)
047 m (confirmatory)
048 da ('there')
(A. points to another hole.)
049 löbes haus ('silly house')
050 lobe ('lion')
(P: a lion house?)
051 dummes haus ('stupid house') (After question from P.)
052 sage warum ('say why')
(You should say why.)
053 du was baue? ('you what build')
(What are you building?)
054 da ('there')
(A. points to Lego.)
055 du.ab ('you.out') (Meaning unclear)
056 baue auto! ('build car!')
(You should build a car.)
057 wo? ('where?')
058 elefante ('elephants')
(P: what's your favourite animal?)
059 ma.eisbär rotliebes löbe ('polar bear lion')
(Meaning unclear)
060 ein laffe.laffe (= Affe, 'ape'; elliptical)
061 laffe ('ape') (elliptical)
062 so.so ('like this')
(P: I don't know how to do the trunk.)
063 äh (P: what did the elephant do in the zoo that time?)
064 ja ('yes') (confirmatory)
065 jetzt messe? ('now measure')
(A. wants to measure both of the houses.)
066 messe ('measure')
(P: should we measure?)

067 du mal.du mal schnell ('you quickly')
(P. should look on.)
068 utz.net utz made ('out.not out make'(?))
(= ?ausmachen ?turn off))
069 lödes haus ('stupid house' = blödes H., ellipt.)
070 schau ('look')
071 deht deht immer net ('goes goes always not')
(House always breaks.)
072 immer net? ('always not?') (Follows on from 71)
073 oh.oh puttdeht immer ('breaks always')
(House always breaks.)
075a daufdück ('push there')
075b puttdeht? ('breaks?')
076a nein ('no')
(P: doesn't it bother you there?)
076b stör mir ('sturbs me')
(That disturbs me = das stört mich.)
077 da ('there') (Follows on from 76)
078 ja ('yes') (confirmatory)
079 rumlaufe du? ('round run you?')
(Are you running around?)
080 du spiele ('you play')
081a nein ('no')
081b des deld ('the money')
(You should take the money. = das Geld)
082 hallo
083 hab deine wurst ('have your sausage')
(I haven't got a sausage. not any = *k*eine)
084 ander mal holen geht ('other time fetch go')
(Another time I'll fetch some.)
085 ja ('yes')
086 eis ('ice')
(P: what have they got today then?)
087 nein ('no') (negative)
088 no was.was no was? ('something else')
089 sage wolfi aud eis ('say wolfi too ice')
(W. said he wants an ice cream, too.)
090 da ('there')
(A. puts an ice cream on the counter.)
091 suppe? ('soup?')
092 deld ganz viel ('money quite much')
(That costs quite a lot of money.)
093 äh.tausend mark ('äh.a thousand marks') (Follows on from 92)

094 zehn mark ('ten marks') (imitative)
095 nein ('no')
096 ja ('yes')
097 da nei tu ('there put in')
(You have to put the money in there.)
098 mat zu! ('close!')
(M. should shut the bag.)
099 auße rumlang ('outside round long')
(You have to get to it round the outside.)
100 ja ('yes') (confirmatory)

Transcript: andreas 2

No.	Utterances and comments
001	zumachen ('close') (A. is drawing the curtains.)
002	licht an! ('light on!') (Somebody should turn on the light.)
003	nein ('no')
004	dabferthater hier ('Kasperltheatre here') (Here's the Punch and Judy theatre.) (A. is pointing at the Punch and Judy theatre.)
005	nein ('no')
006	da ('there') (A. shows where P. should go.)
007	aus ('off') (A. wants to turn a light switch to off.)
008	hier ausmade ('here make off') (Turn it off here.) (A. wants to turn off the light.)
009	weiß net ('know not') (P: how does that go?)
010	dabferltater ('Punch and Judy theatre')
011	hier hinsetze ('sit down here') (A. shows P. a chair.)
012	titalala.hallo ('(fanfare) hello') (A. goes behind the stage.)
013	ja ('yes')
014	ja? ('yes?')
015	komme äh mal ('come on then') (P. should come.)
016	uns komme! ('us come!') (Come to me. = Komm zu mir.)
017	ja.schön ('yes.good') (P: how are you then?)
018	ja ('yes')
019	dabferl burtstag feier ('?Kasperl birthday party') (?K. is celebrating his Birthday.)
020	dabferl burttag feier (P.: what do you have to do?, For meaning see 19)
021	hinsetze! ('sit down!') (P. should sit down.)
022	burtstag feier dabferl ('birthday party ?Kasperl') (For meaning see 19)

023 ja ('yes')
024 sage nit ('say not')
(P: where did you celebrate your birthday?)
025a sage wo? ('say where?')
(Should I say where?)
025b wo? ('where?') (For meaning see 25a)
026 äh.wa (interrupted)
027 s vorbei ('is over')
(It's already over)
028 schön ('lovely')
(P: how was it then..?)
029 goβes fest feier ('big party have')
(A. had a big party.)
030 fuβball.fuβball spiel ('football.football play')
(We played football.)
031 ja ('yes')
032 ga net mitspiele ('not at all play with')
(I didn't play with them.)
033 sad (= schade) ('shame')
034 net mit ('not with') (interrupted)
035 schöne lang net mitspiele ('lovely long not play with')
(A. did not play with them.)
036 sad (= schade) ('shame')
037 äh. au ('eh. ow')
(P: what was going on at the party then?)
038 nase ('nose')
(P: did you hurt yourself?)
039 dogodil da ('dogodile there')
(Crocodile has bitten off his nose.)
040 ja ('yes')
041 hallo ('hello')
042 fi di (Wording of greeting)
043 gleich wiederkomme ('soon come back') (Subj = ich (I))
044 au ('ow')
045 dabferl (= Kasperl)
046 o h.oh.aoh.hua
(Accompanying noises to the entrance of a robber.)
047 jäh.hallo ('yeah.hello')
(Enter robber.)
048 räuber böse ('robber bad')
049 ja ('yes')
050 jo.warum? ('yes.why?')

051a sage ('say')
(P. should say why she's afraid.)
051b warum böse ('why bad') (For meaning see 51a)
052 äää haue.äh behaue ('strike.hit')
(I'll hit you.)
053 nein ('no')
054 ho ('fetch')
(fetch = holen) (A. wants to fetch something.)
055 ho bitte.spielen ('fetch please.play')
(P. should play with them.)
056 ja ('yes')
057 sage net ('say not') (Meaning unclear)
058 immer h (interrupted)
059 daber holen.hole ('kasper fetch')
(A. fetches Kasperl.)
060 räuber wiederdomme ('robber again come')
(The robber's coming again.)
061 ja ('yes')
062 ho ('fetch')
(A. fetches Kasperl.)
063 wiederdomme ich ('again come I')
064 nein ('no')
065 titalala (fanfare)
066 net neischaue ('not look in')
(P. shouldn't look behind the stage.)
067 hallo ('hello')
068 wie ('how') (imitative)
069a weiβ net ('know not')
(P: what is your name?)
069b wie heiβe ('how called') (Continuation of 69a)
070 räuber da? ('robber there')
(Was the robber there?)
071 ja ('yes')
072a sage ('say')
072b warum domme äh räuber? ('why come robber?')
073 weiβ gar net ('know not at all')
074 äh wie äh ('how') (Meaning unclear)
075 anders ('other') (Meaning unclear)
076 nit des ha hinbine ('not that has bring')
(Meaning unclear)
077 böd biβi böd hinbine ('stupid little stupid bring')
(Meaning unclear)
078a sage ('say')

078b wo wohne ('where live')
(Where do you live?)
079 ich ('I') (ellipt.)
080 unterhati (= Unterhaching, a place name; ellipt.)
081 ja ('yes')
082 san dib ('sand there')
(There is sand in Unterhaching.)
083 san dib.san dib aud ('sand there.sand there too')
(There was sand there too.)
084 ja ('yes')
085 nit baute ich ('not need I')
(I do not need the sand.)
086 baute ('need') (ellipt.)
087 fi di (Wording of greeting)
088 schlafe ('sleep')
089 wiederdomme.ja? ('again come.yes?')
(You're coming again, aren't you? OR He's coming again, isn't he?)
090 dododil wiederkomme ('crocodile again come')
(Crocodile coming again.)
091 rufe! ('call!')
(You have to call it.)
092 ch.ch.ch. ('hiss.hiss.hiss')
(onomatopoeic for a snake.)
093 rufe! ('call')
094 sch sch.wa (onomatopoeic)
095 dabferl rufe! ('Kasper call!')
(P. should call Kasperl.)
096 ja ('yes')
097 fallt aber au ('falls but also')
(?The snake also falls)
098 beißen mir ('bite to me')
(The snake is biting him. = mich)
099 ja ('yes')
100 was? ('what?')
101 nein ('no')
102 hole äh räuber ('fetch robber')
(A. is fetching a robber)
103 ja ('yes')
104 hole ('fetch') (interrupted)
105 net wisse ('not know')
(P: why are you fetching the robber?)

Transcript: anja 1

No.	Utterances and comments
001	ein fel noch ('one miss still') (Number one on a dial is missing.)
002	ja ('yes')
003	hier ('here') (M: then she was definitely here)
004	hier ('here')
005a	he ('here')
005b	hier nich war num ('here not was num(ber')) (= Nummer)
006	ein ('one') (M: but the one was here)
007	fel noch ('miss still') (Still missing. As in 001)
008	fel noch ('miss still') (Still missing. As in 001)
009	fel noch ('miss still') (Still missing. As in 001)
010	ja ('yes') (M: is it still missing?)
011	ja ('yes') (M: then we have to paint in a new one?)
012a	ja ('yes') (M: we'll do that after then, shall we?)
012b	ein nu hier ('a number here') (A number should go in here)
013	ein ('one') (M: you put your new one in there)
014	alte we ('old (a) way') (We should get rid of the old number. away = weg)
015	feter dehn ('harder turn') (I'm turning the dial more firmly = fester)
016	feter dehn ('harder turn') (see sentence no. 015)
017	ein ('one')
018	ja ('yes') (To M's question: better?)
019	je mach ebn ('now do just') (je = jetzt = now)

020 ja ('yes') (M's question: do it now?)
021 neue ('new')
(Mother is fetching new pens.)
022 ja ('yes')
(M: now you've got a new number one.)
023 blaun ('blue' = blau)
024 eine ('one') (Meaning unclear)
025 rote scheiben ('red write')
(I'm writing in red; write = sch*r*eiben.)
026 ote reinschreiben ('red write in')
(I'll write it in in red.)
027 ote ('red')
(To stress the previous utterance.)
028 ote (X) ('red (X)')
029 abmache ('take off')
(A. is playing with the telephone dial.)
030 ot (= rot ('red'); points to the telephone.)
031 neue machen ('new make')
032 hier ein neue machen ('here a new make')
(Make a new one here.)
033 wei ('two')
(Question: which number is that then?)
034 hier? ('here?')
(A. is pointing to another number.)
035 dei ('three' = drei; question: which is that?)
036 hier ('here')
(A. indicates another number.)
037 fünf ('five') (Question: which is that?)
038 vier (Imitation)
039 hier ('here')
(Anja indicates another number.)
040 vier ('four') (Question: which is that?)
041 fünf ('five') (Question: welche ist das?)
042 neue ('new') (Meaning unclear)
043 sieben ('seven') (Question: and that?)
044 neu ('nine') (= neun, Question: and that?)
045 ach ('eight') (= acht, Question: and that?)
046 neun ('nine')
047 hier? ('here?')
(A. indicates a number.)
048 eichen ('?own')
(Meaning unclear)

049 (X) im ('(X) in the')
(Meaning unclear)
050 ohne ('without')
051 ohne machen ("?without to do') (Meaning of "ohne" unclear)
052 eigen ('own')
(A. wants to show something.)
053 erwin holen ('erwin fetch')
(I'm fetching Erwin; A. leaves the table.)
054 erwin holen ('erwin fetch')
(I'm fetching Erwin.)
(M: no. we're not going to fetch erwin in now.)
055 neue ('new')
(Question: who is erwin?)
056 (neue) musekater ('(new) pussycat')
(Question: who is erwin?)
057 musekater ('pussycat')
(Question: who is erwin?)
058 musekater (imitative)
059 pielen ('play')
060 aua macht ('ouch makes')
(It hurts.)
061 erwin (possible subject supplementing 60)
062 ja ('yes')
063 meine bett ('my bed')
(in my bed ... Erwin did ouch.)
064 ja ('yes') (Question: in your bed?)
065 hier ('here')
(A. points at her folding bed.)
066 hinlege ('lie down')
067 doch ('yes')
(M: no. erwin's not allowed to do that.)
068 ja ('yes')
(M: erwin's not allowed in your bed.)
069 rein.reinkomme ('in.in come')
070 ein (X) ('one')
071 musekater ('pussycat')
072 aua beine ('ouch legs')
073 ja ('yes')
074 meine ('my') (Reference to what is not clear)
075 grü ('green')
(Question: what colour was it again?)
076 weiβ? ('white?')
077 erwin?

078 musekater? ('pussycat')
079 mümmel ('rabbit')
(M: what other animals are there in the stall?)
080 (X)
081 mümmel ('rabbit')
082 ein (X) neu mümmel ('a new rabbit')
083 ja ('yes')
084 ja ('yes')
085 (X)
086 (X)
087 ja ('yes')
088 neue kuken ('new chicks')
(Question: and what else?)
089 hahn ('chicken')
090 baun ('brown') (= braun)
091 weiβe ('white')
(We've got a white chicken too.)
092 ja ('yes')
093 kikiki (imitative)
094 mogen auch ('morning also')
(In the morning, too.)
(M: the chicken always screeches like that.)
095 (X)
096 mama. ich ('mama. I')
(M: who feeds the animals?)
097 papa
(M: and who else?)
098 itte? ('please') (= bitte)
099 bitte ('please')
100 bitte mam ('please mam')
(M: what please?)
101 (X)
102 (X)
103 heute abend ('today evening')
(M: you may go to andreas's tonight.)
103 ja nein ('yes no')
(M: do you prefer sour milk?)
104 feun ('friend') (= freund)
(M: there's markus his friend.andreas)
105 aufgemache ('open')
(Has anybody opened the door for A.)
106 herhole? ('fetch?')
(Should I fetch him?)

Transcript: anja 2

No.	Utterances and comments
001	heute heute mich aufnehmen? ('today today me tape?') (Are you going to tape me today?)
002	ja ('yes')
003	heute? ('today?') (Follows on from 1)
004	ja ('yes')
005a	ä heute momojan ('today momojan') (Today Krowojan was tense again.)
005b	kampfen ('tense') (M: what was the trouble with krowojan?) (= sich verkrampfen (to be tense))
006	ja ('yes')
007	ich ei ('I egg') (I made an egg.)
008	ja ('yes')
009	ja und dann X mama X kampfen mama ('yes and then X mama X tense mama') (Meaning unclear)
010	ich a morg a: ('I a tomorr a:') (interrupted)
011a	montag komme ich .nich kampfen ('monday come I .not tense') (If he comes on Monday, he will not be tense.) (With 'ich nich' (I not), she corrected herself.)
011b	nich krampfen ('not tense') (Continuation of 11a)
012	ne ('no') (M: if he comes on Monday shouldn't he be tense?)
013	heute nich kampfen ('today not tense') (He's not tense today.)
014	ne ('no') (M: today not tense any more?)
015	morgen nich ('tomorrow not') (Follows on from 14)
016	am samtach hause bleiben ('on Saturday at home stay') (He stays at home on Sat.)
017a	dann wümmen wümmen ('then wim wim') (= schwimmen, swim)
017b	halb elf ('half eleven') (Follows on from 17a)
018	ne ('no') (M: at half past ten?)
019	halb sieben ('half seven') (Follows on from 17)
020	halb sieben ('half seven') (After M.'s question)

021 doch ('yes') (to stress)
022 ja ('yes')
023 m go ('m so')
(= like this.)
(M: and what did you do in swimming? go = so ('like this'))
024 der emio mitgekommen ('the E. came with')
(E. came with us.)
025 kein wimm zeug mit ('no wim stuff with')
(E. didn't have any swim things with him.)
026 ne ('no')
(M: he didn't have any swim things with him?)
027a unahose ('pants')
(Karsten swam in his pants.)
027b de karchen (= der Karsten, i.e. Karsten)
028 katen katen teinme unahose gewommen
('katen katen teinme swam in pants')
(K. Steinmetz swam in his pants.)
029 emio um badehose ('E. in trunks')
(E. had swimming trunks.)
030 äm is nich ('is not')
(M: who else went swimming with you?, is = ist)
031 ne ('no')
032 momojan is nich ('M. is not')
(Krowojan wasn't there.)
033 fau hein montach mittwoch mit
('mrs. hein monday wednesday with')
(Frau H. was with us on Wednesday.)
034 fau kuchta matin ('mrs kuchta matin')
(M: ... who else was with you?)
035 ja ('yes')
036 go ('so') (Like this.)
(= so (like this) ; A. demonstrates an exercise.)
037 dann rau ('then out')
(Then we went out.)
038 ein uhr ('one o'clock') (Follows on from 37)
039 dann ich m halb sieb a halb elf angezogen
('then I m half six a half ten dressed')
(Then I got dressed at nine thirty.)
040 ja ('yes')
041 halb zwölf halb sieb wassa rausgekomme
('half eleven half six water come out')
(We came out of the water at half past ten.)

042 dann hause gefahrn ('then home drive')
(Then we drove home.)
043 ja ('yes')
044 ers fühstücken ('firs beakfast')
(First we had breakfast.)
045 ja ('yes')
046 m. knäckekot ('m. crispbcad')
(M: what did you have for breakfast today then?)
047 ja ('yes')
048a m die kertin ('m the kertin')
(The girl Kerstin.)
048b ja ('yes')
(M: kerstin?)
048c nich mitgefrühstück ('not breakfast with')
(Didn't have breakfast with (us).)
049 kein fühstück geha ('no breakfast have')
(K. hasn't had b.)
050 ne ('no')
051 doch ('yes') (to stress)
052 ja ('yes')
053 mamama.meine mamama('jam.my jam')
(M: what did you have on it then? = Marmelade (jam))
054 flaumen ('plums')
(M: which was that then?)
055 ne ('no')
056 ich donnertach ('I thursday')
(2x, I have to bring something on Th.)
057 ja ('yes')
058 (bei) (zukucken) ('at watch') (Meaning unclear)
059 montach konen ('monday cook')
(We're cooking on Monday.)
060 m rei ('m rice')
(M: what are you cooking?)
061 ja ('yes')
062 m weiβ ni ('know not')
(I don't know.)
(M: what did you cook last week then?)
063 pudding? ('mousse?')
(Answer to 62)
064 laden kudding ('oclate mousse')
(M: what kind?, chocolate mousse = Schokoladenpudding)
065 (den) (X) (Meaning unclear)
066 das nächs mal vanilekudding
('the next time vanilla mousse')

067 ja ('yes')
068 ladenkudding ('ocolate mousse')
(see 064) (elliptical)
069 ja ('yes')
070 X machen (Meaning unclear)
071 momojan wein ('momojan cry')
072 ja ('yes')
073 momo enio ärgern ('M. E. annoy')
(M. has annoyed E.)
074 ja ('yes')
075 auch ärgern ('also annoy')
(I annoyed him too.)
076 ne ('no')
077 hauen ('hit') (elliptical, A. hit him.)
078 momojan marku klinger meine klasche
('M. Marku Klinger my class')
(M. Klinger was in my class.)
079 ja ('yes')
080 nein ('no')
(They shouldn't row.)
081 ä ne ä m ba
(He is ä and ba, i.e. not nice.)
082 abhauen ('get out')
(It's best he goes.)
083 ja ('yes')
084 X ni mehr emio nich mehr ärgern
('X not more E. not more annoy')
(E. won't annoy us any longer.)
085 ne ('no')
086 ä X majon.X (Meaning unclear)
087 majo
(M: what's his name?, Mario)
088 ä anda klasse ('another class') (ellipt.)
089 ja ('yes')
090 m nein ('no')
091 papa hingefah ('papa drove')
(P. took Mario to school.)
092 papa maja papa hingefah ('papa maya papa drove')
(Papa drove Mario there.)
093 ja ('yes')
094 nule ('nool')
(M: did they take him there?, to school = zur Schule)
095 ja ('yes')

096 heute ('today')
(M: when?)
097 majo papa hingebra ('mayo papa took there')
(Mario's Papa took him there.)
098 hier hi ('to here')
(He's coming back.)
099 herr feu m. herr feudmann weitafahn majon
('mr. F. drive further mayon')
(Mr. F. drove Mario further.)
100 ja ('yes')
101 heute ('today') (Follows on from 99)

Transcript: jonas 1

No. Utterances and comments

001 fat mattu de? ('what do you there?')
(What're you doing there?)
(= Was machst du da?)
002 fat mattu? ('what do you?')
(What're you doing?)
(= Was machst du?)
003 feiti nich ('know I not')
(I don't know.)
(= Weiß ich nicht.)
004 alcha feiche möche hihoche ('?all ?know want listen')
(Meaning unclear)
005 na! ('well!')
006 prima ('great') (imitative)
007a bett hintuje ('bed put here')
(I'll put the bed here.)
007b und hier sank hintuje ('and here cupboard put')
(And I'll put the cupboard here.)
(= Und hier tu ich den Schrank hin.)
008 hu (High pitched whistling from the microphone)
009 e hupe e hupe ('e horn e horn')
(E: that was a horn)
010 komma her! ('come here!')
011 ferteche nit? ('understand not?')
(Don't you understand?)
(= Verstehst du nicht?)
012 fahum verteche sie nit? ('why understand you not?')
(Why don't you understand?)
(= Warum verstehen sie nicht?)
013 und das da? ('and that there?')
(And what is that there?)
(= Und was ist das da?)
014 fau chos weiβe ('mrs. J. knows')
(= Frau Jost weiβ es.)
015 fa is das da? ('what's that there?')
(See 13) (= Was ist das da?)
016 hier umfahe immer ('here fall always')
(Something always falls over. = Etwas fällt immer um.)
017a na fau chos ('well mrs. J.')
(= address)

017b sie auch nit feis? ('you too not know?')
(Don't you know either?)
(= Wissen sie das auch nicht?)
018 umfahe immer ('fall over always') (see 016)
019a ahso ('aaah')
019b hier große ding.umfalle immer
('here big thing.over fall always')
(This big thing always falls over.)
020 hier ding umfalle immer
('here thing over fall always')
(This thing always falls over.)
021 na! ('well!')
022 (X) puppehaus (x) ('dolls' house')
023 puppehaus ('dolls' house')
(E: what're you doing there?)
024 da ('there') (interrupted)
025 hier tieche obehin
('here animals up top')
(I put the animals in at the top = Die Tiere tu ich oben hin.)
026 na ('well')
027 hier obe tieche hinhoje
('here top animals in fetch')
(I'll fetch the animals into the top here.)
(= Hier oben hol ich die Tiere hin.)
028 na.na jo.
029a sag ich. puppehaustiere ('say I. dollhouseanimals')
(= I have already said: P.)
029b puppehaustiere ('dollhouseanimals')
(For meaning see 29a)
030 un wohinne tchirm hintuche?
('and where brella put?')
(And where does the umbrella go? = Und wohin kommt Schirm?)
031 feiß i nit ('know I not')
(I don't know.)
032 sache sie! ('say you!')
(You should say it.)
033 viellei otto? ('praps otto?')
(Otto perhaps?)
(E: what are their names?)
034 aje tieche otto heiße ('all animals otto call')
(All of the animals are called Otto = Alle Tiere heißen Otto.)
035 feis i nis atehe tieche heiße
('know I not other animals call')

(I don't know what the other animals are called.)
(= Ich weiß nicht, wie die anderen Tiere heißen.)
036 un das da? ('and that there?')
(J. takes an animal.)
037 (XXX) tieche ('animals') (Meaning unclear)
038 vielei hautieche ('peraps pets')
(Maybe they're pets. = Das sind vielleicht Haustiere.)
039 na X X ('well X X')
040 XX und hier higeschirm ('XX and here mbrella')
(And here is an umbrella. = Und hier ist ein Regenschirm)
041 eh.eh.(X) na.na hop (accompanying an action)
042 vielei hier ('praps here')
(The child opens a cupboard.)
043 (XX) na mattu (XX) ('well ?make ?you') (Meaning unclear)
044 fa i tas ta? fa its tas da?
('what is that there?') (x2 = Was ist das da?)
045 (X) kaputt.mm ('broken.mm') (Meaning unclear)
046 na sowas X X eima ('well, well, well X X once')
(Meaning unclear)
047 brauche fer net kaputte tier ('need we not broken animal')
(= Wir brauchen das kaputte Tier nicht.)
048 kaputt ('broken')
(We don't need the broken animals.)
(Follows on from 47)
049 da ('there')
050 fas? ('what?')
051 farum pss pss? ('why pss pss?')
052 na sofas.pss pss (Meaning unclear)
053 setz kss kss (Meaning unclear)
054 chchch.XX mm.so (Meaning unclear)
055 XX u kann nit stehe ('XX mal can not stand')
(The animal can't stand. = Das Tier kann nicht stehen.)
056 XX hier ('XX here')
057 zas zu groß ('tha's too big')
(That's too big. = Das ist zu groß.)
058 mhm (confirmatory)
059 zu kein puppehaus ('too little dolls' house')
(The dolls' house is too small. = Das Puppenhaus ist zu klein.)
060 ha.wo denn? ('ha.where then?')
061 viellei hier hintuche ('praps over here put')
(I'll put it over here. = Ich tu es hierhin.)
062 na hoppla ('oops')
063 fa? (= was, 'what?')

064 de zu voll von ('that too full of')
(The wall is too full. = Die Wand ist zu voll.)
065a also ('well')
065b obe hintuche viellei? ('up top put praps?')
(Should I put it on top?)
066 viellei obe hintuche ('praps up top put')
(Maybe I'll put it on top.)
067 XX umfahe nit ('XX fall over not')
(Something isn't falling over. = Etwas fällt nicht um.)
068 na ha (Meaning unclear)
069 un du geh obe hinterher ('and you go over behind')
070 un tu? ('and chair?')
(= Und der Stuhl?)
071 fohi? ('where?') (= Wohin?)
072 tuei ('chair')
(= Stuhl, E: what have you got in your hand?)
073 da hierhin tuche ('there here put')
(I'll put it there.)
074 ah.na sowas hier ('ah.well something like this here')
075 umfahe immer ('falls over always')
(It always falls over. = Der fällt immer um.)
076 ei tis ('egg this')
(It's an egg.)
(E: what's this then?)
077 (teib stehe) tch (Meaning unclear)
078 und hier? ('and here?')
(= Und hier das?, J. is holding a tin in his hand.)
079 fohin X hier? ('where to X here?')
(Where does this here go? = Wohin kommt hier das?)
080 aha.so.na ('well.like this')
081 puppe ('doll')
(E: ... what's all that in there?)
082 na eima gucke an ('well once look at')
(I'll look at it once. = Ich sehe es einmal an.)
083 m.komma her ('m.come here')
084 na XX ein ecksank ('well XX a corner cupboard')
(ellipt., = ein Eckschrank)
085 un hier.ha. den löffel ('and here.ha. the spoon')
(And this here's a spoon. = Und hier ist ein Löffel.)
086 na.ei tuh sieche ('well a door see')
(I see a door. = Ich sehe eine Tür.)
087 ja. un ei eßzimmertieche ('yes. and a dining roomtable')
(Yes, I see a dining room-table)

(E: what else can you see?)
088 ich.un be ('I.a be')
(J. is interrupted by E.)
089 dak tieche.obeauf ('roof animals.ontop')
(There are animals on the roof. = Auf dem Dach sind Tiere.)
090 ja ('yes')
091 XX darfe nit ('may not')
(They mayn't do that. = Das dürfen sie nicht.)
092 feis i nit ('know I not')
(I don't know.)
093 e sie.ei du. ei du. ei du.
(K. mimics animal noises.)
094 so geche nit.geche nit ('so goes not.goes not')
(It doesn't work like that.)
(= So geht das nicht.)
095 iaah (Animal noises)
(E: was können die anderen tiere sagen?)
096 hier hier iaah matte ('here here 'iaah' makes')
(= J. points to a donkey.)
097 chchch (Animal noise)
(E: what do the other animals say?)
098a hier tier ('here animal')
(Here is an animal. = Hier ist ein Tier.)
098b und hier tier ('and here animal')
099a un X gue morjen ('a X good morning')
(Continuation see 99b)
099b und fau sagen gue moje ('and mrs. say good morning')
(And the woman is saying good morning.)
(= guten Morgen)
100 ahso napeche darfe nit ('well after talk may not')
(You mayn't mimic. = Du darfst nicht nachsprechen.)

Transcript: jonas 2

No.	Utterances and comments
001	ja ('yes')
002	warum? ('why')
003	kann ich hinsetze hier? ('can I sit down here?') (J. wants to sit down.)
004	un sie? ('And you?') (Follows on from 3)
005	un sie? ('And you?') (Follows on from 3, J. points to the other teacher.)
006	kann se hier auch hinsetze ('can you here also sit down') (You can also sit down here = Sie können sich auch hier hinsetzen.)
007	ja ('yes')
008	ja ('yes')
009	joh.kanne i ('joh.can I') (Yes, I can.) (E: show Nico how to play that.)
010	daf ich jetz aufbaue meine dame? ('may I now build my woman?')
011	der nico kucke zuerst ('the nico watch first')
012	ja.warum? ('yes.why?')
013	si: tu X heute ('si: do X today') (Meaning unclear)
014	äpfel ('apples') (E: what's in there then?)
015	siche doch ('see yes') (You can see it. = Siehst du doch.)
016	joh? ('yes?')
017a	also hierhin tellen ('so over here put') (We've to put them here like this.) (E: what do you have to do with the apples now?)
017b	und dann so nei gucke ('and then so in look') (And then you look in like this. = Und dann so reingucken.)
018	ja.diese baum der nico komme ('yes.this tree the nico come') (Nico gets this tree. = N. bekommt diesen Baum.)
019	meike ei apfel hier immer din ('Meike (name of a girl) an apple always in here')
020	noch keine äpfel appematte ('yet no apples taken away') (There aren't any apples taken away yet.)

021 und da? ('and there?')
(J. points.)
022 leite ite mitte rundbieje
(Meaning unclear)
023 und da ei ('and there')
024 diese äpfel rucke runter ('and these apples pick up')
025 und da auch äpfel ('and there apples too')
026 diese äpfel rucke runter ('and these apples pick up')
027 oga.oga diese äpfel pflücke
('or.or these apples pick')
028 diese äpfel pflücke ('these apples pick')
029 oga ei junge esse auf äpfel
('or a boy eat up apples')
(= oder, Continuation of 28)
030 it? ('I?')
(it = ich, E: who's starting?)
031 meike it feit.meike it feit picke
(Meaning unclear)
032 wat? ('what?')
033 rucke noch einmal X ('move again X') (Meaning unclear)
034 id ei apfel pflücke ab ('I an apple pick off')
(id = ich (I))
035 fertig? ('ready?')
036 vielleich.vielleich rucke diese äpfel? (= ?pflücken)
('peraps.peraps ?pick these apples?')
037 danebe? ('next to?')
038 its au danebe ('is also next to')
039 wat sake sie? ('what say you?')
(What're you saying?)
(= Was sagen sie?)
040 nei.nei ('no.no')
041 da.vie vieje tück äpfel ('there.ma many pieces apples')
042 soviel tück äpfel ('so many pieces apples')
(Follows on from 41, points finger)
043 sovie äpfel du kanne am baum (schucke)
('so many apples you can on tree (?pick)')
044 it die kamera an.it die kamera an ('is the camera on.is the camera on')
(The camera is on. = Die Kamera ist an.)
045 it die kamera alleine fieme? ('is the camera alone film?')
(Does the camera take pictures by itself? = Filmt die K. alleine?)
046 hh? wat heit dat? ('hh? what mean that?')
(What does that mean?)
047 danebe ('next to')

048 du anfänge ('you start')
049 wat? ('what?')
050 danebe ('next to') (Imitation)
051 mats nits ('makes nothing')
(Doesn't matter. = Macht nichts.)
052 its au danebe ('is also next to')
053 itze ummeiβe korb (itze = ich (I)) ('I throw over basket')
054 oke nein ('or not') (= oder nicht, Follows on from 53)
055 hh? der zeiger da? ('hh? the pointer there?')
056 hm (confirmatory)
057 wat? ('what?')
058 ja.da ('yes.there')
059 ja.du ei apfel pflücke ('yes.you an apple pick')
060 hei.du noch ein apfel pflücke ('hei.you another apple pick')
061 das ei ('that nuff') (That's enough. = Das reicht.)
062 is mir zu X X ('is for me too X X')
063 du dann komme ('you then come')
(Then you'll get it. = Du bekommst es dann.)
064 ja ('yes') (confirmatory)
065 danebe ('next to')
066 du korb ummmeiβe ('you basket throw over')
067 ma tu noch eimal ('do you once more')
068 meite nochmal ('throw again') (= schmeiβen)
069 der junge? ('the boy?')
070 wat? ('what?')
071 (X) der junge klaue äpfel ('the boy nick apples')
072 sieche dok ('see you')
(Follows on from 71, = siehst du doch)
073 ja.der junge klaue äpfel ('yes.the boy nick apples')
074 meitje.dieser junge äpfel in de hand?
('throw.this boy apples in his hand?')
075 und dann klaue. weje.äpfel ('and then nick.away.apples')
(= Er klaut die Äpfel weg.)
076 un dei pau. ('and your tree') (= Baum)
077 oga sieche nit ('or see not')
(Or can't you see it. = oder siehst du den nicht.)
078 mach.mach ('do.do') (encouraging)
079 weitermatte ('further make') (encouraging)
080 danebe? ('next to?')
081 jez meite it ei apfel noch am baum
('now throw I an apple still on the tree')
(meite = schmeiβen (throw))
082 nochmal daneben ('again missed')

083 hund? hund? ('dog? dog?')
084 meintje is noch ma ('throw I again')
085 eh.nein.dahin.so (setz eintje) ('eh.no.there.so')
(= Meaning unclear)
086 da zeiger hin eima.nok ma
('there pointer to once.nok make')
087 hei.zeiger doof ('hei.pointer silly')
088 du matte mist mit mir ('you make rubbish with me')
(You're messing me about.)
089 nochmal ('again') (Imitation)
090 was? ('what?')
091 koab? ('basket?')
092 mutte koab ummisse diese ('must basket throw over this')
(You have to hit this basket. = Du mußt diesen Korb umschmeißen.)
093 na gut ('alright')
094 its ummisse (its = ich (I)) ('I throw over')
095 wat?wat? ('what?what?')
096 du is pflücke nix (große) ('you is pick nothing (big)')
097 du nochma dafe einma matze ('you again may once make')
(You may do that one more time.)
098 abe wenn ('but if') (interrupted)
099 nei.nei.nei ('no.no.no')
100 zeiga .du feit matte.dahin
(Meaning unclear)
101 matje so ('doit so')
(Do it like this. = Mach es so.)
102 daneben? ('next to?')
103 nein ('no')
104 was? ('what?')
105 wat? wat? ('what? what?')
106 oder so ('or so') (elliptical)
107 wat? ('what?')
108 und du? ('and you?')
109 du dann komme ('you then come')
(you'll get it then. komme = bekommen (get))

Transcript: julia 1

No.	Utterances and comments
001	nein ('no') (M. encourages J. to tell a picture book story.)
002	ja ('yes') (L: today's flecki's birthday)
003	so (L: what's he up to there?)
004	so (L: what's he doing then?)
005	so (L: how's he doing then?)
006	*weiβ* nich ('know not') (L: yes, what's he doing with the dogs, you must tell us.)
007	ja ('yes') (L: is he keeping his eyes closed?)
008	da wecki. da wecki burtstag? ('there wecki. there wecki birthday?') (Is it Flecki's Birthday? = Hat Flecki Geburtstag?)
009	(bölte) (i.e. a name) (L: And that is?)
010	flecki mama ('flecki mummy') (L: Who's that?)
011	ja ('yes') (L: and flecki counts)
012	eins zwei drei vier fünf sechs ('one two three four five six') (L. interrupts the utterance with his laughter.)
013	sieben acht neun zehn elf ('seven eight nine ten eleven') (Continues counting)
014	flecki (L: where did you learn to count so well?)
015	fab.fabian (L: who taught you to count then?)
016	nein ('no') (L: right, to see I have to put on my glasses)
017	fabians (Fabian's glasses. = Fabians Brille)
018	fabians (L: what what please?)
019a	nein ('no'). (L: Are these your glasses?)
019b	fabians (Continuation of 19a)
020	ja ('yes') (L: Do you want to try them on?)

021 nein ('no')
(L: Look here, I'd like to put on my glasses.)
022 aufziehn will ('put on want')
(I want to put them on.)
(L: only if you tell me that you want to put them on.)
023a nein ('no').
(L: say: I'd like to put on the glasses.)
023b sag ich ('say I')
(L. interrupts Julia)
024 doch ('oh yes')
(L: then you won't get them from me either)
025 doch ('oh yes')
(L: no)
026 doch ('oh yes')
(L: no)
027 ja ('yes')
(L: what's flecki shouting? I'm coming)
028 datati (= Krokodil) ('crocodile')
(Julia's looking at the picture book again.)
029 haben ('have')
(L: a crocodile)
030 (Schau mal bleck weg) (Meaning unclear)
(M: there is a crocodile under the carpet)
031 da ich komme ('there I come')
(L: and flecki. what is flecki calling?)
032 bär.bär ('bear.bear')
(L: there's another one behind the curtain))
034a essen da ('food there')
(L: and what's the bear doing?)
035 eine tuchen ('a cake') (= einen Kuchen)
(L: yes what's he eating then?)
036a (lennt wecki ba lennt su) (Meaning unclear)
036b wecki funden hat ('wecki found has')
(= Flecki has found cake.)
037 unter vorhang ('under curtain')
(L: flecki has found it.)
038 (hillich) (Meaning unclear)
(L: oh who's in the cupboard?)
039 nein ('no')
(L: the snake?)
040 nein ('no')
(L: isn't that a snake?)

041 n'nilpferd ('h'hippo')
(L: what's that then?)
042a nich nilpferd ('not hippo')
(L: pardon?)
043 nein ('no')
(L: ah the hippo?)
044a nein ('no')
(L: that's a snake)
044b nil (Continuation of 44a) (is interrupted)
045 dumen ('flowers') (= Blumen)
(L: look that's a jug and a plate)
046 pott ('mug')
(J. is looking at the picture book.)
047 teller ('plate')
(J. is looking at the picture book.)
048 und teller ('and plate')
(L: plate)
049a teller. ('plate.')
(L: and another plate)
049b lila teller ('mauve plate') (Continuation of 49a)
050 und ('and')
(L: mauve plate yes, L. interrupts J.)
050b da? ('there?')
(J. now asks L. about the objects in the book.)
(L: mauve plate yes)
051 da? ('there?')
(L: that's a yellow plate)
052 da? ('there?')
(L: a yellow plate too)
053 lila paffekanne ('mauve poffepot')
(It's a mauve coffeepot.)
(J. answers her own question. L: I don't know)
053 da? ('there?')
(L: a mauve coffeepot)
054 weiβ nich ('know not')
(L: I don't know)
055 belben tasse ('yellow cup')
(J. is looking at the picture book)
056a nein ('no')
(L: a yellow cup?)
056b belb belbe ('yell yello')
(Yellow.) (Continuation)

057a nein ('no')
(L: a yellow plate?)
057b belbe unterlage ('yellow saucer') (Continuation)
058 da lila tasse ('there mauve cup')
(L: a yellow saucer. great)
059a höma ('listen')
(= hör mal)
059b lila bas ('mauve lass')
(mauve glass; = Ein lila Glas)
060 da. da nilpferd ('there. there hippo')
(L: a mauve glass. yes)
061 ja ('yes')
(L: a hippo. gracious! does that manage to fit into the bathtub?)
062 einbin in badewanne ('jump in bathtub')
063 haare nei werd ('hair wet become')
(The hair'll get wet; = die Haare werden naβ...)
064a ja. ('yes')
(L: the hippo's hair'll get wet yes. if there's any water in there, eh?)
064b fama so. haare naβ wird ('fama so. hair wet become')
(If it goes like this, its hair gets wet.)
(L: the hippo's hair'll get wet yes. if there's any water in there, eh?)
065 julia legen badewanne.haare naβ wird
('julia lie bathtub.hair wet become')
(If I lie in the bathtub, my hair'll get wet.)
(L: yes yes. that's how your hair gets wet)
066a naβ (wird) ('wet (become)')
(L: if Julia lies down in the bathtub...)
066b haare naβ wird ('hair wet become') (Continuation of 66a)
067 jetzt nicht haare naβ ('now not hair wet')
(L: ..your hair gets wet))
068 nein ('no')
(L: but you're not in the tub)
069 batt ('sheet') (= Blatt)
(Julia is looking at the picture book)
070 löwe ('lion')
(L: that's a sheet. and who's behind the sheet?)
071 ch chau ch (Animal noise)
(L: the lion what's the lion doing then?)
072 da auch blatt ('there also sheet')
(J. is still busy with the picture book)
073 da nicht abmachen ('there not take off')
(He didn't remove the sheet here; = Das Blatt hat er nicht abgemacht.)

074 oh. nicht julia ('oh. not julia')
(L: he simply ripped the other sheet off)
075a nein.nein ('no.no')
(L: didn't julia rip that off?)
075b fabian (Continuation of 75a)
076 ja ('yes')
(L: fabian ripped it off?)
077 julia. julia buch ('julia. julia book')
(Julia is looking at the picture book)
078 da mit fabian. fabian auch reiβen mit den löwe
('there with fabian. fabian also rip with the lion')
(F.ripped the sheet with the lion.)
079 löwe batt fetthalten ('lion sheet hold')
(The lion is holding onto the sheet; = Der Löwe hält das Blatt fest.)
080 da ('there')
(J. is looking at the book)
081 da. dabeben ('there. there stick')
(L: the lion is holding onto the sheet yes)
(It should be stuck there.)
082 ja ('yes')
(L: it should be stuck there?)
083 affe ('monkey')
(L: who's behind the door?)
084a hihi ('here')
(L: how do you know it's a monkey?)
084b (bitt) ('please')
(Continuation)
084c affe ('monkey')
(L: how do you know it's a monkey?)
085 unsinn ('nonsense')
(L: what's the monkey doing behind the door?)
086 mama wecki ('mama wecki')
(L: and who's under the table?)

Transcript: julia 2

No.	Utterances and comments
001	rat (= Soldat?) ('soldier') (Julia is looking at another picture book with a child.) (K.: What's this here?)
002	trarat (K.: What's this here? whispers: Ritter ('knight'))
003	ritter ('knight') (K.: That's not a knight ... M.: a soldier?)
004	ritter ('knight') (K.: You have to say that into here.)
005	(Lune) (uncomp.) (K.: What's this here?)
006	ziehpferd ('pull horse') (A cart-horse.) (K.: Right, what's that there?) (M. laughs.)
007	lanzen ('lances') (K.: They're lances. Lances. Two lances.)
008	pferd ('horse') (K.: And this here?)
009	hut ('hat') (K.: And this here?)
010	ein ratenhut ('a soldhat') (soldier hat; = Soldatenhut) (K.: What's this here?)
011	nein ('no') (M.: A soldier's hat. Or a knight's hat?)
012	ritter ('knight') (K.: Knight, Knight, that's a knight.)
013	auch ritter ('too knight') (K.: this here?)
014	auch ritter ('too knight') (K.: this here?)
015	nonen ('cannon') (= Kanonen) (K.: What're these here?)
016	ja ('yes') (K.: Cannon balls?) (M.: cannon balls, 'Nonen')
017	julia vögel essen ('julia birds eat') (Julia is telling about all of the things she wants to do in Spain.)
018	meck gut vögel. ham. ('taste good birds. ham.') (Birds taste good; = Vögel schmecken gut.) (V.: What?)

019 so und.und julia.und fisch ('so and.and julia.and fish')
(Meaning unclear)
020 ja.fische ('yes fishes')
(V: you want to eat fish too?)
021 ja ('yes')
(V.: Fish?)
022a ja.und raupferde ('yes.and horses')
(V: many fishes?)
022b und mausen ('and mouses') (Continuation)
023 ja.und betten ('yes.and leaves') (= Blätter?)
(V: mice too?)
024a und metterlinge essen banien. Ham.
('and utterflies eat spain. Ham.')
(And I'll eat butterflies in Spain; = Und Schmetterlinge esse ich in Spanien.)
(V.: What's up?)
024b julia metterling dut meck. ('julia utterflies good taste.')
(Julia likes eating butterflies; = Schmetterlinge schmecken Julia gut.)
025 nein ('no')
(V.: Have you eaten butterflies before?)
026a ja ('yes')
(V.: You're going to try all of this in Spain?)
026b aubiern ('try out') (= ausprobieren)
027 essen ('eat')
(V: Yaya'll be suprised at everything you...)
028a ja.julia fische ('yes.julia fishes')
028b vogeln ('birds')
028c und maus ('and mouse') (Cont.)
028d und bumen ('and lowers') (flowers; = Blumen) (Cont.)
028e und bienen.julia essen ('and bees.julia eat') (Cont.)
029 und raupen ('and caterpillars')
(V.: What are going to eat?)
030 und mausen ('and mouses')
(V.: A caterpillar too.)
031a ja.und und lange julia essen.
('yes.and and nake julia eat') (snake; = Schlange)
(Yes, and Julia eats the snake.)
031b lange nut ('snake good') (= Die Schlange schmeckt gut.)
031c mecken lange ('taste good snake') (= Die Schlange schmeckt.)
031d metterling ('butterfly') (= Schmetterling)
031e und und tildöte julia ('and and tortoise julia') (=Schildkröte)
032 ja.und das Julia essen. Ham ('yes.and the Julia eat. Ham')
(Yes, and Julia eats that.)

(V: tortoise yes)
033 ja ('yes')
(V.: You're a greedy-guts, aren't you?)
034 nein ('no')
(V.: Oh yes, you're a greedy-guts.)
035a nein.nein ('no.no')
(V.: not?)
035b julia äpfel essen ('julia apples eat')
036 äpfel banien essen.(dern) ('apples spain eat.(like)')
(V.: Yes apples. You like eating those here too. dern = gern (like)?)
037 ja ('yes')
(V.: Only in Spain? And here?)
038a fisch julia essen. ('fish julia eat.')
(V.: see.)
038b und (bit) ('and (bit)')
038c und better ('and leaves') (= Blätter)
038d und tefen ('and beetles') (= Käfer)
039 tefer julia essen banien ('beetles julia eat spain')
(V.: That is a 'Käfer'. That is a 'Käfer'.)
040 tefer essen banien ('beetles eat spain')
(V.: oh you!)
041 yaya tefer.yaya tefer kochen ('yaya beetles.yaya beetles cook')
(V.: You want to eat a lot of things, don't you?)
042 ja ('yes')
(V.: What? Yaya's going to cook beetles?)
043 julia tefer essen. Ham. ('juia beetles eat. Ham.')
(V.: Gracious me!)
044 fisch ('fish')
(V.: Yes.)
045 ja ('yes')
(V.: And what about when you're five?)
046 angeln('fishing')
(V.: What're you going to do..; he means: ... when you're five.)
047 ja.vier julia nicht angeln ('yes.four julia not fish')
(V: then you want to go fishing?)
048 nein ('no')
(V.: When you're four, then you aren't allowed to go fishing.)
049 ja ('yes')
(V.: but when you're five you can go fishing?)
050 yaya ('yaya')
(V.: Who told you that then?)
051a ja.banien yaya tel ('yes.spain yaya tel')
(Yaya said)

051b (let) julia fische angeln will ('julia fishes fish want')
052 fünf bin ('five am')
(V.: Aha; Follows on from 51b. Something like: 'when I'm five'.)
053 ja ('yes')
(V.: When you're five.)
054 ja ('yes')
(V.: Did you ring Yaya?)
055a julia fünf ('julia five')
(V.: What did she tell you? Something like: 'whenjulia's five, ...')
055b julia angel kaufen. ('julia rod buy')
056a ja.nicht bielen ('yes.not play')
(Not for playing with = nicht zum Spielen.)
(V: buy a rod?)
056b echte angel ('real rod')
057 fische ('fishes')
(V.: Not a game...)
058a ja.fische ('yes.fishes')
(V: not a toy rod but real one)
058b julia angeln echt ('julia fish real')
059 julia saufel mitnehm ('julia spade take with')
(Julia's going to take a spade with her.)
(V.: And has Yaya also told you about the beach, about the sand? What's she told you then?)
060a fabian auch ('fabian too')
(V.: You ought to take a spade?)
060b (pafen bauen pafen) (Incompr.)
061 kaufen Yaya Julia (boen) waufel ('buy Yaya Julia spade')
(waufel = Schaufel (spade))
(V.: What's he buying?)
062 ja ('yes')
(V.: Yes?)
063 (dern) (Incompr.)
064 das ('that')
(Julia wants to look at a picture book.)
065 das ('that')
(V.: Which one do you want to look at?)
066 das ('that')
067 ja ('yes')
(V.: Which? The one with the fishermen at the seaside?)
068 nein ('no')
(V.: Julie, I can't speak Spanish. You'll have to tell me.)
069 julia weiβ nich ('julia knows not')
(Julia doesn't know.)

(V.: I can't speak Spanish. Mama's got that ... You've listened to that before.)

070 julia kann nicht lesen. ('julia can not read.')
(Julia can't read.)
(V.: Well you know, I don't know either, Julie.)

071a julia. julia kann nicht telen ('julia. julia can not tell')
(= Julia kann nicht erzählen, ...)

071b das boden ('the floor')
(something's happened on the floor; = 'was auf dem Boden passiert'.)

072 ja ('yes')
(V.: Can't you tell me what happened on the floor there?)

073 ja.hund ('yes.dog')
(V: yes? can you tell me?)

074 hund ('dog')
(V.: What is that there?)

075 theo dicken wieder wauwau ('theo gets again woofwoof')
(Theo's getting the dog again; = Theo kriegt den Hund wieder.)

076 nein ('no')
(V.: Have you been to the doctor's at all before, Julie?)

Transcript: klaus 1

No.	Utterances and comments
001	(w)o? ('where?')
	(L: there are more things in there.) (L.unpacks the box.)
002	oh
	(While unpacking the box.)
003	nein nein ('no, no')
	(L: have you found another pole?)
004	hm
	(L: do you mean the train or the ducks on the lake?)
005	und da? ('and there?')
	(K. points to the object.)
006	rege(n)wurm ('earthworm')
	(L: could that be a snake or an earthworm?)
007	und das? ('and that?')
008	und da delbe ('and that yellow')
	(K. points at straw.)
009	hierhin ('over here')
	(K. puts it down.)
010	hinlaufen ('run there')
	(The cow should run to the straw.)
011	muh ('moo')
	(L: who's running there?)
012	da kuh ('there cow')
	(K. points to the cow.)
013	neb ('nex')
	(= neben. That comes next to the stall.)
014	abbau ('take dow n')
	(K. wants to knock the things down.)
015	alles? ('all?') (Follows on from 14)
016	ja ja ('yes yes')
	(L: do you want to build up the rest?)
017	(fa) (Meaning unclear)
018	und das? ('and that?')
	(K. points to the calender.)
019	hm?
020	mama au so ein ('mama too so one')
	(Mama's got a calender too.)
021	mama nich ('mama not')
	(= M.'s calender's not like that, it's different.)
022	dünner ('thinner')

(L: it looks different, mama's)
023 der's auch biβchen lang ('the's too bit long')
(That's a bit long too.)
024 länger ('longer') (Follows on from 023)
025 und das? ('and that?')
(K. points at another object.)
026 haffe (= giraffe)
(K. indicates a giraffe.)
027 raushole? ('fetch out?')
(K. wants to get the doll out of the box.)
028 das haus bau (auch)? ('that house build (too)?')
(K. asks, whether he should build a house (too))
029 ja.ja ('yes.yes')
(L. asks K., whether he needs the house too.)
030 tiere ('animals')
(That's the animals' house.)
031a nein ('no')
(L.: oh, that's the giraffe's house.)
031b tiere ('animals')
(Continuation of elliptic utterance 31a)
032 mehr tige.tiere. (funde) ('more animals (found)')
(K. has found more animals in the box.)
033 und dann x tiere ('and then x animals') (Meaning unclear)
034 da.mehr tige ('there.more animals')
(There are even more animals.)
035 fant ('phant')
(K. wants the elephant.)
036 fafant au bauchen? ('phaphant too need?')
(Do we also need the elephant?)
037 runterteiger. tilge ('step down. animals')
(K. wants to let the animals get down.)
038 haffe (= 'giraffe')
(K. wants the giraffe to get down.)
040 un' dann mi de'reger.d'haffe ('an' then with the wheels the giraffe')
(And then the giraffe with the wheels should get down.)
041 da ('there')
(K. points at the object they are looking for.)
042 feunden.feunde.fründe('friends')
(K.wants to indicate the relationship between two toys.)
043 wat machen mit den tab? ('what do with the pole?')
(What do we do with the pole?)
(= Was machen wir mit dem Stab?)
044a runterhupfen ('jump down')

(K. pushes the figures off the table.)
044b runtermachen ('make down')
045 fafant?('phaphant?')
(K. isn't sure whether he should push the elephant down.)
046 ne ('no')
047 laufen immer ('run always')
(K. indicates that the animals always run.)
048 und das? ('and that?')
(K. points at an object.)
049 und da? und da? ('and that? and that?')
(Question about the animals' possible actions.)
050 so geht? ('so goes?')
(K. asks whether he should put the dolls into the box.)
051 un' das? ('an' that?')
(K. asks where he should put a doll.)
052 bauche? ('need?')
(= Brauchen wir das? Do we need that?)
053a nein ('no')
(K. seems to want to correct one of his actions verbally.)
053b falsch ('wrong')
054 un' das? ('an' that?')
055 tor? tore? ('gate? gate?') (Tor = gate; Tür = door)
(Question, whether an object is a door.)
056 he. affe? ('he. ape?')
(= Ist hier ein Affe? Is there a monkey here?)
057 wutsch. wa (Meaning unclear)
058 den tuch ('the cloth') (Tuch = cloth; Zug = train)
(To that L.: Ah, you're looking for the train.)
059 und da? ('and that?')
060 hm?
(Comprehension question after L.'s explanation.)
061 wo is'n de? ('where is it then?')
(= Wo ist denn der(Anhänger)?)
062a wo? ('where?')
(K. is looking for the trailer in the cupboard.)
062b den? ('this? masc. acc. form.')
(= die? fem. form.: K. has found the doll) (die Figur (doll) = fem.)
063 faß ('barrel')
(K. wants to show that there is also a monkey barrel in the drawer concerned.)
064 auch affen bauchen? ('also apes need?')
(Do we also need the monkeys?)
065 richtig tumachen. richtig ('right close. right')

(K. is trying to close the drawer properly.)
066 un'der tetel au' bauchen? ('an' the paper also need?')
(= Brauchen wir den Zettel auch? Do we also need the piece of paper?)
067 ja ('yes')
(To the question whether the piece of paper is needed.)
068 lesen ('read')
(Question: What is the paper needed for?)
069 was da dra' ('what out there')
(Rest incomprehensible)
070 viele? ('many?')
(Answer from L.: yes, we've got a lot of monkeys.)
071 ja ('yes')
(Stressing L.'s comment.)
072 aufmuma affen ('buy muma apes')
(Interpretation on the basis of 073: "Mama soll auch Affen kaufen." Mama should buy monkeys too.)
073 muma auch affen taufen ('mama also apes buy')
(Supplement to 072)
074 enö affen ('monkeys')
(= keine Affen, ('no apes'))
075 ne ('no')
(To the question whether K. has any monkeys.)
076 die mama tauf' hein ('the mama buys no')
(= Die Mama kauft keine (Affen). Mama doesn't buy any.)
077 nein ('no')
(After L.'s encouragement to ask for one.)
078 möcht' 'nen arzkoffer ('want a doctor bag')
(= Ich möchte einen Arztkoffer.)
079 auch 'n'n baker ('also a digger')
(= auch einen Bagger.)
080 tistind (Follows on from 079, = Christkind, 'Christ-child')
081 noch 'n x ('another 'n')
(K. has another wish which is incomprehensible.)
082 auch 'n x ('also one')
(Meaning unclear)
083 das auto ('the car')
(K. interrupts his attempts to explain this matter further. Reference to a new theme; here: more dolls)
084 hier durchfahren ('drive through here')
(= Das Auto kann/soll hier durchfahren. The car can/should drive through here.)
085 de' naha
(Utterance to go with an action. K. is looking for something.)

086 das dies fahren ('that this drive')
(Again as in 085; K. is looking for something.)
087 viele ('many')
(L.: And here's another car.)
088 finten ('ahind')
(Behind.)
(To guide L.'s actions.)
089 bus ja ('bus yes')
(L.: I've only got a train and a bus.)
090 d' eisebah ('t' railway')
(Reference to a toy.)
091 hm.hm

Transcript: klaus 2

No. Utterances and comments

001 ja ('yes')
002 hm (Agreement)
003 aber den auch ('but the too')
(But I know him (lion) too; = Aber den (Löwen) kenne ich auch.)
004 ein anderen ('another')
(I have already been to another circus; = (ich war schon) in einem anderen (Zirkus).)
005 löwe un'daufen ('lion a above')
(To L.'s question whether there was a lion there.)
006 bär au' ('bear too')
(There was a bear too; = Da war auch ein Bär.)
007 ne ('no')
008 und da? ('and there?')
009 wo? ('where?')
010 un' hasen ('a hare')
(To supplement L.: that's the magician. with the topper and the magic wand.)
011 auch hasen? ('also hare?')
(Now as a questi on to L.)
012 noch welche? ('still more?')
(Is he going to magic some more?; = Zaubert er noch welche?)
013 un' viel taup. taube ('an' many duf.dove')
(He's conjoured a lot (of doves); = Viele Tauben hat er gezaubert.)
014 oben viele? ('above many?')
(Are there a lot of doves up there (in the marquee)?; = Sind oben (am Zirkuszelt) viele (Tauben)?)
015 hiar? ('?here?')
(K. is pointing at a point in the puzzle.)
016 ans ('scare')
(K. wants to indicate that the doves are scared.)
017 eine ('one')
(Only one of the musicians is scared of the doves; = Nur der eine (Musiker) hat Angst vor den Tauben.)
018 so
(Agreement with L.'s interpretation.)
019 na.x ('well.x')
(K. tries to take off a part.)
020 den abnehmen ('that take off')
(K. takes a part of the puzzle off again.)

021 nein ('no')
022 alle ab ('all off') (After a completed action)
023 tommel.tommel ('drum.drum')
(K. points at the clown's drum.)
024 ja ('yes')
025 alles ('all') (Agreement)
026 alles? ('all') (Question)
027 ver.x.x (Action accompanied by utterance)
028 antucken bär ('look bear')
(Let's have a look at the bear; = Wir gucken uns den Bären (mal) an.)
029 ein toba ('a drum')
(= Eine Trommel)
030 ein tein toba ('a little drum')
(= Eine kleine Trommel.)
031 bum.bum (K. imitates the banging of a drum.)
032 wo's die da die da? ('where's it there it there?')
033 und das? ('and that?')
034 und da? ('and there?')
035 nein ('no')
036 und das? ('and that?')
037 d'töte.töte ('t'lute.lute')
(K. wants to say 'Flöte' (flute), but points at the tuba.)
038 tubè.tuba (Attempts to find the word for 'tuba')
039 der paβt ('it fits')
(As he puts down the puzzle)
040 det paβt ('that fits')
(To stress the previous statement.)
041 un' die? ('an' them?') (Points at the spectators)
042 ahm ('er') (Indecision)
043 das in die mitte ('that in the middle')
(That (part of the game) goes in the middle; = Das kommt in die Mitte.
(= das Spielteil))
044 und das ('and that')
(And that (comes in the middle.))
(To complete: = Und das (kommt in die Mitte).)
045 und das x ('and that x') (Renewed explanation)
046 paβt nist? ('fits not?')
(Doesn't it fit?; = Paβt (es) nicht?)
047 woran lit das? ('why's that?')
(Why's that; = Woran liegt das? (that it doesn't fit))
048 dahin paβt? ('there fits?')
(Does it fit in there?; = Dahin paβt es?)
049 un' der tauberer da? ('and the magician there?')

(= Und der Zauberer da?)
050 da obe' da? ('there above there?')
(Playing with the puzzle: (Up there?) Da oben da?)
051 un' d' füβe tauberer? ('an' th' feet magician?')
(And where are the magician's feet?; = Und wo sind die Füβe von dem Zauberer?)
052 unten ('under')
(K. indicates that the puzzle should be continued 'unten'.)
053 da x x. ('there x x.') (to accompany an action)
054 das mein. ('that mean.')
(I mean that; = Das meine ich.)
055 und so? ('and so?')
056 und dann so ('and then so')
057 und paβt ('and fits')
(On successfully placing something.)
058 so ('so')
059 paβt nist ('fits not') (= Paβt nicht.)
060 und da? ('and there?')
061 daun ('lown')
(K. points at the clown.)
062 keine daun ('little lown')
(That's the little clown; = Das ist der kleine Clown.)
063 doβe daun musik machen ('big clown music make')
(The big clown is making music; = Der groβe Clown macht Musik.)
064 hoch machen ('high make')
(The little clown is propping the weight up (high))
(= Der kleine Clown stemmt das Gewicht hoch.)
065 wist ('weight') (Attempt to pronounce the word 'Gewicht'.)
066 und das hinpaβt? ('and that fits in?')
(And where does that fit in?; = Und wo paβt das hin?)
067 tuckendas ('look that')
(In the sense of: Mal gucken, wo es hinpaβt/Wir müssen gucken, wo es hinpaβt. Let's see where it fits in/We'll have to see where it fits.)
068 nä auch wie x ('nä also like x') (Accompanying an action)
069 anders suchen ('other look for')
(Look for another (part); = Ein anderes (Teil) suchen.)
070 wu's das? ('where's that?')
(Where's the (big part); = Wo ist das (groβe Stück)?)
071 wo is'n d'grote tück? ('where's t' big part?')
(Where's the big bit then?)
(= Wo ist denn das groβe Stück?)
072 wo's tei tarke mann? ('where's the strong man?')
(=Wo ist der starke Mann?)

073 doßer bär ('big bear')
(K. points at the big bear.(= großer Bär))
074 ein tück 'n bär suche ('a piece a bear look for')
(K.'s looking for a piece of puzzle with a bear.)
075 da han an tück von bär funden ('there have a piece of bear found')
(There, I've found a piece with a bear; = Da habe ich ein Stück vom Bär gefunden.)
076 wohin paßt? ('Where fits?) (= Wohin paßt es?)
077 nein ('no')
078 da ('there')
(It belongs there; = Da gehört es hin.)
079 bißchen boden ('bit floor')
(There's a bit of the circus floor; = Da ist ein bißchen vom Zirkusboden.)
080 der mann noch mal 'rausnehmen ('the man another time take out')
(Let's take the man out again; = Wir nehmen den Mann noch einmal heraus.)
081 ma suchen das ('let's try that')
(I'll have a go; = ich versuche das mal.)
082 guck! ('look!')
083 da ('there')
084 beine un' füße? ('legs and feet?')
(L.: legs and feet are missing there.)
085 an auto ('a car') (Indicates a car.)
086 unter ('under')
(In looking for a missing piece of puzzle.)
087 nein.nein ('no.no')
088 tück 'n tauber ('piece 'n magic')
((That is) a piece of the magician; = (Das ist) ein Stück von dem Zauberer.)
089 oder? ('or?') (Question)
090 nein ('no')
091 da ('there')
092 so pat da 'rein ('so fit there in')
(It fits in like that; = So paßt es darein.)
093 wo is' an d' vorhaung? ('where is on t' curtain?')
(Where is there a/the curtain?; = Wo ist ein/der Vorhang?)
094 hier in de' vorhaung ('here in t' curtain')
(Here in the curtain (there is a piece missing); = Hier an dem Vorhang (fehlt ein Stück).)
095 n' toßes tücken vohaung feht noch
('a big part curtain miss still')
(A large part of the curtain is still missing; = Ein großes Stück Vorhang fehlt noch.)

096 wo's 'n d' zirkzel? ('where's t' circusten')
(Where's the circustent?; = Wo ist das Zirkuszelt.)
097 des ne ('that no')
098a hasen weggeläuift ('hare ranned away')
(see Continuation in 98b)
098b lauft unter den tisch ('run under the table')
(Continuation of 098a)
099 ne('no')
(Answer to the question whether L. should give him a tissue.)
100 nein ('no')
(In answer to the question whether he'd like the tissue as a present.)

Transcript: patrick

No.	Utterances and comments
001	ja ('yes') (T. and P. are sitting on the floor. T: ... slid properly?)
002	umfallen nicht machen ("fall over not make') (P. doesn't want to make it fall over.)
003	nö ('no') (T: ..or was that dangerous?)
004	ja.mein vater auch ('yes.my father also') (T: mama can definitely drive well.)
005	ja ('yes') (T: your father too?)
006	nä ('no') (T: you needn't be scared.)
007	hier das ('here that') (T: what do you like playing with the most? P. takes two bricks out of the toy box.)
008	XXX / geht nich so eine ('goes not such one') (P. puts two bricks together (and they don't fit).)
009	geht so eine nich ('goes so one not') (P. puts two bricks to the side.)
010	nä ('no') (T: do you think we haven't got those?, referring to bricks)
011	ja? ('yes?') (T: I saw some.only yesterday on the street)
012	ja? ('yes?') (T: there was a building site. you know?)
013	raupen? ('Caterpillars?') (T: and there were Caterpillars like this.)
014	ja? ('yes?') (T: they pushed loads of sand.)
015	nö ('no') (T: have you never seen any?)
016	hmhm ('uh uh') (T: really never?)
017	noch was drinne? ('still something in?') (P. takes bricks out of the toy box.)
018	nich was hier drinne? ('not something here in?') (Meaning see 17)
019	ja ('yes') (T: yes, there's still something in there.)

020a ne ('no')
(T: I'll get the telephone out.)
020b brauch ich nich ('need I not') (Follows on from 20a)
021 ohaXXX (Meaning unclear)
022 ja ('yes')
(T: do you know her?)
023 hm ('uh huh')
(T: have you ever seen a real one?)
024 holland
(T: where then?)
025 hm ('uh huh')
(T: in Holland?)
026 noch elefante ('still elephants')
027 hm
(T: elephants too?)
028 das se (Meaning unclear)
029 brauch ich nich ('need I not')
(I don't need it.)
(T: there's an elephant; P. puts it to one side.)
030 ja? du brauchen ('yes? you need')
(Yes; do you need it?)
(T: I think it's pretty; P. gives T. the figure.)
031 auch noch einen ('also another one')
(P. needs another one.)
032a nä ('no')
(T: another elephant.)
032b so nen ('such a one') (Follows on from 32a)
033 ehm.löwe ne? ('uhm.lion no?')
(T: it's a goat.a billygoat. P. places the figure on the floor)
034 tiger ('tiger')
(T: that's a tiger.)
035 löwe nich? ('lion not?')
(Is it not a lion?; = Ein Löwe ist es nicht?)
036 jo? ('yes?')
(T: a lion looks like this.)
037 ich hab so was ('I have so thing')
(I've got something like that.)
(P. gets a figure out of the toy box.)
038 ich auch so einen ('I also so one')
(I want one like that, too.)
(P. gets another figure out of the box.)
039 tonne is das ('tonne is that')
(T: boar)

040 tonne (Follows on from 39)
041 ehm
(T: my elephant comes on top of that.)
042 eh was? ('er what?')
(T: we're building a right little zoo.)
043 zoo? ('zoo?')
(T: a proper zoo.)
044 doch.zoo ('yes.zoo')
(T: don't you know what that is?)
045 die hier ('these here')
(P. takes figures out of the box.)
046 zoo ('zoo')
(T: am I building one there now?)
047 ne wiese? ('a meadow?')
(T: a meadow.)
048 zoowiese? ('zoomeadow?') (Question)
049 zoowiese gibts nich ('zoomeadow exists not')
(there's no such thing as a zoomeadow.)
(T: a zoomeadow.yes)
050 nä ('no')
(T: doesn't that exist?)
051 hm
(T: no?)
052 ja? ('yes?')
(T: it exists in my book.)
053 au wei. alles umfalle ('oh no. everything fall over')
054 ja ('yes')
(T: really?)
055 pferd steh nich ('horse stands not')
(My horse won't stay standing.)
(P. tries to stand the figure up.)
056 tiere? ('animals?')
(T: now I need a few more animals.)
057 ja.ich auch paar brauchen ('yes.I also a few need')
(T: would you pass me over the box please.)
058 eh XX (Meaning unclear)
059 nä ('no')
(T: do you know what that is?)
060 kamel ('camel')
(T: that's a camel.)
061 ja ('yes') (Follows on from 60)
062 eh.eh. gibts nich ('uh.uh. exists not')
(T: a giraffe is going into my zoomeadow now.)

063 ja.manchmal ('yes.sometimes')
(T: you've set up a nice few animals there.)
064 noch einen männchen brauchen ('still one little man need')
(P. takes a figure out of the box.)
065 noch nen.noch einen männchen brauchen
('still an.still one little man need')
(I still need another little man.) (to T.)
066 jo ('yes')
(T: do you need another little man?)
067a ne ('no')
(T: Look in here. I've got proper little dolls in there.)
067b brauch ich nich ('need I not') (Follows on from 67a)
068 haus brauche bei ('house need with')
(P. wants the dolls' house from the last session.)
069 ja? ('yes?')
(T: yes.we had this house last time.didn't we?)
070 is das haus? ('is that house?')
(Where is the house?; = Wo ist das Haus?)
071 nä? ('no?')
(T: I couldn't find it today.)
072 ja ('yes')
(T: so I thought we could play with the building bricks today instead.)
073 hm
(T: do you think that's a good idea, too?)
074 ja bald XX ('yes soon XX') (Meaning unclear)
075 ja? ('yes?')
(T: there are maybe a few more little men here.)
076 baum brauchen ich ('tree need I')
(I need a tree.)
(P. delves into the box.)
077 ja.hm ('yes.mm')
(T: exactly.we need flowers too.)
078 hier is die ('here is he')
(Here it is.)
(P. puts the tree out.)
079 einen hier ('one here')
(P. puts another figure next to it.)
080 he noch (XX) (Meaning unclear)
081 hier is der ('here is he')
(P. carries on building.)
082a XXX ne. ('no.')
(T: you're making a great forest patrick.)

082b ich noch was bei ('I still some with')
(I've still got some.)
(P. moves T.'s figure away.)
083 hm.den auch bei ('mm.the also with')
(T: here's the lion you were just looking for. P. puts the lion next to it.)
084 och.hier is der ('oh.here is he')
(P. pushes figures to and fro.)
085 hier kommen der ('here come he')
(P. pushes figures to and fro.)
086 und tehn nich ('and stan not')
(And they won't stand.)
(P. tries to make the figure stand.)
087 nä ('no')
(T: won't he stay standing?)
088 ja.mach son ('yes.do already')
(Yes. Have a go.)
(T: should I have a go? P. leaves it to T.)
089 ja? ('yes?')
(T: he's tired.)
090 slafen muß der ('sleep must he')
(He has to sleep.)
(T: he always has to sleep.)
091 hä? rollo? ('huh? roll?')
(P. picks up a roll of wood.)
092 rolle?.eine rolle ('roll?.a roll?')
(T: a roll.)
093 tiere drinnen hier ('animals inside here')
(P. builds a fence around the animals and points to it.)
094 hier grinne tiere ('here inside animals')
(There are animals inside here.)
(T: pardon?)
095 ja.kleine ('yes.little')
(T: you've also made a little barn?)
096 du nich kleinen tall? ('you not little barn?')
(barn = Stall, T: I think that's nice.)
097 hä? is das? ('huh? is that?')
(P. takes a figure out of the box.)
098 ablepper ('tow-er') (recovery vehicle; = Abschlepper)
(T: what's that meant to be?)
099 ablepper aussieh ('tow-er looks like')
(It looks like a recovery van.)
(T: huh?)

100 mh
(T: that's what it looks like.)
101 nä ('no')
(T: do we need th at?)
102 noch einen.noch einen ('another one.another one')
(T: I'll put some more pigs out for you.)

Transcript: petra 1

No.	Utterances and comments
001	= ja ('yes') (xx) (P. wants to paint a picture; L: then fetch another piece of paper)
002	ja ('yes') (L: can it be a big piece like that too?)
003	dies x ma so son x zeiten ('this x well like x times') (P. points at a picture.)
004a	guck ma ('look here')
004b	so swänzchen ('so little tail') (A little tail like this.) (P. points at paws.)
005	foten so lecken.so lecken ('paws so lick.so lick') (They're licking their paws; = Die lecken ihre Pfoten.)
006a	ja ('yes') (confirmatory)
006b	ga mutzig ('full dirty') (completely dirty; = ganz schmutzig)
007	muschi nö.muschi nö xx ('muschi no.muschi no xx') (L: sometimes they say muschi to them.)
008	oma.oma a ('gran.gran a') (Extension to 009)
009	de oma soein muschi heiβt.muschi heiβt ('the gran so a muschi called.muschi called') (At Grandma's an animal like this is called muschi)
010	ja endlich ('yes at last') (Drawing paper is passed round.)
011	ja ('yes') (confirmatory)
012	em.so ein männchen.so ein männchen ('er.such a little man.such a little man') (P. wants a little man painted.)
013a	nein ('no') (L: a little man like this with a suitcase like this.)
013b	so ('like this') (P. corrects L.)
014	ja ('yes')
015	ja ('yes')
016	em.das ('er.that') (L: which are you taking first for yourself?)
017	ja ('yes')
018	ich ein männchen ('I a little man') (I want to paint a little man.) ((paint) malen = 0)

019 ich ein kein männchen ('I a not a little man')
(I'm not a little man.)
((not a) kein = correcting herself)
020 du mir helft? ('you me helps?')
(Will you help me?)
021 ja ('yes')
022 hier.hm ('here.er')
(L: where are you going to sit down?)
023 ich he ('I he') (interrupted)
024 ja ('yes')
025 augen ('eyes')
(L: what are you painting?)
026 ein mund ('a mouth') (Follows on from 025)
027 schulstiften ('schoolpens')
028 = kindergarten x ('kindergarten/play group')
(L: and now we're going to draw with wax crayons.)
029a ne. ('no.')
(L: the hair?)
029b mütsche ('cap') (= Mütze)
030 ein mütsche kann ('a cap can')
(I can draw a cap.)
031 ja so ('yes so')
(L: take a look at it..)
032 ja ('yes')
(L: just have a go.)
033 hm.haltsch ('er.throat')
(throat; = Hals, L: what's still missing?)
034 un kopf ('a head') (Follows on from 033)
035 ehm bauch ('a stomach')
(L: ..the throat and the?)
036 hm
037 nich kann ('not can')
(I cannot do that; = Ich kann das nicht.)
038 jetsch ('now') (= jetzt, Encouragement to carry on.)
039 ja ('yes')
040 jetsch ('now') (see 038)
041 nein ('no')
(L: is it already ready?)
042 ein bau.ein bau ('a boman.a boman')
(P. points at a woman (= Frau). It's her picture.)
043 ja ('yes')
044 ne ('no')
(L: that is one of the legs.)

045 jaha ('yeahs') (yes)
046 ein ein sock ('a a sock')
(L: and what are you just painting now?)
047 ja ('yes')
048 hm ja hm warze.warze.warze ('er yes er lack.lack.lack')
(P. is painting black (= schwarz) stripes.)
049 hm aufpassen ('er careful')
(P. wants to attract attention.)
050 hm kuma hm ('er look er') (see 049)
051 jaha ('yeahs') (yes)
052 xx hose is ('xx trousers is')
053 kuck ('look')
054 un baby ('a baby')
(L: what else is the woman getting?)
055 jaha ('yeahs') (yes)
056 in lankenhaus ('in 'spital (hospital)'; = Krankenhaus)
057 sein.sein kopf ('his.his head')
(P. points at her picture again.)
058 augen ('eyes') (see 057)
059a mein meine mama imma so ein baby
('my my mama always such a baby')
(My mama had a baby like that too; = ..hatte auch ein Baby.)
059b isch ein baby ('I a baby')
(?I'm going to draw a baby too; = ?Ich male/habe auch ein Baby.)
060 ja ('yes')
061 hals ('throat')
(P. draws a throat for the baby.)
062 XXXX (Meaning unclear)
063 hm.jetsch ('er.now') (it's ready; = Jetzt ist es fertig.)
064a ja ('yes')
064b ein ein baby ('a a baby')
(L: the woman is missing one more thing, I think...)
065 und ein bändschen ('and a little tail')
(Follows on from 064, (little tail) = Schwänzchen)
066 ein junge ('a boy')
(P. points to her picture.)
067 babyjunge ('babyboy') (imitative)
068 (X) (Meaning unclear)
069 bänzchen ('little tail')
(L: and what's he getting there?)
070 armen ('arms')
(L: look what they're still missing.)
071 oh

072 kuck ma ('look here')
073 ein baby ('a baby')
(P. looks at her picture.)
074 X X haut ('?skin') (Meaning unclear)
075 ehm morden nan nehmen ('er morrow ?man take')
(?Tomorrow I'll take it with me; = ?Morgen nehm ich es mit.)
076 verjessen? ('forgotten?')
(L: and the woman?) (P. had forgotten the woman.)
077 noch spiel ('still play')
(I still want to play)
078 noch ein mann mal ('still a man draw')
(I want to draw another man.)
079 un ein auto ('and a car') (Follows on from 078)
080a kuck ma.kuck ma ('look here.look here')
080b da ei auch ein auto ('there a also a car')
(P. points to the board on the wall.)
081 X X (Meaning unclear)
082 ja ('yes')
083 ich ein mann ('I a man')
(I want to paint a man.)
((paint) malen = 0)
084 un ein kaubie ('and a cowboy') (Follows on from 083)
085 un ein blusi ('and a flower') (= Blume, Follows on from 083)
086 wase wase ('lawn lawn') (= Rasen)
087 imma so was wasen so was ('always so thing lawn so thing')
(A lawn is always like this.)
(P. paints a lawn.)
088 ja ('yes')
089 keine angst ('no fear')
090 X X (Meaning unclear)
091a nein ('no')
(L: can the baby then play on the meadow?...)
091b noch bauch ('still stomach')
(It's still in the stomach; = Es ist noch im Bauch.)
092 ja ('yes')
093a nein ('no')
(L: then the mother sits down on the lawn...)
093b da sitzen ('there sit')
094 das is ein kopf ('that is a head')
(P. points at her picture.)
095 lu kuck ('look')
096 ich ängen auf das ('I ang on that')
(I'm going to hang the picture on there.)
(P. hangs up the picture.)

Transcript: petra 2

No.	Utterances and comments
001	ich weiβich nich ('I know I not')
	(I don't know.)
	(L: what do we want to play today then?...)
002	oder das ('or that')
	(P. points at the monkey game.)
003	ja ('yes')
004a	du anders spiel ('you other play')
	(You should play the other monkey; = Du sollst den anderen Affen spielen.)
004b	nehm gelb ('take yellow')
	(Take the yellow monkey; = Nimm den gelben Affen.)
005	ich ('I')
	(L: and who's taking the red one?)
006	jupps ('oops')
	(6x, P. jumps up and down with the monkey.)
007	und meiner hier ('and mine here')
	(L: and mine ... he's hanging over there.)
008	und deiner? ('and yours?') (Continuation of 007)
009	ja ('yes')
010	nich ganz oben ('not quite above')
	(Not quite at the top.)
011	meiner viel gröβer ('mine much bigger')
	(My monkey is much bigger; = Mein Affe ist viel gröβer.)
012	dei deiner viel kleiner ('yo yours much smaller')
013a	nein ('no')
013b	dei dein ganz klein ('yo yours quite small')
	(Yours is quite small.)
014	ganz klein du deins ('quite small you yours')
	((you yours) du deins = correction of herself)
015	du ganz klein ganz winzig dein affen
	('you quite small quite tiny your monkey')
	(You have got quite a small monkey; = Du hast einen ganz kleinen A.)
016a	nee ('no')
	(L: my monkey is quite small?)
016b	mein ganz groβ ('my quite big')
	(Mine's quite big.)
017	vie deiner viel ganz klein
	('mu yours much quite small')
	(Yours is much smaller.)

018 nein ('no')
(L: my monkey is exactly the same size as yours.)
019 dei deiner immer zukucken
('yo yours always watch')
(Yours always watch.)
020 meiner so ('mine like this')
(P. lets her monkey climb up.)
021a wills auch? ('want too?')
(Do you want to, as well?)
021b kleiner? ('smaller?') (Continuation of 021a, Vocative)
022 aber du ganz klein ('but you quite small')
023 immer helfen ('always help')
(I help you; = Ich helfe dir.)
024 äng äng du äng äng so sag
('äng äng you äng äng like this say')
(You should say 'äng'; = Du sollst äng sagen.)
025 äng äng (onomatopoeic)
026 aber du gar nicht mehr hoch ('but you not at all more high')
(You can't get higher; = Du kannst nicht höher.)
027 petraX X unten ('below') (Meaning unclear)
028a du du jetzt zukucken ('you you now watch')
(You should watch now; = Du sollst jetzt zugucken...)
028b ich macht ('I make')
(Follows on from 28a, what I do = was ich mache)
029 ja ('yes')
030 nein nein ('no no')
(L: did you practise that for a long time?)
031 aber du nich darf ('but you not may')
(But you're not allowed to.)
(= ... climb.)
032 ja ('yes')
033 ich n vase un fenster sieh
('I a vase an a window see')
(L: can you tell me all about what you can see from up there?)
034a du dann runterfällt ('you then down falls')
(Then you fall down)
034b dann un du passiert ('then an you happens')
(And then it's happened; = Und dann ist's passiert.)
034c dann du du tot ('then you you dead')
(And then you're dead)
035 nein ('no')
036 du mir helf besser.ja? ('you me help better.yes?')
(You'd better help me.)

037 du besser helf ich ('you better help I')
(It's better that I help you; = Ich helf dir besser.)
038 aber ich viel größer ('but I much bigger')
(But I'm much bigger.)
039 aber du ganz klein ('but you quite small')
(But you're quite small.)
040a du jetzt fallen ('you now fall')
(Now fall.)
040b ja: ('yes: ') (encouraging)
041a du jetzt ganz fallen ('you now quite fall')
(Now let yourself fall completely.)
041b so: ('like this')
(Continuation of 41a, accompanying an action)
042a nee ('no')
(L: but I'm holding on pretty tightly...)
042b du ganz fallen ('you quite fall')
(Fall completely.)
042c so ('like this') (Continuation of 42b, accompanying an action)
043a du ganz fallen ('you quite fall')
(See 42b)
043b ja bitte ('yes please') (encouraging)
044 du un du .au au ('you an you .ow ow')
(breaks off, L. should shout.)
045 siehst du! ('see!')
046 du aber in in du in aber in ritschra
('you but in in you but in slide') (Meaning unclear)
047 du in käfig ('you in cage')
048 warum du immer so so so wil ('why you always so so so wild')
(Because you..are wild; = weil du..wild bist, P. laughs.)
049 (im) gefängnis ((in) prison')
(L: where am I then behind there now?)
050 du in fängnis ('you in prison')
(= Gefängnis)
051a nix ('nowght')
(L: what have I done now then? P: Nothing.)
051b nur du immer fallen ('only you always fall')
(It's just that you always fall; = Du fällst nur immer.)
051c dann immer ('then always') (Continuation)
052 ja ('yes')
053a so ('like this') (Introduction to encouragement)
053b du setz ('you sit')
(L. should sit down.)

054 du in popo hauen ('you in bum hit')
(You'll get your bottom smacked; = Du bekommst den Popo verhauen.)
055a mh (encouraging)
055b zeig deine pofoten ('show your paws')
056 da foten ('there paws')
057 aber dein dein po dein po kaputt
('but your your bum your bum bust')
(But your backside is broken.)
058 du ein tanken.tanken tanken auto?
('you a ambul.ambul ambul car?')
(Have you got an ambulance?; = Hast du einen Krankenwagen?)
059 ja ('yes')
060a jetzt ein auto ('now a car')
(Now the car goes; = Jetzt fährt das Auto. P. makes the car drive.)
060b tatütata ('beep beep')
(P. imitates driving noises.)
061 so fahren ('drive like this')
(P. shows how L. should drive.)
062 ja ('yes')
063a einer lett da ('one hurt there')
(someone there is hurt; = ist verletzt)
063b den affen ('the monkey') (Continuation of 63a)
064a ja ('yes')
064b in po buten ('in bum bleed')
(His backside is bleeding; = bluten)
065a nee ('no')
(L: is the monkey hurt?)
065b dein tanken.tanken boot ('?your ambul.ambul boat')
(Meaning unclear)
066 jetz in kankenhaus ('now in hospital')
(Now we're driving to the hospital; = Jetzt fahren wir ins Krankenhaus.)
067 und du ein du ein schrankenschwester?
('and you a you a nurse?') (= Krankenschwester)
068 ja ('yes')
069 ehm po letzt ('er bum hurt')
(The backside is hurt; = Der Po ist verletzt.)
070 doch ('yes')
(P. contradicts L.)
071a ehm immer ein malen ('er always a paint')
(We have to make a note of that; = Wir müssen das aufschreiben.. see 71b)
071b ein tranken verletzt ('a ill hurt')
(If a sick person is hurt; = wenn ein Kranker verletzt ist, Cont. of 71a)

072 oder ein affen oder ein tier? ('or a monkey or an animal?') (Are you a monkey or an animal?) = Sind sie ein Affe oder ein Tier?)
073 ein tier? ('an animal?')
074 tier ('animal') (Continuation of 73)
075 X ein tier ('X an animal') (Meaning unclear)
076 ganz kleiner mhm ('quite small mhm')
(A small monkey; = ein kleiner Affe)
077a passiert ('happened')
(Something has happened; = Etwas ist passiert.)
077b ganz tot tot ('quite dead dead')
078 ni ganz ('not quite') (Continuation of 77)
079 un das po letzt ('and the bum hurt')
(= Und der Po ist verletzt.)
080a also erst ehm ('so first er')
080b auto ('car')
(We'll fetch the patient out of the car; = Wir holen den Patienten aus dem Auto.)
081a also ('so')
081b eben kucken ja? ('just look yes?')
082 du ganz wa wa ('you quite wa wa')
(L. should cry.)
083 i kuck mal ('I look here')
084 du ganz böse (2x) ('you quite angry')
085 X sein X böse ('X be X angry') (Meaning unclear)

Transcript: petra 3

No. Utterances and comments

001 ich male ('I paint')
002 ja ('yes')
003 mein stifte setz schon weg
('my pens now already away')
(P. already has no more pens.)
004 hmhm (negating)
(L: haven't you got a single pen left?)
005 die einfach getrocknen die
('they simple dry they')
(The pens have dried out; = Die Stifte sind ausgetrocknet.)
006 weil ich wollte die suchen
('because I wanted they look for')
(Because I wanted to look for the (lid).)
(L: did you forget to put this lid back on again?)
007 aber dann ich finde keins mehr
('but then I find no more')
(But then I couldn't find one.)
008 dann ich immer muβ hier malen
('then I always must here paint')
009 hier geht schöner ('here goes more pretty')
(It's prettier here.)
(P. points at a place where her painting is better.)
010 aber der ('but he')
(P. indicates a pen which isn't empty.)
011 sosa ('pink'.) (rosa)
012 da is da gelb? ('there is there yellow?')
(Is that yellow?; = Ist das gelb?)
013 weiβ ich nich.ne ('know I not.no')
(I don't know.)
(L: maybe that's pink too?)
014 jetzt da an ('now there at')
(In the roof a fire is burning; = Im Dach brennt ein Feuer.)
015 da brennt ('there burning') (see 014)
016 ich das mache jetzt ('I make that now')
(P. paints the fire brigade.)
017 ne ('no')
(L: That's the ambulance.)
018 doch ('yes')
(L: no?)

019 hier will ich was malen ('here want I something paint')
(I want to paint something here)
020 da ehm der das gibt es ('there er the that gives it')
(There's the Red Cross; = Das gibt das rote Kreuz.)
021 krankenwagen ('ambulance')
(L: was that the fire brigade or the ambulance?)
022 und da n mann ('and there a man')
(And a man is sitting there; = Und da sitzt ein Mann.)
023 da kein mann ('there no man')
(L: but there's another man.)
024 das ein ('that a') (interrupted)
025 ja ('yes')
026 das ein blut ('that a blood')
(The woman is bleeding; = Die Frau blutet.)
027 ja ('yes')
028 jetz die feuerwehr ich mal ('now the fire brigade I paint')
(I'm going to paint the fire brigade now.)
029 dann mann ('then man')
(?Then I'll paint the man; = ?Dann mal ich den Mann; as a continuation of 28)
030 das der noch spritzt das wasser ne?
('that the still sprays the water no?')
(He's still spraying the water, isn't he?)
031 das X ('that X')
032 das lustig ne? ('that funny no?')
033 und jetzt ('and now')
(incomprehensible because P. is whispering.)
034 ich dir sag gar nicht ('I to you say not at all')
(I'm not saying a thing about it to you.)
(L: what're you doing now?)
035 feuerwehr feuerwehr ehm noch malst
('firebrigadefire brigade, er, still paint')
036 doch nochmal das heiβt ('yes again that called')
(Meaning unclear)
037 ja ('yes')
038a mond mond ehm das mond ('moon moon er the moon')
(If the moon shines; = wenn der Mondscheint.) (Cont. of38b)
038b ehm polizei ('er police')
((comes the police) ... kommt die polizei)
038c die polizei ('the police') (Continuation of 38b)
038d lustig ('funny')
(P. finds the idea funny, see 38a, b)
039 ja ('yes') (confirmatory)

040 der polizeimond ('the police moon')
041 das die stern sterne ('that the star stars')
(P. points at her picture.)
042 krankenwagen ('ambulance')
(P. points at her picture.)
043 groβer stern ('big star')
(L: but that's a wonderful star)
044 wir in kindergarten ein kissenschlach
('we in kindergarten/play group a cushion fight')
(We had a cushion fight at play group)
045 aber gleich jetzt ('but right now')
(We're having the cushion fight in a minute; = Wir machen die Kissenschlacht gleich.)
046 wir in kindergarten ('we in play group')
(We've got cushions at play group; = Wir haben Kissen im Kindergarten.)
047 kuck mal ('look here')
048 das ein kissen ne? ('that a cushion no?')
(ist = 0) (That's a cushion, isn't it?)
049 und dann immer werft ('and then always throws')
(Subj. = ich ('I'))
050 und dann der andere we wieder werft
('and then the other ag again throws')
051 kissenschlach das so nennt
('cushion fight that so called')
052 ja ('yes')
053 und ein hund ('and a dog')
(L: and each person has to bring a cushion for that?)
054 ein schmusetier ('a cuddly toy') (Continuation of 53)
055 ja ('yes')
056 noch nich fertig ('not yet finished')
(The picture isn't finished yet; = Das Bild ist noch nicht fertig.)
057a du sach ('you say')
(You ought to say; = Du sollst sagen,..)
057b was ich malen soll ('what I should paint')
(Follows on from 57a)
058 ich mal was ('I paint thing')
059 so. so ('like this. like this')
(accompanying an action, whilst painting)
060 ne ne ('no no') (negating)
061 jetzt ich eins ehm noch mal ('now I one er another paint')
(malen = 0)
062a (XX) (Introduction to 62b)

062b was ich jetzt noch malen muß
('what I now still to paint must')
(What I still have to paint now.)
063 (jetzt hab ich XX) ('now have I XX')
(P. whispers.)
064 hmhm (negating)
065 ich dir sage? ('I you say?')
(Should I tell you?; = Soll ich es dir sagen?)
066 schneeflocken ('snowflakes')
067 schneeflöckchen weiß röckchen ('snowflakes white little skirts')
(P. sings.)
068 das ein esel ('that a donkey')
069 ja ('yes')
070 da der da weihnachten ('there he there christmas')
071 und der immer der geschenke ('and he always he presents')
(He brings presents; = Der bringt Geschenke.)
072 das ein geschenk ('that a present')
073 der tragt ('he carries') (Continuation of 72)
074 danke gleichfalls ('thanks the same to you')
075 ja ('yes')
076 der muß auch ('he must too')
(L: but he's got a heavy load, the donkey.)
077 von weihnachten der gesagt ('of christmas he said')
(He said...; = Er hat gesagt..)
078 daß der band da nich da drunterfällt
('that the string there not there fall down')
(So that the string (from the Christmas tree) doesn't fall down there.)
079 so und dann ('like this and then') (interrupted)
080a in haus ('in house')
(L: where's the donkey going then?)
080b wo die dontusch wohnen ('where the d. live')
080c und der weihnachtsmann ('and the christmas man')
(Continuation of 80b)
081 ja ('yes')
082 und der esel ('and the donkey')
(L: does Santa also live in the house?)
083 aber kuck mal ('but look here')
084 ich ein weihnachtsmann ne? ('I also a santa no?')
085 da (XXXX) ('there')
086 und dann die haben elche ('and then they have elks')
087 aber ich ein esel ('but I a donkey')
088 is was anderes ne? ('is something else no?')

089 die auch ein.ehm ein ('they also one.er one')
(L: the elks have such big horns...)
090 ich jetz mach ('I now make')
091 das ganz gefährlich ('that quite dangerous')
092 (X) ein hirsch ('a deer') (Meaning unclear)
093 aber in finnland da hirsche ('but in finland there deer')
(But there are deer in Finland.)
094 ja ('yes')
095 da immer so und (berse) und so und füschse
('there always such and (?bears) and so and foxes')
(Meaning unclear)
096 da da ehm der papa ne.der immer.papa.ne der immer füsche ehm fische angelt
('there there er papa no.he always.papa.nohe always foxes er fishes fish')
097 und da immer da schläft ('and there always there sleeps')
(Father sleeps in the boat; = Der Vater schläft im Boot.)
098 nee ('no') (negating)
099 im boot ('in the boat')
(L: where does papa sleep then?)
100 der schon mal ('the already once')
(P. begins a longer story.)

Transcript: stefan

No.	Utterances and comments
001	tuck ma hier ('look over here') (= guck; S. puts the telephone on the Punch and Judy theatre.)
002	da ('there') (S. points.)
003a	ja ('yes') (Th1: then we can maybe somehow put something on there)
003b	das ('that') (see the comment for 003a)
004	(...) weg ('away') (incompr.)
005	tu ges machen ('close now make') (= zu jetzt machen (I'm now going to close them)) (S. wants to draw the theatre's curtains.)
006a	oh . oh
006b	noch ein telefon ('another telephone') (S. finds a second telephone.)
007	del telefon ('the telephone') (incompr.)
008	alle beide ('all both') (S. watches (both of) the telephones)
009	das euer ('that your') (S. gives Th1 a telephone.)
010	das mein telefon ('that my telephone') (S. means the second telephone)
011	nein ('no') (Th1: Should I make a call?)
012	da hinten euer haus ('there behind your house') (S. points into the room)
013	ja ('yes') (Th1: oh, we have to go to the back?)
014	mann ('man') (shows impatience)
015a	ich detz suppetapfter ('I now soupfan') (= ?Suppenkasper; S. picks up the Punch doll.)
015b	(XXX) (Meaning unclear)
016a	ne ('no') (Th1 and Th2 want to call S., but S. wants to play Punch; Th1 and Th2 should watch.)
016b	det nich . det nich ('goes not . goes not') (see the comment for 016a)
016c	det hier ('goes here') (see the comment for 016a)

017a ne ('no')
(Th1: oh, we should ring Punch? S. shows that he wants to play.)
017b so machen ('like this make')
(see the comment for 017a)
018 ja ('yes')
(Th2: Do you want to play?)
021 hier (sitz ich) XXX ('here sit I') (incompr.)
022 tschüß... ('bye...')
(Makes Punch disappear, whereby the theatre's telephone falls. Rest of the sentence incompr.)
023 dib mal mein telefon ('give here my telephone')
(bends down, wants to have the telephone back)
024 danke ('thank you')
(Th1 puts the telephone back onto the stage.)
025 tschüß ('bye')
(waves with Punch, disappears with it behind the theatre.)
026 dep.dep.dep. ...
(plays with the doll behind the theatre)
027 hallo ('hello')
(makes the monkey doll appear, squeaks)
028 auu ('oww')
(The telephone falls down again.)
029a ah
029b dib mal mein telefon ... wieder ('give here my telephone ... again')
(speaks in a "monkey voice")
030 meiner ('mine')
(Th1: whose telephone is it then now?)
031 ja ('yes')
(Th1: yours?)
032a nein ('no')
(Th1: or the monkey's?)
032b mir ('to me') (see the comment for 032a)
033 i setz euch anrufen ('I now you ring')
((I now); = ich jetzt ... S.takes the telephone away from Th1)
(I'm going to ring you now.)
034 i setz euch anrufen ('I now you ring')
035 ja ('yes')
(Th1: yes?)
036 hallo ('hello')
(makes the telephone ring)
037 hier. binich. ich ('here. amI. I')
(Th1: who's that then?)

038	stephan (Th1: who's "I"?)
039	haha. witzig ('haha.funny') (giggles into the telephone)
040	tschüβ nächste mal ('bye next time')
041	schon auflegen ('already hang up') (S. has hung up the receiver.)
042	null un vier ('zero and four') (Th2 wants to ring S., asks for the number)
043	ja ('yes') ('makes the telephone ring, answers)
044	hallo ('hello') (Th2: hello Stephan!)
045	hallo ('hello')
046	hier telefon nummer achtzehn ('heretelephone number eighteen') (Th2: what a lovely house you've got, where are you living there?)
047	ja ('yes') (Th2 asks about it again)
048	ja ('yes') (Th2: Regine wants to speak to you again too)
049	hallo ('hello')
050	gehts dir? ('goes you?') (How are you; = wie geht's dir?)
051	wie gehts dir? ('how're you?')
052	auch ('also') (Th1: I'm great, Stephan, and you?)
053	tschüβ ('bye') (puts the phone down)
054	(schon) auflegen ('(already) hang up') (S. has hung up the receiver.)
055	hallo ('hello') (makes a new doll appear)
056	hallo ('hello') (Th. says that the doll is a girl)
057	doch ('yes') (Th2: that's not a girl. Th1: not a girl?)
058a	nein ('no') (Th2: I reckon that's a boy.)
058b	ich ein mädchen . bin ich ('I a girl. am I')
059	dine a.a ('dine a.a') (Th1: what's your name then?) (dine = Regine)

060 ja ('yes')
(Th2: Gine Aa?)
061 tschüß ('bye')
(makes the doll disappear)
062 setz antwort was ('now answer something')
(Now you'll answer; = jetzt ... S. has dialled and wants Th. to go to the other phone)
063 ja ('yes')
(Th: oh,did it ring?)
064 hallo ('hello')
065 hier bin ich . stephan ('here am I . stephan')
(Th1: who's there then?)
066 ja ('yes')
(Th1: Stephan?)
067 bin ich ('am I')
(Th1: who's there then?)
068a ne ('no')
068b ich dine und a.a scheißer bin ich
('I dine and a.a shitter am I')
(dine = Regine. S. giggles)
069 ja ('yes')
(Th1: Is Gine on the loo at the moment?)
070 a.a scheiße machen ('a.a shit make')
(Th1: what's Doro doing?)
071 ja ('yes')
(Th1: is she on the loo too?)
072 tschüß ('bye')
(hangs up)
073 ämämäm ...
(makes the car drive around the stage)
074 schüß ('bye')
(waves and draws the theatre curtain)
075 nein ('no')
(Th1: aren't I allowed to look any more?)
076 dann ich schlafen ('then I sleep')
(Th1: what're you going to do now then?)
077 tschüß ('bye')
078 dut nat ('ni' ni'')
(night night)
(Th1: good night!)
079 deh euer haus ('go your house')
(get into your house; = geh in euer Haus)

(Th1 has gone behind the theatre and "woken" S. up; S. draws the curtain.)

080 morgen ('morning')
(Th2: good morning!)

081 ne . ater ('a . eatre')
(theatre; = Theater, Th2 asks whether S. and Th1 want to play something for her. S. wants Th1 to go.)

082 hier mein ater ('here my eatre')
(Here is my theatre; = hier ist mein Theater)

083 deh ('go')
(= geh!)

084 ja ('yes')
(Th1: oh, your theatre?)

085 da hinten dein weund ..dehn
('there behind your frend .. go')
(= Freund (friend); Th1: and what should I do?)

086 ja ('yes')
(Th1: then I'm a spectator too? S. goes to Th2 in front of the theatre)

087 heute.tinder.('setzen') eine affe tommen
('today.children.(sit) a monkey come')
(Today, children, (now) a monkey is coming.)
(= Heute,Kinder, kommt ein Affe, setzen = jetzt (now))
(Th2 afterwards: Today a monkey came)

088 hallo ('hello')
(makes a monkey appear)

089 i.i . heiβ ich ('I.I. called I')
(Th2: what's your name then, monkey?)

Transcript: sven

No.	Utterances and comments
001	nachher ('after') (T: Sven.why's your mother fetching you today? so early?)
002	ja.katen ('yes.carsten') (T: do you still want to go off somewhere?; (= Carsten, name of a child))
003	katen (T: where?)
004	papa taf nich ('papa may not') (= P. mayn't come with us.)
005	ne ('no') (T: papa may not go with you?)
006	ja.nachher ('yes.after') (T: and mother's fetching you then?)
007a	das is ('that is') (interrupted)
007b	u uh hä das kenn ich ('that know I') (That I know.) (Follows on from 007a.)
008	hm (T: you know that uh)
009	ein puzzle ('a puzzle') (T: a puzzle)
010	hü ohoho (Meaning unclear)
011	den? ('the?') (That one?) (T: take a look first at what's in the box.)
012	hi.poho oh ho ho (S. opens the lid.)
013	ich nimm ich den ('I take I the') (I'll take that one.) (S. takes a cow and then puts it back.)
014	ooh poh (S. takes a crocodile and looks at it.)
015	äh äh (S. moves the crocodile and puts it onto the table.)
016	das is puppen? ('that is doll?') (P. takes a doll out of the box.)
017	da ein hund ('there a dog') (S. takes out a dog.)
018a	oh.das hier nehm ('oh.that here take') (S. takes a rod of wood out of the box.)
018b	das is? ('that is?')

019 aufmachen ('open')
(S. wants to unscrew the lid.)
020a ne ('no')
(S. can't get the lid open.)
020b auf du machen ('open you make')
(S. gives the rod to T.)
021 ja ('yes')
(T: should I open it?)
022 ne? ('no?')
(T: oh you can't open that, it won't budge)
023 warum is? ('why is?')
(S. takes the cow and fiddles with its moveable legs.)
024 muh ('moo')
(T: what's that Sven?)
025 du den ('you the')
(S. places the doll in front of T.)
026 ich ('I') (interrupted)
027 das is? ('that is?')
(S. takes a doctor-doll.)
028 doktor ('doctor')
(T: what kind of doctor could that be?)
029 tarum ('because')
(T: how can you see that then? T. asks how S. can tell that the doll is a doctor.)
030 ja.das ganz machen ('yes.that make whole')
(T: he's got a kind of white apron, hasn't he? S. wants to put a train and waggon together.)
031 oh.äh keht nicht ('oh.äh goes not')
(This doesn't work)
(S. is making an effort; S. puts the train back into the box.)
032 ich mach (XXX) ('I make')
033 oh.ein auto ('oh.a car')
(S. sees cars in the box.)
034 ich porsche nehm ich ('I porsche take I')
(I'll take the Porsche.)
(S. takes 2 cars out of the box.)
035 hi.das is schupo ('hi.that police')
(S. points at the car and holds it up.)
036 ehm ä ü ü. das bist du.ä ä
('er ä ü ü. that are you.ä ä')
(S. makes driving noises and gives the car to T.)
037 oh.ein brennt.ein brennt ('oh.one burns.one burns')
(Something's burning or a fire; = Etwas brennt, or = ein Brand)

038 ne ('no')
(T: the car's burning?)
039a ne ('no')
(T: no?)
039b haus ('house')
040 oh.da ('oh.there')
(S. knocks against a crocodile; T: where are the cars supposed to drive? S. points.)
041 ja ('yes')
(T: to the crocodile?)
042 na nä ohu ch ch
(S. makes the crocodile run.)
043 das.da steht? ('that.there stands?')
(S. points underneath the cars.)
044 ja ('yes')
(T: it's standing?)
045 ja ('yes')
(T: should we have a look at what's on there?)
046 ford? ('ford?')
(T: ford is written on there.)
047 oh ü. ford
(T: who's driving the car then Sven? Driving noises)
048 der ausscheign (XXX) ('he get out')
(He's getting out.)
(S. opens the doors.)
049 ein brennt (XXX) ('one burns')
(Something's burning or a fire; = Etwas brennt, or = ein Brand)
050 hühü.nem nem nem wau wau ü ü ü
(S. runs with the figures and makes the cars drive.)
051 ja ('yes')
(T: is the car driving over the dog?)
052 das is? ('that is?')
(S. points at the screen.)
053 ja ja ('yes yes')
(T: that's a screen...)
054 das das gehört da ('that that belongs there')
(S. puts paper into the box.)
055 hü? ooh.sind schön ('hü? ooh.are pretty')
(S. takes dolls out of the box.)
056 das is? ('that is?')
(S. points at a female doll.)
057 papa ('papa')
(T: who's that huh?)

058a ne ('no')
(T: that's papa? incredulous)
058b das papa ('that papa')
(S. takes another doll.)
059 mama ('mama')
(T: and that? T. points at another doll.)
060 hier ('here')
(T: and where do they live?)
061 alle hier ('all here')
(S. puts the dolls together.)
062 ja ('yes')
(T: shall we build them a house?)
063 (XXX) haus bauen ('house build')
(T: you see, here are bricks for building a house.)
064a ne ('no')
(T: you can build them a house with these)
064b lieber (XXX) ('better')
(?I'd prefer...)
065 das is? ('that is?')
(S. grabs a piece and lifts it up.)
066 das ab? ('that off?')
(Should I take that off?)
(S. wants to take the insert out.)
067 ich fahrich weg ('I driveI away')
(S. drives the car.)
068 oh oh.ein tot ('oh oh.one dead')
(S. puts the crocodile, which has fallen down, back onto the table.)
069 ja.komm Jonny.komm ('yes.come Jonny.come')
(T: is that dead? S. takes a second car.)
070 ja.da tanken.tankenstelle ('yes.there fill.filling station')
(Yes, let's fill her up there, at the filling station)
071 ja.ja. ('yes.yes.')
(T: a filling station is this a filling station?)
072 der geht nich auf ('it goes not open')
(I can't get it open)
(S. tries to open the car doors.)
073 hier ('here')
(T: where's the attendant then Sven?)
074 da drinne ('there inside')
(T: where is he then? S. points at a car.)
075 ja ('yes')
(T: should daddy do that for you?)
076 oh.warum ganz viele beine?

('oh.why quite many legs?')
(Why has the doll got so many legs? S. indicates the doll's legs.)
077 zwei ('two')
(T: how many has it got then?)
078 wa (XXX)
(S. jumps onto the car with the doll.)
079 ja.du fahren ('yes.you drive')
(T: so.the car's now full,isn't it.it can drive on.)
080 ich ich warte hier ('I I wait here')
081 taxi kommt gleich.ü ü ('taxi's coming in a minute.ü ü')
(Driving noises)
082 komm hier parken die.ü ü ('come here park the.ü ü')
(S. stays at the filling station with the car.)
(Driving noises)
083 kute tag ('good day')
(T: good day)
084 ja ('yes')
(T: would you like some petrol?)
085 ja ('yes')
(T: like this.full yes?)
086 hier ('here')
(T: good.then you still have to pay; S. gives T. money.)
087 du kommen ('you come')
(S. indicates a place to T.)
088 hier ('here')
(T: where?)
089 ja.ja ('yes.yes')
(T: I come here ... to the zoo?)
090 (XXX) komm her.hier ('come here.here')
(Scene hidden; S. fiddles about.)
091 du da uü pch (Driving noises)
092a wir auch (XXX).kuck.wir auch (XXX) .kuck
('we also (XXX).look.we also (XXX) .look')
(Meaning unclear)
092b so einen ('such a one')
(One like that.)
(S. points at a car.)
093 ja ('yes')
(T: you've got one like that at home too?)
094a mann ('man')
(T: who drives it then?)

Transcript: wolfgang

No.	Utterances and comments
001	uschi.falte runter ('uschi.fold under') (Uschi, they keep falling down.) (W. tries to make pieces of Lego stay on a board.)
002	uschi.fall runter die.fall ('uschi.fall under the.fall') (Meaning see 001)
003	die hier auch ('the here too') (W. points to another sign.)
004	die hier auch ('the here too') (U: hm?)
005a	tata (Meaning unclear) (W. points at Torsten who's putting up a sign too.)
005b	hier ein feets ('here one miss') (W. points at his signs.)
005c	da ('there') (Continuation of 5b)
006	ja ('yes') (U: Wolfgang would you like another tree?)
007	is hab ('I have') (I've got one.) (U: have you got a long one too? W. shows a stone.)
008	oh.is hab ('oh.I have') (Oh, I want to have that.) (W. takes the stone which U. is giving to him.)
009	oh.putt ('oh.break') (W.'s car is broken (down).)
010	uschi.piele ('uschi.play') (= spielen)
011	abfall.uschi ('down fall.uschi') (still referring to the broken (down) car.)
012	oh.wieda ab ('oh.again off') (W. tried to repair the car.)
013	auto ('car') (H: what are you doing there wolfgang?)
014	meine auto ('my car') (W. tries to take a car away from T.)
015	dat mein auto ('that my car') (W. takes another car.)
016	uschi.hier bommchen ('uschi.here little trees') (W. takes two Lego-trees.)

017 hier drauf is ('here on is')
(They go on here.)
(W. wants to put the trees onto the board.)

018 hier zwei bäum is ('here two trees is')
(W. wants to put them onto the board.)

019 zwei bäume ('two trees')
(H: what's that.two tree.wolfgang!)

020a uschi.hier noch ein feesch
('uschi.here another way')
(W. points at a path on the board.)

020b hier auch.hier auch ('here too.here too')
(W. points to paths.)

020c die noch ('the too')
(These as well.)
(U: what? W. shows further with his finger.)

021a uschi hier? ('uschi here?')
(Does Uschi live here?; = Wohnt U. hier?)

021b uschi hier wohn? ('uschi here live?')
(See 21a)

021c uschi.uschi hier wohn? ('uschi.uschi here live?')
(See 21a)
(U: pardon?)

022 ich ('I') (= I do, or = me.)
(H: who lives there wolfgang?)

023 ein haus ('a house')
(H: what are you doing there?)

024 uschi.geht rein nich ('uschi.goes in not')
(Uschi, it won't go in.)
(W. is trying in vain to fix the Lego brick together.)

025 uschi.so auch.uschi.so auch
('uschi.like this too.uschi.like this too')
(W. has pushed the Lego brick in.)

026 is au fenzer bauch ('I also window need')
(W. needs a window.)

027 ma.tür plau ('ma.door nick')
(= klauen; W. takes the door away from T.)

028 tossa (= Torsten, name of a child)
(U: would you like a window? W. looks at T.)

029 tür abplaut ('door nicked')
(The door has been stolen.)
(means to say: Die Tür ist abgeklaut.)

030 uschi.hier auch ein tür reinkomm
('uschi.here too a door income')

(Uschi, a door goes in here, too.)
(W. inserts a door.)
031 uschi.is ein fenzer bauch ('uschi.I a window need')
(Uschi, I need a window.)
032a ein haus hoch.ne? ('a house high.no?')
(= ?ein Hochhaus (a block of flats)? Meaning unclear)
032b mein hoch is haus ('my high is house')
(Meaning unclear)
033 oh.haus putt ('oh.house break')
(The Lego bricks fell over.)
034 oh.mein baume fall ('oh.my trees fall')
(My trees have fallen over; = Bäume sind umgefallen.)
035 mein bauma runterfall wieda ('my trees falls over again')
036 mein baum runterfall ('my tree falls over')
(After question from U.)
037 zwei ('two')
(H: your tree fell over?)
038 is hierhin ('is to over here')
(I'll put them over here.)
(W. puts the trees up somewhere else.)
039 anner bau haus ('other build house')
(W. builds his house differently.)
040 so au.ne? (Reference unclear)
041 hm. so muß.so muß ('er. like this must.like this must')
(U: has your house gone wrong or do you want to make it different?)
042 falz mach ('wrong do')
(H: what did you do wrong then wolfgang?)
043 di ding nich (XXX) nich
('the thing not (XXX) not')
(Meaning unclear)
044 die ding klein toff nich ('the thing small fit not')
(This doesn't fit anything.)
(W. shows a little building brick; toff = paßt (fits))
045 uschi.die toff nich ('uschi.the fits not')
(After question; toff = paßt(fits))
046 die ham kleiner nich ne? ('the have smaller not no?')
(Meaning unclear)
047 die auch nich bauch ('the also not need')
(I don't need this either.)
(W. gives U. a Lego brick.)
048 dat i bauch ('that I need')
(W. takes a Lego brick from U.)

049 is toβer haus bau ('I big house build')
(I'm building a big house.)
(W. builds a big house.)
050 is auch ein männlei ham ('I also a little man have')
(W. wants to have a little man too.)
051 ein metsa ('a girl')
(U: what're you doing with the boy now wolfgang? W. corrects her: ein Mädchen (a girl))
052 hier metsa hintomm.ne?
('here girl comes in.no?')
(W. puts the girl on the table.)
053a noch ein kleiner bauch nich ('still a smaller need not')
(W. gives the little brick back.)
053b uschi.noch ein kleiner.kleiner auch bauch nich
('uschi.still a smaller.smaller also need not')
053c noch ein kleiner ('still a smaller')
(Continuation. W. gives U. a brick.)
054 mach hoch deht nich ('make high goes not')
(It won't come out.)
(W. tries invain to pull the figure out of the Lego car.)
055 is auf tis nis stes ('I on table not put')
(Meaning unclear)
056 is auf tis stes ('I on table put')
(W. wants to put the figure on the table.)
057 mh.is tis aufstel ('I table put up')
(H: do you want to put it on the table?)
058 oh.haus runterfall ('oh.house fall down')
(The house has fallen down; = Das Haus ist runtergefallen.)
059a is au ein metsa.uschi.is au ein metsa.ne?
('I too a girl.uschi.I too a girl no?')
(W. has got a girl too.)
059b is auch ('I too') (Continuation)
060 (...) metsa totmach ('girl dead make')
(Meaning unclear)
061 auto ('car')
(U: who's doing that?)
062 totmach auto ('deadmake car')
(U: what's it doing with the girl? The car drives over the girl.)
063 auto ('car')
(H: kill?)
064 hm (H: has the girl been run over wolfgang?)
065 oh.ein tenzer is bauch ('oh.a window I need')
(= Fenster (window). W. needs a window.)

066 oh.is ein tür nich ('oh.I a door not')
(W. is looking for a door.)
067 uschi.is ein tür nich ('uschi.I a door not') (see 066)
068 nee ('no')
(U: yes.you had a door)
069 ein tenzer feit ('a window miss')
(A window is missing; = Ein Fenster fehlt.)
070 oh.metsa runterfall.metsa runterfall
('oh.girl fall down.girl fall down')
(A figure has fallen down.)
071 oh.du das runter ('oh.you that down')
(W. points at R., who knocked the girl over.)
072 das runterfall ('that fall over')
(That girl's fallen over.)
(W. points at the girl.)
073 ah.noch ein feits ('ah.still one miss')
(There's still one missing; = Eins fehlt.)
074 frank klaua ab ('frank nick away')
(= klauen (nick/steal))
075 da ein feits ('there one miss')
(One's missing.)
(= Eins fehlt.)
076 hier eins feits ('here one miss')
(W. points at signs.)
077 hier ('here')
(U: what's missing there?)
078 da eins feets ('there one miss')
079 du mis ein geb ('you me one give')
(Give me one.)
080 is auch ein auto fahr ('I too a car drive')
(I'm driving a car, too.)
081 diese hier ('this here')
(W. takes a figure and puts it on his car.)
082 uschi
(W. addresses the teacher.)
083 hier drauf muß ('here on must')
(It has to go on here.)
(W. puts a figure onto his car.)
084 verkehrt mach ('wrong do')
(When the teacher puts his hair right.)
085 meine metsa auch reintom detz ('my girl also come in now')
(= Mädchen)

086 ein metsa will ('a girl want')
(I want a girl; = ich will ein Mädchen.)
087 fei metsa ne? ('two girls no?')
(Points at two figures of girls.)
088 du auch ein metsa hol ('you too a girl fetch')
(Fetch a girl, too.)
089 ein metsa du ham ('a girl you have')
090 oh (= Exclamation)
100 wieda ('again')
(W. tries to put two figures onto a car, but they fall down.)
101 diesa nich ('this not')
(W. gives the figure back to the teacher.)
102 diesa nich auch ('this not too')
(Not this one either; = auch nicht)

Bibliography

Baker, C. 1979. Syntactic theory and the projection problem. *Linguistic Inquiry 10*: 533-581.

Baker, C. and J. McCarthy ed. 1981. *The logical problem of language acquisition*. Cambridge, Mass.

Bates, E. 1976. *Language and context. The acquisition of pragmatics*. New York.

Bates, E. and B. MacWhinney 1979. A functionalist approach to the acquisition of grammar. In: E. Ochs/B. Schieffelin (ed.), *Developmental pragmatics*. London, pp.167-211.

Bates, E. and B. MacWhinney 1982. Functionalist approaches to grammar. In: Wanner and Gleitman (ed.), pp.173-218.

Bates, E., MacWhinney, B. and St. Smith 1983. Pragmatics and syntax in psycholinguistic research. In: S. Felix and H. Wode (ed.), *Language development at the crossroads*. Tübingen, pp.11-30.

Becker, K.-P. and M. Sovak 1975. *Lehrbuch der Logopädie*. Köln.

Berman, R. 1985. A step-by-step model of language learning. In: I. Levin (ed.), *Stage and structure: Human development*. Vol. 1. Norwood, N.J., pp.191-219.

Bickerton, D. 1981. *Roots of language*. Ann Arbor, Mi.

Bickerton, D. 1984. The language bioprogram hypothesis. *The Behavioral and Brain Sciences 7*: 173-188.

Bloom, L., Lightbown, P. and L. Hood 1975. Structure and variation in child language. *Monographs of the Society for Research in Child Development*. Vol. 40.

Bloom, L., Lahey, M., Hood, L., Lifter, K. and K. Fiess 1980. Complex sentences: Acquisition of syntactic connectives and the semantic relations they encode. *Journal of Child Language 7*: 235-261.

Borer, H. 1984. *Parametric syntax*. Dordrecht.

Borer, H. and K. Wexler 1987. The maturation of syntax. In: T. Roeper and E. Williams (ed.), *Parameter setting*. Dordrecht, pp.123-172.

Bowerman, M. 1973. *Early syntactic development*. London.

Bowerman, M. 1982. Reorganizational processes in lexical and syntactic development. In: Wanner/Gleitman (ed.), pp.319-346.

Bowerman, M. (1985) What shapes children's grammars? In: D. Slobin (ed.), pp. 1257-1320.

Braine, M. 1963. The ontogeny of English phrase structure: The first phase. *Language 39*: 1-13.

Braine, M. 1976. Children's first word combinations. *Monographs of the Society for Research in Child Development*. Vol. 41.

Bresnan, J. ed. 1982. *The mental representation of grammatical relations*. Cambridge, Mass.

Brown, R. 1973. *A first language. The early stages*. Cambridge, Mass.

Budwig, N. 1985. Me, my and 'name': Children's early systematizations of forms, meanings and functions in talk about the self. *Papers and Reports on Child Development 24*.

Bunzel, U. 1978. Spracherwerb und Dysgrammatismus. Unpublished thesis (Staatsexamensarbeit). Universität Köln.

Bybee, J. 1985. *Morphology: A study of the relation between meaning and form*. Amsterdam.

Chomsky, N. 1965. *Aspects of the theory of syntax*. Cambridge, Mass.

Chomsky, N. 1981. *Lectures on government and binding*. Dordrecht.

Clahsen, H. 1982. *Spracherwerb in der Kindheit. Eine Untersuchung zur Entwicklung der Syntax bei Kleinkindern*. Tübingen.

Clahsen, H. 1982a. Dokumentation von Daten zur frühen Kindersprache. *Wuppertaler Arbeitspapiere zur Sprachwissenschaft 4*.

Clahsen, H. 1983. Some more remarks on the acquisition of German negation. *Journal of Child Language 10*: 465-469.

Clahsen, H. 1984a. Der Erwerb von Kasusmarkierungen in der deutschen Kindersprache. *Linguistische Berichte 89*: 1-31.

Clahsen, H. 1984b. Linguistische Aspekte der Spontansprachdiagnostik im Frühbereich. *Sprache-Stimme-Gehör 8*: 38-44.

Clahsen, H. 1985. Parameterized grammatical theory and language acquisition. A study of the acquisition of verb placement and inflection by children and adults. Paper presented at MIT, October 1985. (Since then published in: S. Flynn and W. O'Neill (ed.), *Linguistic Theory in Second Language Acquisition*. Dordrecht.)

Clahsen, H. 1986. *Die Profilanalyse. Ein linguistisches Verfahren für die Sprachdiagnose im Vorschulalter*. Berlin.

Clahsen, H. 1986a. Verb inflections in German child language. Acquisition of agreement markings and the functions they encode. *Linguistics 24*: 79-121.

Clahsen, H. and B. Mohnhaus 1985. Die Profilanalyse. Einsatzmöglichkeiten und erste Ergebnisse. In: Füssenich and Gläß (ed.), pp.76-97.

Clahsen, H. and P. Muysken 1986. The accessibility of Universal Grammar to adult and child learners. A study of the acquisition of German word order. *Second Language Research 2*: 93-119.

Comrie, B. 1981. *Language universals and linguistic typology*. Oxford.

Cromer, R. 1978. The basis of childhood dysphasia: A linguistic approach. In: Wyke (ed.), pp.85-134.

Crystal, D. 1974. Review: R. Brown, A first language. *Journal of Child Language 1*: 289-306.

Crystal, D. 1981. *Introduction to language pathology*. London.

Czepluch, H. and H. Janßen ed. 1984. *Syntaktische Struktur und Kasusrelationen*. Tübingen.

Dannenbauer, F. M. 1983. *Der Entwicklungsdysgrammatismus als spezifische Ausprägungsform der Entwicklungsdysphasie*. Birkach.

Dannenbauer, F. M. 1985. Anmerkungen zur Sprachtherapie bei dysgrammatisch sprechenden Kindern. In: I. Füssenich/B. Gläß (ed.), pp.142-164.

Deutsch, W. 1985. Language production and comprehension: two sides of the same coin? *Research Group on Perception and Action at the Center for Interdisciplinary Research (ZiF)*. Vol. 72. Bielefeld.

Deutsch, W. ed. 1981. *The child's construction of language*. London.

Dixon, R. 1979. Ergativity. *Language 55*: 59-138.

Dorn, U. and H. Spencker 1984. Mehrdimensionale Analyse für Sprachproben sprachentwicklungsgestörter Kinder. Unpublished thesis (Staatsexamensarbeit). Universität Hannover.

Emonds, J. 1976. *A transformational approach to English syntax*. New York.

Felix, S. 1984. Maturational aspects of Universal Grammar. In: A. Davies, C. Cripper and A. Howatt (ed.), *Interlanguage*. Edinburgh, pp.133-161.

Felix, S. 1985. More evidence on competing cognitive systems. In: *Second Language Research 1*: 31-52.

Ferguson, Ch. and D. Slobin ed. 1973. *Studies of child language development*. New York.

Ford, M. 1982. Sentence planning units: Implications for the speaker's representation of meaningful relations underlying sentences. In: J. Bresnan (ed.), pp. 797-828.

Forster, O. 1984. Kindlicher Dysgrammatismus und Grammatiktheorie. In: J. Kriz (ed.), pp.131-160.

Fried, L. 1982. Sprachdiagnose im Vorschulalter. In: K. Ingenkamp (ed.), *Tests und Trends*. Weinheim, pp.43-69.

Füssenich, I. 1982. Zum Landauer Sprachentwicklungstest (LSV). In: *Osnabrücker Beiträge zur Sprachtheorie 19*: 130-141.

Füssenich, I. and B. Gläß ed. 1985. *Dysgrammatismus. Theoretische und praktische Probleme bei der interdisziplinären Beschreibung gestörter Kindersprache*. Heidelberg.

Full, P. 1984. Spontansprachdiagnose – Richtlinien zur Erhebung repräsentativer Spontansprachproben und die 'Profilanalyse' als eine Möglichkeit ihrer Auswertung. Unpubl. thesis (Staatsexamensarbeit). Universität München.

Garman, M. 1979. Early grammatical development. In: P. Fletcher and M. Garman (ed.), *Studies in first language development*. London, pp.177-208.

Gazdar, G., Klein, E., Pullum, G. and I. Sag 1985. *Generalized phrase structure grammar*. Cambridge, Mass.

Givón, T. 1976. Topic, pronoun and grammatical agreement. In: Ch. N. Li (ed.), *Subject and Topic*. New York, pp.151-188.

Gopnik, I. 1985. Featureless grammar. Unpublished manuscript. McGill University of Montreal.

Greenberg, J. 1963. Some universals of grammar with particular reference to the order of meaningful elements. In: J. Greenberg (ed.), *Universals of language*. Cambridge, Mass., pp.73-113.

Grimm, H. 1973. *Strukturanalytische Untersuchung der Kindersprache*. Bern.

Grimm, H. 1975. On the child's acquisition of semantic structure underlying the wordfield of prepositions. *Language and Speech 18*: 97-119.

Grimm, H. 1983. Kognitions – und interaktionspsychologische Aspekte der Entwicklungsdysphasie. *Sprache und Kognition 3*: 169-186.

Grimm, H. and E. Kaltenbacher 1982. Die Dysphasie als noch wenig verstandene Entwicklungsstörung: sprach- und kognitionspsychologische Überlegungen und erste empirische Ergebnisse. *Frühförderung interdisziplinär 1*: 97-112.

Grimshaw, J. 1981. Form, function, and the language acquisition device. In:Baker and McCarthy (ed.), pp.165-182.

Gross, M. 1972. *Mathematical models in Linguistics*. Englewood Cliffs, N.J.

Grunwald, A. 1982. Ein neues Kategorisierungsmodell der Dysgrammatismen – unter Berücksichtigung ätiologischer und psycholinguistischer Fragen. *Die Sprachheilarbeit 27*: 162-174.

Günther, H. 1981. Untersuchungen zum Sprachverhalten agrammatischer Kinder mit Ziel- und Modellsatzmethode. In: G. Kegel and H. Günther (ed.), pp.35-59.

Hawkins, J. 1983. *Word order universals*. New York.

Hay, G., Hummel, Y., Günther, H. and J. Meßing 1981. Dokumentation von Daten und Fehleranalysen zum kindlichen Agrammatismus. In: G. Kegel and H. Günther (ed.), pp.81-213.

Heidolph, K. et al. 1980. *Grundzüge einer deutschen Grammatik*. Berlin (DDR).

Homburg, G. 1981. Methodische Überlegungen zur therapeutischen Arbeit mit dysgrammatisch sprechenden Kindern. *Die Sprachheilarbeit 26*: 267-281.

Hopper, P. and S. Thompson 1980. Transitivity in grammar and discourse. *Language 56*: 251-299.

Huang, J. 1982. Logical relations in Chinese and the theory of grammar. MIT Diss. Cambridge, Mass.

Huss, V. 1980. Anmerkungen zur Theoriediskussion in der Spracherwerbsforschung. In: B. Kettemann and R. St.Clair (ed.), *New approaches to language acquisition*. Tübingen, pp.157-175.

Hyams, N. 1984. The null subject parameter in language acquisition. In: O. Jaeggli and K. Safir (ed.), *Syntax and semantics*. New York.

Hyams, N. 1986. *Language acquisition and the theory of parameters*. Dordrecht.

Ihssen, W. 1978. Der Psycholinguistische Entwicklungstest (PET) aus linguistischer Sicht. In: G. Peuser (ed.), pp.95-114.

Ihssen, W. 1978b. Psychologie, Linguistik und Primärsprachdiagnostik. *Studium Linguistik 5*: 89-98.

Jackendoff, R. 1977. *X-bar syntax: A study of phrase structure*. Cambridge, Mass.

Johnston, J. and T. Schery 1976. The use of grammatical morphemes by children with communication disorders. In: D. Morehead and A. Morehead (ed.), *Normal and deficient child language*. Baltimore, pp.239-258.

Kaltenbacher, E. and W. Kany 1985. Kognitive Verarbeitungsstrategien und Syntaxerwerb bei dysphasischen und sprachunauffälligen Kindern. In: Füssenich/Gläß (ed.), pp.180-219. .

Kanngießer, S. 1984. Anlagebedingungen und Devianzen der Sprachbeherrschung. In: Kriz (ed.), pp.26-94.

Kaplan, D. and J. Bresnan 1982. Lexical-Functional Grammar: A formal system for grammatical representation. In: Bresnan (ed.), pp.173-281.

Kean, M.-L. ed. 1985. *Agrammatism*. London.

Kegel, G. 1981. Zum Einfluß von Syntax und Semantik auf die Nachsprechleistungen agrammatischer Kinder. In: G. Kegel/H. Günther (ed.), pp.61-80.

Kegel, G. 1985. Kind ohne Sprache. In: Füssenich/Gläß (ed.), pp.220-237.

Kegel, G. and H. Günther ed. 1981. *Psycholinguistische Untersuchungen zum kindlichen Agrammatismus*. München.

Kelley, K. 1967. Early syntactic acquisition. (Report Nr.P-3719). The Rand Corporation. Santa Monica, Ca.

Kerschensteiner, M. and W. Huber 1976. Grammatical impairment in developmental aphasia. *Cortex 11*: 264-282.

Koster, J. 1984. Die konfigurationelle Matrix. In: H. Czepluch and H. Janßen (ed.), pp.17-35.

Kratzer, A. 1984. On deriving syntactic differences between English and German. Unpublished manuscript TU Berlin.

Kriz, J. ed. 1984. *Sprachentwicklungsstörungen*. München.

Lapointe, S. 1985. *A theory of grammatical agreement*. New York.

Lenerz, J. 1985. *Syntaktischer Wandel und Grammatiktheorie. Eine Untersuchung an Beispielen aus der Sprachgeschichte des Deutschen*. Tübingen.

Liebmann, A. 1901. Agrammatismus infantilis. *Archiv für Psychiatrie 34*: 240-252.

Lightfoot, D. 1979. *Principles of diachronic syntax*. Cambridge.

Macnamara, J. 1982. *Names for things*. Cambridge, Mass.

Mallinson, G. and B. Blake 1979. *Language typology. Cross-linguistic studies in syntax*. Amsterdam.

Martens, K. and R. Schmid 1979. Zum Problem der Sprachentwicklungsdiagnostik: Der Heidelberger Sprachentwicklungstest. *Praxis Deutsch 36*: 5-9.

Meisel, J. 1986. Word order and case marking in early child language. Evidence from simultaneous acquisition of two first languages: French and German. *Linguistics 24*: 123-183.

Meixner, F. 1976. Dysgrammatismusverfahren. *Sprachheilpädagoge 8*: 44-52.

Menyuk, P. 1978. Linguistic problems in children with developmental dysphasia. In: Wyke (ed.), pp.135-158.

Miller, M. 1976. *Zur Logik der frühkindlichen Sprachentwicklung*. Stuttgart.

Mills, A. 1985. The acquisition of German. In: D. Slobin (ed.), pp.141-254.

Morehead, D. and D. Ingram 1973. The development of base syntax in normal and linguistically deviant children. *Journal of Speech and Hearing Research 16*: 330-352.

Muysken, P. 1985. Taalontwikkelingen en grammatika. *Interdisciplinar Tijdschrift voor Taal- en Tekstwetenschap 5*: 219-230.

Nelson, K. 1975. Individual differences in early semantic and syntactic development. *Annals of the New York Academy of Sciences 213*: 132-139.

Ochs, E. 1982. Ergativity and word order in Samoan child language. *Language 58*: 646-671.

Park, T.-Z. 1976. Imitation of grammatical and ungrammatical sentences by German-speaking children. In: W. von Raffler-Engel and Y. Lebrun (ed.), *Baby talk and infant speech*. Amsterdam, pp.202-217.

Peuser, G. ed. 1978. *Brennpunkte der Patholinguistik*. München.

Pinker, S. 1979. Formal models of language learning. *Cognition 7*: 217-283.

Pinker, S. 1982. A theory of the acquisition of lexical interpretative grammars. In: J. Bresnan (ed.), pp.655-726.

Pinker, S. 1984. *Language learnability and language development*. Cambridge, Mass.

Platzack, C. 1983. Germanic word order and the COMP/INFL parameter. *Working Papers in Scandinavian Syntax 2*: 1-45.

Ramge, H. 1976. *Spracherwerb und sprachliches Handeln. Studien zum Sprechen eines Kindes im dritten Lebensjahr*. Düsseldorf.

Reis, M. 1982. Zum Subjektbegriff im Deutschen. In: W. Abraham (ed.), *Satzglieder im Deutschen. Vorschläge zur syntaktischen, semantischen und pragmatischen Fundierung*. Tübingen, pp.171-211.

Roeper, T. 1973. Connecting children's language and linguistic theory. In: T. Moore (ed.), *Cognitive development and the acquisition of language*. New York, pp.187-196.

Schieffelin, B. 1981. A developmental study of pragmatic appropriateness of word order and case marking in Kaluli. In: W. Deutsch (ed.), pp.105-120.

Schöler, H. 1985. Überlegungen zum Erwerb morphologischer Strukturformen bei dysgrammatisch sprechenden Kindern am Beispiel des Pluralmorphems. In: Füssenich/Gläß (ed.), pp.165-179.

Schöler, H. 1986. Untersuchungen zum Entwicklungsdysgrammatismus als spezifischer Ausprägungsform der Entwicklungsdysphasie. Unpublished manuscript Pädagogische Hochschule Heidelberg.

Scholz, H.-J. 1978. Einige psycholinguistische Bemerkungen zum Entwicklungsdysgrammatismus. In: Peuser (ed.), pp.275-289.

Scholz, H.-J. 1983. Zur Frage der Bildung und sprachheilpädagogischen Förderung sprachentwicklungsverzögerter Kinder. Vortrag auf dem 5.Kongreß der Österr. Gesellschaft für Sprachheilpädagogik. Krems.

Schuurmanns, K. 1986. Möglichkeiten und Grenzen linguistischer Analyse von Spontansprache. Unpubl. thesis (Diplomarbeit). Universität Dortmund.

Scupin, E. and G. Scupin 1907. *Bubis erste Kindheit*. Leipzig.
Selkirk, E. 1982. *The syntax of words*. Cambridge, Mass.
Skinner, B. 1957. *Verbal behavior*. New York.
Slobin, D. 1973. Cognitive prerequisites for the development of grammar. In: Ch. Ferguson and D. Slobin (ed.), pp.175-208.
Slobin, D. 1981. The origins of grammatical encoding of events. In: W. Deutsch (ed.), pp.185-200.
Slobin, D. 1982. Universal and particular in the acquisition of language. In: Wanner/Gleitman (ed.), pp.128-170.
Slobin, D. 1985. Crosslinguistic evidence for the language-making capacity. In: D. Slobin (ed.), pp.1157-1256.
Slobin, D. ed. 1985. *The cross-linguistic study of language acquisition*. Hillsdale, N.J.
Slobin, D. and T. Bever 1982. Children use canonical sentence schemas: A cross-linguistic study of word order and inflection. *Cognition 12*: 229-265.
Staats, A. and C. Staats 1963. *Complex human behavior*. New York.
Stachowiak, F.-J. 1987. Spracherwerb, Semantik und menschlicher Cortex – vom lautbegabtem zum sprachbegabtem Wesen. In: Deutsche Gesellschaft für Sprachheilpädagogik (ed.), *Spracherwerb und Spracherwerbsstörungen*. Hamburg, pp.391-411.
Steele, S. 1981. *An encyclopedia of Aux. A study in cross-linguistic equivalence*. Cambridge, Mass.
Stephany, U. 1982. Der Entwicklungsdysgrammatismus aus psycholinguistischer Sicht. In: W. Welte (ed.), *Sprachtheorie und angewandte Linguistik*. Tübingen, pp.263-275.
Stern C. and W. Stern 1928. *Die Kindersprache*. Leipzig.
Tracy, R. 1984. Fallstudien: Überlegungen zum Erwerb von Kasuskategorie und Kasusmarkierung. In: H. Czepluch and H. Janßen (ed), pp.271-313.
Tracy, R. 1986. The acquisition of case morphology in German. *Linguistics 24*: 47-78.
Travis, L. 1984. Parameters and effects of word order variation. MIT Diss. Cambridge, Mass.
Wanner, E. and L. Gleitman ed. 1982. *Language acquisition. The state of the art*. London.
Wexler, K. 1981. Some issues in the theory of learnability. In: Baker and McCarthy (ed.), pp.30-52.
Wexler, K. and P. Culicover 1980. *Formal principles of language acquisition*. Cambridge, Mass.
White, L. 1985. The pro-drop parameter in adult second language acquisition. *Language Learning 35*: 47-62.
Wiese, R. 1986. Schwa and the structure of words in German. *Linguistics 24*: 697-724.
Williams, E. 1981. Predication. *Linguistic Inquiry 11*: 203-260.

Wode, H. 1981. *Learning a second language. An integrated view of language acquisition*. Tübingen.

Wunderlich, D. 1985. Über die Argumente des Verbs. *Linguistische Berichte 97*: 183-227.

Wunderlich, D. 1985a. Zur Nominalflexion im Deutschen. Unpublished manuscript Universität Düsseldorf.

Wurst, F. 1973. *Sprachentwicklungsstörungen und ihre Behandlung*. Wien.

Wurzel, W. 1970. *Studien zur deutschen Lautstruktur*. Studia Grammatica VIII. Berlin (DDR).

Wyke, M. ed. 1978. *Developmental dysphasia*. New York.

Zakharova, A. 1973. Acquisition of forms of grammatical case by pre-school children. In: Ferguson and Slobin (ed.), pp.281-284.

Index